W9-DJD-819

Leslie Sklair has been a lecturer in Sociology at the London School of Economics since 1967. Born in 1940, he was educated in Glasgow and the University of Leeds. At present he is the International Secretary of the British Society for Social Responsibility in Science (BSSRS). His first book, *The Sociology of Progress*, was published in 1970.

Organized Knowledge is published in a sociology series under the general editorship of Professor John Rex.

Leslie Sklair

Organized Knowledge

A Sociological View of
Science and Technology

Paladin

Granada Publishing Limited
Published in 1973 by Paladin
Park Street St Albans Herts

First published in Great Britain by Hart-Davis, MacGibbon Ltd 1973
Copyright © Leslie Sklair 1973
Made and printed in Great Britain by
Richard Clay (The Chaucer Press) Ltd
Bungay, Suffolk
Set in Monotype Ehrhardt

Contents

Introduction

The world in which we live is made possible by science and technology. The food we eat, the houses we live in, the clothes we wear, the fuel that warms us and powers our machines – the characteristic forms of all of these in the modern world are the results of what our scientists and technologists do. Science and technology affect us all in direct and indirect ways. In the following pages I shall argue that although the layman, in one sense, usually has no knowledge of science or technology, in another and equally important sense we are all participants in a scientific and technological society. We do not need knowledge of the principles and practices of science and technology in order to experience their consequences.

The inhabitants of Hiroshima and Nagasaki needed no grasp of the development of twentieth-century physics to experience their suffering on those dreadful days in August 1945 when the atomic bombs were dropped on them, nor do those who live in industrial societies need much expertise in the chemistry of gases to appreciate that the air they breathe is often dangerously polluted. However much we are told that the Bomb was dropped by the politicians and that atmospheric pollution is principally an economic issue, and however true these claims may be, it is clear that science and technology do have extremely important consequences for the lives of us all. It is no longer the case that scientists and technologists are people who fiddle around in their workshops or back gardens in the way that many people nowadays carry on their hobbies. The 'fiddling around' of scientists and technologists today can result in mass destruction or in mass salvation, in the transformation of the cities in which we live and of the open spaces on which our ancestors romped, in the creation of totally new styles of living for some and the abolition of traditional styles for others. We cannot ignore science and technology for they will not leave us alone.

Governments, among other groups in society, have not been slow to pick up this point in the twentieth century and, as time goes on, the involvement of governments with science and technology increases at a swift rate. Their interest in science and its political applications is by no means new, and the extent of this interest, not surprisingly, seems to have become greater as the scale of science, in terms of its costs and its manpower, has grown. Napoleon, building the new France at the turn of the eighteenth century, was perhaps the first political leader to take scientists and technologists systematically into the sphere of government and to put their talents to use as part of a political plan (cf. Crosland, 1967). A hundred years later, Lenin is reputed to have said in an interview with H. G. Wells that 'Soviets *plus* Electrification equals Communism' (Dobb, 1966, p. 339); and the Soviet Union was certainly the first large country to attempt to harness the power of science and technology and to construct its future through these means.

These efforts, impressive as they were, pale before the story of what has come to be accepted as the watershed in the relations between science and government – the Manhattan Project. This project, which accomplished the manufacture and successful explosion of the atomic bomb, heralded the beginning of a new stage in the relations between the political and the scientific worlds (see Bush, 1945). As I shall have more to say on these matters in later chapters, I shall restrict myself here to pointing out and emphasizing with as much force as possible that science and technology do matter to everyone in the modern world, not only to scientists and technologists and those unlucky enough to get in their way. Whether we like it or not, we will all get in the way of science and technology in some respects sooner or later, and *now* is the time to start thinking about this and making plans to avoid the worst disasters and to maximize the benefits.

It is easy to be alarmist, and it is even easier to give the impression of desperation when confronted with the literally countless examples of the catastrophes and near-catastrophes that science and technology have presented us with in recent years. In some areas, fortunately, the impact of science and technology has aroused public passions and the worst abuses have been regulated with varying degrees of success.

Industrial society, to take the largest and most obvious example, makes possible a high standard of living and a high level of material comfort for most of its citizens by virtue of the fact that the factory system can produce many goods cheaply. But we find that industrial areas have polluted environments, in the air and in water and in the soil – pollution which goes much farther than simply spoiling amenities. It can actually change the so-called balance of nature and perhaps even the metabolism of individuals exposed to the pollutants. Governments have passed legislation to control these abuses of science and technology, without very much success, as the causes of the pollution (in all parts of the environment) appear to be expanding faster than the controls. In any case, it is argued, if we want an affluent, i.e. industrial, society, then we will have to put up with these sorts of inconveniences: thus we may construct the modern aphorism – he who says affluence, says effluence.

It is not always a clear-cut question of abuse or solutions, for what science and technology appear to promote are contradictory states of affairs.

These are the sorts of problems to which I shall return many times in the following pages; and they are serious problems because if we continue to tamper with land, air, and water (the so-called 'eco-system'), then we may end up by destroying the conditions necessary for human life as we know it. The consequences of science and technology are the business of all of us.

Another sensitive area that has roused public passions and private anxiety over the past few years is that of the bio-medical sciences. It is here, more than in any other context, that science and technology become personal, for it is here that science and technology are coming into direct contact with our bodies and the bodies of our unborn children. The technology of organ transplants and the isolation of bacterial genes, the debate around the manufacture and use of chemical and biological weapons, the controversy surrounding the widespread use of the contraceptive pill, the avoidable tragedy of the thalidomide babies and the arbitrary attempts to avoid similar accidents by the abolition of various food additives – all of these are examples of the ways in which bio-medical science and technology may affect all of us in our day-to-day lives. You do not need to work in a laboratory to confront science, nor do you encounter technology only in automated factories. They surround us and they have access to our private places.

How, then, can we get to grips with this situation which, on the most optimistic assessment, will continue to create much pain and unpleasantness for as long as we feel committed to the types of societies that we have at present in the 'developed' world? Many people feel confident that science or technology or both will clear up the mess without outside interference, and that in any case the disadvantages will always be vastly outweighed by the advantages of science and technology. These include some distinguished and informed men as well as others who are plainly ignorant of the issues involved. (One of the polemical purposes of this book will be to persuade those of goodwill who fit into either of these categories that they are wrong and that their views are dangerous.)

We cannot all be expected to become scientists and technologists, although an increasing number of men and women in the modern world will enter scientific and technological occupations. If it is argued that only experts are entitled to comment on and to evaluate the results of science and technology, then the argument stops here. The role of the specialist in society suggests problems that will demand attention in later chapters, but, for the moment, let us assume that in any society that has a claim to be democratic, the powers and discretion of the experts must be limited, although the actual limitations themselves, and how they are organized and enforced, are matters that are probably best decided upon as a result of our experiences. Therefore, it is important that those who are genuinely disturbed about some of the consequences of science and technology, but who do not start out with detailed, specialized knowledge, should not be inhibited from voicing doubts because of their layman status. That is to say – although scientists and technologists themselves are clearly the best qualified in some ways to consider the effects (harmful and otherwise) of their work on the societies in which they operate, the layman must be given the opportunity both to express his opinions on these matters and also to have access to as much relevant non-technical information as possible.

It is here that the sociology of science and technology becomes more than an interesting and faintly esoteric intellectual pursuit. It becomes a means of exposing the workings of science, to those without the benefits of formal scientific and technological education, and of stripping away some of the mystique that has surrounded the world of science, mostly to its detriment. The sociology of science and technology is an attempt to describe and explain how science is organized and to discuss what are the consequences of its activities for the rest of society. As long as the mystique of science is maintained, there will be little likelihood that people outside science (though, as I have emphasized, *we are all affected by it*) will be encouraged to assume an attitude of healthy scepticism towards its impact on the societies in which they live. Science, which was supposed to have abolished dogma and arguments from authority, itself engenders dogma and canonizes its own self-appointed authority.

The sociology of science, therefore, has two aims. In the first place we pin down knowledge *about* science rather than knowledge *in* science, though these are not always entirely independent areas. In the second we indelicately lift the veil which has shrouded science from the proper attentions of the non-scientists, the paying customers who have seen the vision in its hazy outlines vacillate between the beautiful and the ugly, the glorious and the disgusting, the hopeful and the hopeless.

Plan of the Book

The book falls into three unequal parts. In Part One this general introduction is followed by a long chapter, the main purpose of which is pragmatic. In it I shall show that in the richest countries in the world very large amounts of money are devoted to, and very large numbers of trained people work in, science and technology. I shall also draw some contrasts between rich countries and poor countries in these respects, and introduce some of the relationships between them, in order to demonstrate that big science is the most important material basis on which knowledge is organized in the modern world.

Part Two is concerned with two interrelated tasks. It presents a critical account of some of the main tendencies in the sociological study of science. It also suggests a model of the *social institution*, and proceeds to modify and use this to construct a more adequate approach to the sociology of science.

In Part Three, some of the problems generated by the approach outlined in Part Two are discussed. In particular, I shall be paying attention to some of the political consequences that the social institution of science and technology has for the societies in which it operates.

At this stage science and technology, as separate activities, are not systematically distinguished. The reason for holding over discussion of this vital issue until Chapter 2, where it is dealt with in some detail, is that my intention in Part One is to show the importance of science and technology as a whole for modern societies in terms of the material apparatus and manpower involved. The view that technology is the public face of science suffices, for the moment, to describe the current state of affairs in what is known as big science.

Part One
Big Science

1 Big Science: Money and Manpower

One of the most amazing facts about twentieth-century science and technology is that it was only very recently that people started to count its financial cost in a serious fashion. This is all the more amazing when we reflect that science grew up in the modern world largely in the countries where the protestant ethic and the spirit of capitalism were thought to have prevailed. And furthermore, as Max Weber argued, these phenomena, along with the sociological corollary of the bureaucratic form of organization, were indirectly and directly supposed to have been tied up with accounting systems. Thus, when a recent report remarks that 'most countries have better statistics on poultry production than they do on the activities of their scientists and engineers' (Lakoff, 1966), we can begin to appreciate the nature of the problem involved in obtaining quantitative material on any aspect of big science.

Two major difficulties in measuring science and technology expenditures present themselves immediately. The first concerns the problem of *what* we wish to measure; and the second arises if – as is very likely – we wish to *compare* measurements over time and place. These are, of course, very much related problems.

The normal classification which is used in the measurement of scientific activities is 'research and development' (R & D), and, in the last decades, both governments and international organizations have been increasingly gathering quantitative and qualitative information about R & D. Many people doing this data collection appear to be quite conscious of the difficulties involved (see Freeman, 1969, 1970; UNESCO, 1970, I); and there is intensive work in progress, the purpose of which is to establish reliable foundations for the collection and comparison of data on scientific and technical activities (see OECD,

1970). In an appendix at the end of the chapter I shall critically evaluate some of the attempts to distinguish between various scientific and technological activities.

The reasons why governments of most countries which spend significant sums of money on R & D now collect these data are complex, but the fact that it is generally accepted that R & D activities are very much related to economic achievement is the most important single reason. International organizations, principally the Organization for Economic Cooperation and Development (OECD), and the United Nations Educational, Scientific and Cultural Organization (UNESCO), with the not always perfect cooperation of the individual governments, have developed important agencies to deal with these matters.

It is not my intention here to launch an all-out attack on the unreliability of R & D statistics, because (a) as I have mentioned, some of the practitioners of the art are quite conscious of its elementary state, and (b) the sociologist of science should be only too grateful that steps are being taken (by others) to provide the subject with a necessary empirical basis. While not denying the often essential link between theory and practice which is generally ignored by those in the science policy field, it would be incorrect to condemn entirely the information which is already at our disposal. The political point of the motives that drive rich countries to glorify *their* big science (which legitimates and is legitimated by the collection of R & D data) should also not be neglected. These are matters to which I shall return in Part Three – here I shall, for the most part, take the figures at face value.

The pioneering study in this field was carried out by Freeman and Young (1965), and the results published in an OECD monograph entitled 'The Research and Development Effort in Western Europe, North America and the Soviet Union'. To quote the subtitle, it was 'an experimental international comparison of research expenditures and manpower in 1962'. Since this first systematic study others have followed, and these will provide the data on which this chapter is based. In the first section I shall deal mainly with money, and in the second mainly with manpower.

The Financial Costs of Big Science

By all accounts, although there are large differences between countries, it is undeniable that Gross Expenditure on Research and Development (GERD) rose substantially in the 1960s. Table 1.1, put together from several OECD reports, gives a general idea of the magnitude of the spending of selected countries on R & D.*

Table 1.1. Total Gross Expenditure on R & D (GERD) in OECD Member Countries (1962–8) (million US$)

Year	1962[1]	1963[2]	1964[2]	1965[2]	1966[3]	1967[3]	1968[3]
USA	17,531	21,035			23,685		
France	1,108	1,299				2,507	
Germany	1,105		1,436			2,127	
UK	1,775		2,160		2,472		
Japan		892				1,684	
Russia[4] (million roubles)	4,300	4,700	5,100	5,914	6,500	7,200	7,900

1. All figures in this column are from F & Y, p. 71.
2. ISY (2), p. 36.
3. CSP, p. 5.
4. SPU, p. 99. The 1966, 1967, and 1968 figures represent planned rather than actual expenditure. On the 'research rouble' see F & Y ch. IV.

* The following tables are all derived from Organization for Economic Co-operation and Development sources. For convenience I shall give the full bibliographical details here, each one followed by the abbreviation I use in attributing sources in the tables.

C. FREEMAN AND A. YOUNG, *The Research and Development Effort in Western Europe, North America and the Soviet Union*, OECD, Paris, 1965 (F & Y).

INTERNATIONAL STATISTICAL YEAR FOR RESEARCH AND DEVELOPMENT (1), *The Overall Level and Structure of R & D Efforts in OECD Member Countries*, OECD, Paris, 1967 (ISY (1)).

INTERNATIONAL STATISTICAL YEAR FOR RESEARCH AND DEVELOPMENT (2), *Statistical Tables and Notes*, OECD, Paris, 1968 (ISY (2)).

E. ZALESKI et al, *Science Policy in the USSR*, OECD, Paris, 1969, (SPU).

COMMITTEE FOR SCIENCE POLICY, *Survey of R & D Statistics* (mimeo), OECD, Paris, 1969, DAS/SPR/69 58 (CSP). It must be emphasized that this latter report is provisional.

Table 1.2 indicates the proportions of funds allocated to R & D in various OECD countries with respect to their Gross National Product.

Table 1.2. GERD as Proportion of Gross National Product (GNP) in Selected OECD Countries[1]

Country	Year	GERD/GNP : %
USA	1966	3·1
UK	1966/7	2·3
France	1967	2·3
Netherlands	1967	2·3
Switzerland	1967	1·9
Germany	1967	1·8
Japan	1967/8	1·5
Canada	1967	1·4
Sweden	1967	1·4
Italy	1967	0·7
Greece	1966	0·2

1. From CSP, p. 5.

Three conclusions can be drawn directly from these figures:

(1) America spends a very great deal more money on R & D than any other country.

(2) The gap between Western Europe and the United States in GERD is very large.

(3) The Soviet Union, though the figures are more speculative here than for the other countries, seems well-placed in the international R & D effort.

However, these figures (like most blanket figures) conceal as much as they reveal. One particularly significant state of affairs that is concealed relates to the areas within which the expenditure takes place – the national R & D objectives, in the words of the OECD. Three broad objectives are identified, namely 'atomic, space, and defence', 'economically motivated R & D', and 'welfare and miscellaneous R & D'. The national differences for 1963/4 are as shown in Table 1.3.

Table 1.3. National R & D Objectives 1963–4[1]

	Atomic Space Defence %	Economically Motivated R & D %	Welfare and Miscellaneous %
USA	62	28	10
France	45	41	14
Germany	17	62	21
UK	40	51	9
Japan	0	73	27

1. From ISY (1), p. 58.

Although the United States still spends more in absolute terms in each of the three areas than any other country in the world, almost two thirds of US total expenditure on R & D is devoted to atomic, space, and defence work. Thus, if we compare the United States to Western Europe as a whole, we find that whereas the US spent seven times as much on atomic, space, and defence R & D as Western Europe in 1963–4, this ratio is only two to one for economically motivated R & D. It is significant that Japan, which is reported as spending nothing on atomic, space, and defence R & D in 1963–4, had the largest investments in welfare and miscellaneous R & D, relatively speaking.

The category of 'welfare and miscellaneous' R & D, in fact, covers such things as health and generally non-directed basic research, and so it is pertinent to expose a relationship that seems to be suggested by the figures. The four countries with the largest proportions of GERD in atomic, space, and defence work (US, France, Britain, and Sweden), all allotting more than a third of their total to this objective, spend the lowest proportion on welfare and miscellaneous R & D, less than 15 per cent in fact, although the US still spends far more in this category in absolute terms than anyone else.

I am not here simply insinuating that certain areas of R & D are being neglected, proportionately, in those countries where the level of funds going into weapons and space is high – much more research is needed before this conclusion can be safely drawn – but it is clearly most instructive to look not only at how much money is spent on R & D in any country but also at how the GERD is distributed among various 'national objectives'. More recent figures for the allocation of *government* R & D funds show an even greater imbalance.

Table 1.4. Government R & D Objectives 1966–7[1]

		Atomic Space Defence %	Economically Motivated R & D %	Welfare and Miscellaneous %
USA	1966	87	3	10*
France	1967	74	17	9*
Germany	—	—	—	—
UK	1966/7	61	25	14*
Japan	1966/7	17	75	8*

* These figures include universities and other research.
1. From CSP, p. 17.

The institutional location of R & D in these countries also reveals some interesting variations.

There are, in the United States, as in most other countries, three main locations where scientific work is carried out. These are the universities, industry, and government laboratories. There are also non-profit-making organizations in many countries which, for these purposes, are usually classified along with the government laboratories. There are also three main sources of funds for scientific research, namely the government, private industry, and 'other sources' – often gifts and bequests from private individuals or foundations. In theory, any funding source could give money to any research group, but what normally happens in the United States is that the government pays for all of its own research, much of university research and some of industry's research. Both industry and the foundations contribute to university research, and industry pays for a good deal of its own research. Table 1.5 illustrates this very complicated state of affairs for the major R & D countries in the late 1960s.

These figures are interesting in two major respects. In the first place it appears that about two thirds of US research and development is carried out in industrial laboratories. However, when we turn our attention to the sources of the money for this R & D we find that the government pays about two thirds of the bill.

In the main R & D countries of Western Europe, as in America, it appears that the governments pay for a large part of the research and development which is carried out in private industrial laboratories.

How can we explain this state of affairs whereby governments pay out vast sums of money to private firms for the conduct of R & D? A clue may lie in the fact that in 1967 the governments of the United States, France, and Britain all apportioned 60 per cent or more of their R & D budgets to atomic, space, and defence objectives, whereas Germany and Japan, for example, appear to spend less than 20 per cent of their government R & D budgets in this way, though the difference appears to be diminishing at the present time. The fact is that the governments of the United States, France, and Britain buy military and space R & D from private industry.

The consequences of these facts, particularly for American science and for American society as a whole, are complex and difficult to disentangle, but as similar situations exist in most other countries that spend large amounts of money on defence, it is certainly worthwhile to inquire further into the American case.

The Contract

The major organizing feature of American R & D is the *contract* between government and business (Dupré and Lakoff, 1962;

Table 1.5. GERD Analysed by Sector of Performance and Source of Funds 1966-8[1]
(% Total National R & D Effort)

		Sector of Performance			Source of Funds		
		Business Enterprise	Government	Private Non-profit and Higher Education	BE	GOV	PNP and HE
USA	1966	66	17	18	31	64	5
France	1967	54	32	14	31	54	15
Germany	1967	67	4	29	55	43	2
UK	1966/7	69	22	9	44	50	6
Japan	1967/8	63	13	25	63	30	7

1. From CSP, pp. 9-10.

Hieburg, 1966; Danhof, 1968). There is no mystery about this – the government decides what it wants and advertises for tenders from appropriate companies who compete with each other for the contract. This simple picture requires some modification, needless to say. In the first place, there is the advertised fixed price contract, whereby a firm agrees to do the job for a specific price and thus accepts the risk of a loss if costs are higher than anticipated and stands to make an excess profit if it can keep costs down. But this has been largely replaced by other types of contract. These are variations around the theme of negotiated costs and fee contracts, where the government approaches particular firms and conducts negotiations with them alone, thus severely restricting competition. The basic form of this is the cost-plus-fixed-fee contract, where the government agrees to pay the costs, whatever they may be, and in addition pays a fixed fee, as direct profit to the firm on the deal.

There is little opposition to the cost-plus-fixed-fee contract in American industrial circles, especially among those companies lucky enough to win the contracts. No risks whatsoever are involved for the company since its costs are guaranteed along with its profits, and further, there is no real incentive to keep costs down. Governments, it may be added, usually pay their bills. This state of affairs has been modified by several other mechanisms intended to give companies good reasons for not wasting or abusing public funds. Chief among these are the cost-plus-incentive-fee, which allows a proportion of any saving of cost to be added to the fee, and the fixed-price-incentive-fee, which does the same by another route.

With the stakes so high, for all such contracts do offer significant fruits to the company at the right place at the right time, it is legitimate to ask whether or not there are sufficient safeguards built into the government contracting system to ensure that the American people, who provide their government with the money for the research and development, are in fact getting good value for their taxes. Many commentators, particularly in the US, are by no means convinced that this is the case and they have not been reticent in giving their reasons.

The main lines of criticism have been concerned with the interdependent issues of the ways in which the government has arrived at decisions for what R & D to pursue, and how the contracts for this work are allocated. Here, as much as in any other problem area, the fact that science and politics are relevant to one another comes through clearly.

To put the criticisms at their crudest: it could be argued that the contract system positively encourages industrialists in key sectors of the economy to propagandize certain political opinions, whose consequences would be to bring pressure on the government to spend enormous sums of money on particular R & D projects. For example, if groups of influential people were to support the continuing notion of the 'red menace' with all the means at their disposal, both nationally and locally, in anticipation of winning lucrative contracts for their companies to carry out R & D work on more and more sophisticated weapons systems, then we should naturally be moved to suspect the possibility that the motives of these people were mixed. This suspicion has indeed been formalized in American law around the analytically clear, though empirically unclear, principle of 'conflict of interests'.

A good example of this was the case of the Ramo-Wooldridge Corporation and the US Air Force in the 1950s. Ramo-Wooldridge had a subsidiary, Space Technology Laboratory, which acted as an advisor to the Air Force on the sorts of R & D contracts for which its parent company was increasingly eager to bid. Thus, a clear conflict of interest was recognized by the appropriate US government committee and the outcome was the creation of a non-profit Aerospace Corporation, set up specifically to advise the Air Force on contracting technicalities. It may be noted that some of the staff of the Space Technology Laboratory went over to the new non-profit corporation (Dupré and Lakoff, 1962, pp. 33-4; Nieburg, 1966, esp. ch. xi).

It is obviously impossible to ensure that organizational, let alone individual conflicts of interest, are at all times revealed and satisfactorily resolved. It is, however, important to be clear about the levels on which these conflicts are to be found, and the ways in which a knowledge of them helps us to understand how science operates in this context. To put the essential point into a few words – a single massive decision about a major R & D project, to land a man on the moon or to build an anti-ballistic missile system, for example, can influence the directions that science will take for years and even decades in any society. Leaving aside for a moment the thorny and vital problem of how much science there is in such projects, it must be emphasized that science, and especially big science, does not just *happen*; it is directed.

One important implication of big science is that the quantitative growth of science has qualitative repercussions. That is, where the scale and costs of science increase beyond a certain point, the nature of the activities of science experiences some significant changes. Science and technology, no less than most social phenomena – and a great deal more than many – are open to determining influences at the hands of economic interests. This can happen in a variety of ways. At one level it is clear that the criteria which determine whether or not sufficient funds will be forthcoming to support extremely expensive research projects are not necessarily entirely cognitive. Science has a political dimension, no doubt forced upon it, but one that is real in its consequences. This has been documented for American science by Greenberg (1969) and for British science by Vig (1968) and Rose (1969), among others, with a wealth of illustrative detail, and only the most stubborn and ignorant inhabitant of the ivory tower could now deny it.

The repercussions that the sociological and political dimensions have for the content of science, however, is another – though, in my view, not totally unrelated – matter. That research proposers will tailor their research plans to suit particular funding agencies is common knowledge, as is the obvious fact that certain kinds of science are possible only with certain kinds of apparatus. Among the main reasons why physics advanced so quickly in the direction that it did in the late 1920s and 1930s in California must be included the availability of Lawrence's *cyclotron*; and its continued progress depends largely on the availability of funds for more and bigger high-energy machines. I shall be returning to the theme of the relations between the socio-political dimensions of science and its cognitive development in Chapter 4. Different funding and decision-making agencies may have different effects, and we might expect that in some branches of science these effects are more or less marked than in others. Similarly, government–industry, government–university and industry–university funding arrangements will all have their special characteristics (see esp. Danhof, 1968; Kidd, in Barber and Hirsch, 1962).

The most outstanding big science projects of modern times, the Manhattan project and the Apollo project, both involved government funding and the use of government, industrial, and academic scientific personnel. As the Manhattan project has been written about in great detail in many places (Hewlett and Anderson, 1962, esp. 657–62 for sources), I shall restrict myself here to a few remarks on the Apollo project.

The Apollo Project

On 29 July 1958, President Eisenhower signed the National Aeronautics and Space Act by which the National Aeronautics and Space Agency (NASA), a government-sponsored independent civilian body, was empowered to direct the American space effort. In its first year the NASA budget was $145 million, almost doubling each subsequent year to $4,990 million in 1965, and reaching about six billion in 1966. Since then it has declined gradually to about $3 million in 1971. No technological project has ever grown so big so fast. During this time NASA expenditure increased from a negligible amount in 1958, to the point in 1962 where it became the second most highly funded R & D agency, behind the Department of Defence. By 1966, NASA costs accounted for about three eighths of total Federal R & D expenditure, and the agency was dealing out billions of dollars annually to private industry whose R & D expertise was ensuring that, for a price, the first men to step on to the surface of the moon would be carrying the stars and stripes. As everyone knows, this historic feat was accomplished, brilliantly on schedule, and watched by countless millions on television, on 20 July 1969.

Quite apart from the question of whether or not the American people wanted to land men on the moon (or, for that matter, to commit the nation to building ever more sophisticated missile and anti-missile systems), the fact of space research and particularly the Apollo programme has meant that vast resources have been found and given over to particular sorts of R & D. Now, it does not necessarily follow that the political, and therefore the financial, priority accorded to NASA's work has led to a drainage of funds from other types of scientific research in the

United States. It could be argued that the nature of the space programme was such that *extra* resources were made available and that these would not have been available for less dramatic and less prestigious projects.

This view is very widely supported from both the scientific and the political communities. There is no denying, in the first place, the enormous influence of the Russian space achievements in the late 1950s, and the traumatic impact of the Sputniks on many aspects of American science and science policy-making is well documented. As Professor Schoettle has shown in her account of the birth of NASA, it would be a mistake to interpret the American space effort simply as a national response to the challenge of Sputnik as a piece of Russian *science*. As she says in her conclusion, the US Space programme

was a broadly conceived and dramatic program which emerged in response to the *political* impact of Sputnik, not a carefully designed, reasoned policy for the support of space science per se . . . the public management of the space enterprise after 1958 involved the pursuit of policy objectives *which go far beyond the benefits for science* and national security to be derived from space exploration. A successful administration of the program requires . . . the simultaneous pursuit of a number of objectives, some clearly *nonscientific* in character (in Lakoff, 1966, p. 262) (Emphasis added).

Thus, although the role of NASA was not exclusively scientific and technological, there clearly were vital political factors involved in its operation. (This is probably obvious to most people by now. I only labour the point because some American space scientists are *still* claiming otherwise. It is unnecessary even to present an argument for this point with respect to R & D in the field of armaments.) In most if not all situations where science and politics meet, science advises and politics decides. The structure of the American scientific advisory arrangements are complex in the extreme, though it is true to say that the leading scientists and technologists do have the ear of the president. As a most important corollary to this, the president and the polity do have the ears of the scientists and, as the story of NASA amply illustrates, the development of science has come to rest on high-level *political* decisions to an increasing and an increasingly direct fashion. Donald Hornig, special assistant to President Johnson for science and technology, makes the point quite explicitly in a semi-official publication reporting a meeting of the National Academy of Sciences, when he says that 'the shape of science and the directions of scientific progress are no longer a matter for the scientific community alone; they have become part of the public enterprise' (Hornig, 1966, pp. 16–17).

This sentiment is admirable. There is nothing that would confirm the most optimistic claims of our civilization more than an informed and interested public debating seriously the use to which its money was being put in the progress of science. But, of course, this is in no way the case, as is made clear by Jerome Wiesner, President Kennedy's special assistant for science and technology. Discussing the ways in which federal R & D decisions are made, Wiesner says: 'Corporation executives, government budget officers and department heads and members of Congress have traditionally made such decisions with confidence and with access to scientific and engineering advice; there is no reason why they cannot continue to successfully' (Wiesner, 1965, p. 60).[1]

Businessmen, civil servants, and politicians, therefore, and not scientists, far less 'the people', decide how science will progress. And they do so by deciding how much of their resources they are willing to pour into the selected areas of big science which account for such an important part of the total scientific research effort.

The conflict of interests of which I have previously spoken occurs at two levels. Not only does it involve the individual unscrupulous contractor or sub-contractor lining his pockets – for this undoubtedly occurs. But also, on a more general level, it concerns the ways in which science and society actually develop, and how this development may be determined by people whose values and purposes may be quite alien to all that science and its practitioners are supposed to stand for.

In this section I have been inclined to understand science and scientists in a fairly wide sense, on the assumption that to restrict the label 'science' to the performance of crucial experiments, in thought or on the blackboard or in the laboratory, and to restrict 'scientists' to those who carried out these experiments, would be to misrepresent them and to fail to draw the most sociologically significant implications of their activities. Thus, the money spent on space research and travel is by no means money spent exclusively on science as such, though it is largely spent on science and science-related activities. Similarly, not all the people working in establishments funded from R & D budgets are themselves scientists – less than half of them have professional qualifications – but they are all science and science-related workers. As long as we are careful to keep this fact in mind, and as long as we have sufficient information to tell us how far from the rather vague scientific core these activities and personnel are, then we shall be in a position to assess the impact of science on society in certain prescribed respects. There is no doubt whatsoever that a significant though undetermined proportion of R & D expenditure goes towards operating and supporting costs of expensive apparatus and facilities, and to the maintenance of many workers who are, to varying degrees, science-related rather than scientific personnel (see Freeman, 1969).

Having reiterated this necessary warning, let us examine some of the changes in the workforce of science that have taken place in recent years.

The Workforce of Big Science

The number of scientists there are depends mostly on how we define 'scientists'. Table 1.6 presents some recent estimates of scientific manpower for the countries spending most on R & D.

As can be seen from this composite table, the relevant category of persons is made up of the 'qualified scientists and engineers' (QSE) and technicians. The usual implication of the adjective 'qualified' in this context is the possession of some paper qualification or its equivalent that would entitle the holder to membership of the relevant professional societies or associations. Technicians, we may suppose, are those who do not hold this type of paper qualification but whose credentials for the jobs they do are based on training and experience in their actual work situations. In addition to these two groups of scientific workers, the OECD investigators speak of 'other supporting staff' which, in the cases of France, Germany, and Japan, as well as in other smaller R & D countries, are almost as numerous

Table 1.6. Estimated Numbers of Qualified Scientists and Engineers (QSE), and Technicians engaged in R & D

	1962[1]	1963[3]	1964[2]	1965[2]	1966	1967[3]	1968[3]
USA	435,000		696,500				
France	28,000	85,430				125,230	
Germany	40,100		105,010			121,394	
UK	58,700			159,538			
Japan	—	187,080					226,298
USSR[4]	669,300			822,900	894,000		

1. All figures in this column are from F & Y, p. 72.
2. All figures in these columns are from ISY (1), p. 14.
3. All figures in these columns are from CSP, p. 7.
4. The Russian figures, for 'specialists with higher education' working in R & D, are from SPU, p. 530.

as or more numerous than the qualified scientists and engineers.

Again, the position of the United States' research and development effort is outstanding. In the first place, the proportion of QSE and technicians per 10,000 of population, at 35·8, is the highest in the western world, though Britain, with 29·4 QSE and technicians per 10,000 population, is not far behind. France, Germany, and Japan are all under 20 on this index. If we look, however, at the split between QSE on the one hand and technicians on the other, a different story emerges. Over 70 per cent of American scientific workers are QSE, and about 60 per cent of the Japanese scientific workforce are QSE. In Britain and France well under a half of the scientific workforce are QSE, and in Germany the figure is even lower. Thus, America has not only a relatively larger proportion of R & D personnel than any of the other advanced countries, but she has a better qualified scientific workforce. (All the figures in this paragraph refer to the situation in 1963–4.)

The Soviet figures are complex and not directly comparable with the figures from the West. The major difficulties involve the particular ways in which science is organized in the Soviet Union and the structure of the system of higher education. These topics are outside the scope of this work, and I can only direct the attention of the interested reader to sources from which information can be derived (see Zaleski et al, 1969). One point, nevertheless, is of such importance that it must be emphasized, for it provides one key to an understanding of Russian R & D. This is the position of the engineer in Soviet science policy in the 1960s.

The OECD report on science policy in the USSR pays particular attention to the engineer and to engineering training in the Soviet Union. Commenting on the fact that of those gaining the *Diplom* (roughly the B.Sc.) in natural science and engineering between 1961 and 1965, over 90 per cent graduated in engineering, the writer J. P. Kozlowski says:

The role of the engineer in particular is a dominant one, as evidenced by the very high percentage of engineers in this group of persons possessing higher degrees . . . it can probably be stated that the hub around which the USSR's scientific and technological development revolves is the engineer. And, as a corollary, that many of the revolutionary advances in space technology, and offensive and defensive weaponry, nuclear energy research, etc., represent a proportionately very large contribution by the engineering community . . . engineers accounted for almost half (45 per cent) of all scientists employed in the national economy in 1965 (SPU, 1969, pp. 148–9).

Although the ratio of engineers to natural scientists is especially high in the Soviet Union, the importance of the engineer as a type of scientist is increasing in most countries involved in R & D.

Neither the Soviet Union nor the United States, nor any other rich country, expends the effort involved in collecting data on scientific manpower for idle amusement or to while away the time of its bureaucrats. As with GERD, these figures are of economic and/or military importance and, indeed, one of the reasons why it is so difficult to achieve accuracy and reliable comparisons in this field is that the nations involved are politically sensitive about their achievements or deficiencies. The international prestige of science and technology is bound up with the high standard of living enjoyed by those in scientifically successful societies. Economic development and scientific manpower, then, are seen to be linked. But this simple association masks a complex of relationships in which big science, rich countries, and poor countries interact.

Scientific Manpower and Economic Development
Although some of the the OECD figures may be little more than intelligent guesswork, it is plain that the most highly developed countries have increased their R & D personnel in the 1960s at a very rapid rate. Indeed, as Harbison and Myers show in their valuable study, *Education, Manpower and Economic Growth*, the number of scientists and engineers per 10,000 population can be used as a good index of the level of development of a society. A simple and vivid illustration of this is given by these authors when they divide over seventy countries into four levels of, what they aptly label, human resource development. The GNP *per capita* in US dollars for each level was 84, 182, 380, 1100. The corresponding figures for scientists and engineers per 10,000 population were 0·6, 3, 25, and 42. (This figure is at odds with the OECD figure of 35·8/10,000 for the US cited on p. 31, but it is the relative rather than the absolute values which are important here.)

The tragic spiral is set in motion whereby the rich countries, who can afford to spend large sums of money in R & D and who can afford to train personnel for such work, become richer because R & D itself is wealth-producing, and investment in education and technical training is extremely fruitful; and the poor countries, who can barely survive at subsistence level, far less invest in R & D and massive educational programmes, get poorer (both relatively and absolutely). The greatest problem of international politics, without exaggeration, is that of breaking out of this spiral. Even a brief glance at science and science-related personnel in the rest of the world demonstrates the stupendous task of bringing the scientific and technological revolution to the underdeveloped nation.

Not surprisingly, it is very difficult to get any reliable contemporary let alone past statistics on scientific and technological manpower in the less developed parts of the world. Harbison and Myers, writing in 1964, report that information on scientists and engineers per 10,000 population was not available then for 14 out of 17 underdeveloped countries; for 18 out of 21 partially developed countries; and for 13 out of 21 semi-advanced countries. For the 16 advanced countries, however, only 5 had no information available on science and engineering personnel (Harbison and Myers, 1964, ch. 3).

A more recent attempt to show how large the gap really is between the scientific populations of the rich and the poor nations stems from the work of Price. It is easy to criticize Price's methods, but here I simply report his interesting and stimulating examination of the number of scientific authors in various countries. Price counted the numbers of first authors of scientific papers by country and city in which the research presented in the paper took place. Even though this is a very arbitrary criterion of science or scientists, it is an important measure in its own right.

The results are staggering – though not unexpected in the light of the discussion of the last few pages. The top fourteen science nations have 90 per cent of all scientists (science and scientists as understood in terms of Price's one-sided definition, of course). The top forty countries account for about 99 per cent of all scientists; and the rest of the world, about ninety countries, have the other 1 per cent of scientists. Price gives the number of scientists in the world as 126,055, so that we can say, approximately, that there are just over 1,000 scientists in most of Africa and Asia, excluding India (2,882), Israel (1,125), and a few other nations with totals in the lower hundreds (Price, 1969).

Although he does not claim much accuracy for the figures themselves, Price does argue that they accurately represent the order of relative differences between the nations. An even more vivid demonstration of this point is illustrated by a table he constructs comparing the percentage shares of world population, GNP, and scientific publishing manpower in different parts of the world. Table 1.7 is an abbreviated version of Price's table.

Table 1.7. % Shares of World Population, GNP, and Scientific Publishing Manpower (1967)

Country	Population	GNP	Publishing Scientists
USA	5·9	32·8	41·5
USSR	7·0	15·6	8·0
UK	1·6	4·8	8·1
France	1·4	4·5	5·4
Japan	2·9	3·6	4·1
India	14·4	2·2	2·3
Israel	0·08	0·15	0·9
Rest of Near East	2·5	0·85	0·4
Latin America	7·0	3·7	0·9

As can be seen, the more developed parts of the world have a greater share of GNP than population, and a yet greater share of scientists. The USSR seems to be an exception to this, but when we recall the preponderance of engineers in Soviet science, it is clear that Price's method of selection of authors of papers under-represents Soviet science because of the well-known fact that engineering scientists publish less than other types of scientists.

India is something of a middling case, where scientists and GNP are almost on a par in terms of world share, but far less than population. Latin America, on the other hand, has about half the GNP it should have if the world's wealth were spread evenly by population, and only one eighth of the number of scientists it should have if these were spread evenly throughout the world by population.

Once again let me reiterate that these figures are merely illustrative of those countries in so far as their scientists get their names first on the authors' list of scientific papers. They are *suggestive* of the differences between countries with regard to scientific personnel, but it would be quite irresponsible at this stage to assess science and scientists as a whole in terms of these proportions.

What is beyond doubt, nevertheless, is that scientists and engineers are far less numerous in the less developed parts of the world than in the more developed countries, no matter what criteria we employ to assess the differences. From this difference stem two major issues, both of immediate, if inadequately recognized, concern in present-day international politics, though like most science issues they have not been accorded the attention and study that they require. The first is the problem of the brain drain, the second that of the problem of the requirements that different societies have for scientific and technological workers.

The Brain Drain

The brain drain refers to the phenomenon of large numbers of trained men leaving certain countries and settling in others.[2] In large part this boils down today to the emigration of scientists and engineers and, indeed, professionals of all sorts from practically every country in the world to the United States. True in part though it is, this formulation conceals some very important dimensions of the total problem, such as the stages at which these people emigrate and the rates of return from the United States (and other developed countries) to their countries of birth. Let us first look at some of the facts of the matter before jumping to policy conclusions.

One indirect way of approaching the problem is to ascertain the numbers of foreign scientists working and apparently settled in the United States. Taking those born and educated to the secondary school level outside of the US as 'foreign scientists', Herbert Grubel estimates from 1964 figures that about 7 per cent of all American scientists are of foreign origin, rising to 11·5 per cent of US scientists holding Ph.D.s. As would be expected, the figures vary considerably from one branch of science to another. For example, nearly 10 per cent of physicists are of foreign origin, and 8 per cent of chemists and biologists, whereas under 4 per cent of earth and agricultural scientists and meteorologists fall within this group. As for Ph.D.s of foreign origin, the spread includes meteorology and physics at around 20 per cent and biological and earth sciences with about 9 per cent.

Grubel speculates in an interesting fashion on the further fact that the representation of scientists with respect to their national group strength in the US population is in some cases very high. The Japanese one meets in America, for example, is seven times more likely to be a science Ph.D. than the native-born American. From this Grubel argues that he 'would attach great weight to the explanation that the US immigration laws discriminate in favor of the highly skilled' (Grubel, 1968, p. 67).

This is one source of the problem. The developed countries make it rather easy for highly trained personnel to immigrate, and their obvious range of opportunities for trained and untrained, though educationally qualified, people supplies a powerful incentive for those who wish to follow particular occupations. Another aspect of this general problem is the lack of proper educational facilities in the underdeveloped world and the dilemma in which governments of these countries find themselves in trying to cope with the brain drain in its many facets.

Where a country decides that it needs a certain number of physicists, chemists, engineers, etc., and has the facilities to train only half of those it requires, then there would seem to be no alternative to sending its bright students abroad for their higher education. Thus we find large numbers of overseas students in all of the universities and technological colleges of Europe and North America, many being financed by their own governments or by other funding bodies. This is necessary where a country cannot adequately fulfil its own requirements, whether these requirements are set by one or other of the decision-making bodies within the country or even, in some cases, by outside pressures.

The paradox emerges when we observe the situation that arises for highly trained students who return home only to find that their skills are under-utilized, even when they can find satisfactory employment. There are many cases in which the aspirations of governments are not matched by the structural arrangements of the societies which they govern. Scientifically sophisticated personnel need scientifically sophisticated jobs.

The difficulty is summed up in the apparent contradiction contained in the following excerpt from a report to a UNESCO conference on Education, Scientific and Technical Training in Africa, held in Nairobi in 1968.

In addition to the imbalance that appears to exist in the distribution of trained personnel in the scientific fields, the 'brain drain' is seriously affecting many African countries. Although the number of trained Africans employed in research and teaching falls far short of *those needed for the adequate development of science*, it is evident, even so, that large numbers of African scientists trained abroad in various fields fail to return to their home lands.

... In the countries [of Africa] for which data are available, the ratio of scientists, engineers and technicians to the adult literate population is surprisingly high, being comparable to ratios in Western Europe and North America. This implies that a more balanced development of education at all levels is necessary since the rate at which trained scientists, engineers and technicians can raise the technological level of a country depends on the fraction of its population which can acquire new skills and take part in the organized economic life of the country. *Further increase in the number of scientists, technicians and others with university level training, without broadening the base of those acceding primary and secondary education would, have little point, and would result in less than an optimum progress* (Legum and Drysdale, 1969, pp. 867–8) (Emphasis added).

The brain drain, therefore, may be regarded in terms of both 'push' and 'pull' factors, those forces that drive scientists from their countries of origin, and those that draw them to other countries. In the passage just quoted there appear to be two types of 'push' factors operating; those that encourage bright students from secondary schools to acquire scientific training to fulfil the stated need for more scientists in Africa, and those that result from the shortage of adequate employment for them. Although the proportion of all African students who study abroad has declined in the 1960s from 50 to about 40 per cent, the absolute number has more than doubled as African higher education itself has expanded (ibid., p. 866). The other distinctive factor, which precipitates this situation, is that of jobs. Whether or not there are possible employment opportunities for Africans in Africa or Asians in Asia, with few notable exceptions the opportunities are very much better in Europe and in North America. Comparisons of work conditions and facilities show up the relativity of the above distinction, though it is still rather useful.

This is fully and clearly demonstrated in a paper put together by Oldham as a report on a conference organized by the Ditchley Foundation to discuss 'International Migration of Talent from and to the Less-Developed Countries'. Seven push factors and three pull factors are isolated in the discussion. The former, as I have already indicated, revolve around the issue of the uses of manpower, and the first three of these factors are elaborations of points I have made about the difficulty that trained personnel can experience in trying to find suitable employment in under-developed countries. The fourth push factor concerns salaries. Although the highly educated worker might enjoy a salary level far above the average for his own country, he could earn even more abroad. The fifth factor draws attention to the important dimension of the traditional social structure in many poor countries where certain forms of work are considered socially un-desirable. Next, Oldham mentions the problem of discrimination against minority groups, often groups with a high propensity for education; these groups may be forced to migrate, thereby depriving the host country of their talents and skills. Lastly, and similar to the sixth push factor, political conditions in very many countries can force academics and scientists who seek freedom in their work to migrate. The list of countries from which men and women have been forced to flee is still de-pressingly large, and, though this is a phenomenon that has operated for a long time, it is still, and even more so today, an affront to the civilized world.

Two of the three pull factors are, in fact, mirror images of the push factors. The developed countries, it is argued, are in a position where demand for qualified personnel exceeds the supply, and so vacancies arise which attract people from overseas. Secondly, each of the push factors is better accommodated in the developed world, thus draining off those best qualified. Thirdly, as Grubel suggested, the immigration laws of North America, Britain, and Australia, to mention only the most blatant examples, positively encourage the most highly skilled foreign immigrant.

It is at this point that one problem of scientific and technological manpower specific to underdeveloped countries, the brain drain, runs into a second problem, the actual manpower requirements that different societies claim to have. A proper study of this would involve an analysis of science policy decision making in order to discover who decides what scientific manpower requirements are, and the criteria on which these decisions rest. Here I can do no more than make a few suggestions as to how these questions might be answered and the ways in which these answers throw light on the social organization of science.

Policy, Excesses, and Shortages

In the first instance it must be noted that not all countries have science policy-making bodies. In a working paper prepared for the Science Policy Research Unit at the University of Sussex, El-Said, himself involved in Egyptian science policy-making, presented details of such bodies for 61 countries. Of the 21 OECD nations (basically Western Europe, North America, and Japan), all but five had centralized science policy making bodies – totalling 69 separate agencies in all. Of the 17 countries in North Africa and the Middle East, only three have bodies with executive as opposed to advisory powers. In South and South-East Asia 7 out of the 15 countries examined have no science policy bodies. Thus, as might be expected, the less developed part of the world seems to have far less of a basis for assessing needs for scientists and technologists than the more developed countries.

The broader decisions that the governments of poor countries have to make are difficult in the extreme. The argument often runs something as follows: to raise the standard of living we must have a better educated populace – to achieve a higher level of education for the mass of the population we must have more teachers and this requires greater investment in all educational facilities – investment in education can cost a great deal of money and can take up a great deal of resources – this means that wealth must be created from other sources to support large educational expenditures – but this is predicated on a wealthier society, a higher standard of living. We have come full circle. The problem of science policy-making is a special, though an exceptionally important, case of this general dilemma, and I shall return to these problems in the last chapter.

It is unrealistic to discuss these matters without some reference to the widespread incidence of illiteracy in the underdeveloped world, for this *fact* highlights both the desperate nature of the educational problem and also the gap between the rich and the poor nations.

At the Teheran Conference of UNESCO in 1965, called to tackle illiteracy in an international context, it was reported that although proportionately illiteracy had declined somewhat between 1950 and 1962, the number of illiterates had actually risen with population increase. In 1962 the rough estimates were that over 80 per cent of Africans, about 80 per cent of Arabs, and anything between 75 and 99 per cent of Asians in various countries were illiterate. The experts are speaking of 'a world of a thousand million illiterates' (see Jeffries, 1967, pp. 26 ff.). Though the magnitude of the problem is stupendous, determined campaigns have achieved almost unbelievable results. The best modern example is that of Cuba, where a well-planned and popularly supported effort, backed by government money and organization, taught over 700,000 people to read and write in the course of 1961. Another and earlier case is the Indian province of Bihar, where nearly three-quarters of a million people were taught to read in 1938–9. It is obviously possible.

The main point is that we may take many things for granted in the affluent and wealthy parts of the world, that simply do not apply to the rest of the world. Illiterate parents cannot read stories to their children nor can they help them with their sums; reading and writing habits which some children acquire at an early age may be entirely missing in the experiences of other children.

Having said this, it is safe to turn the coin over and to note an almost surrealist contrast. In spite of the high rate of illiteracy, in spite of the paucity of educational facilities, in spite of a myriad of pressing social and economic crises, there is evidence to suggest that certain developing countries may be producing too many of the wrong kinds of scientists and highly trained personnel. In addition, in spite of arguments about the drift from science and the shortage of technically skilled manpower that appear constantly in developed countries, there seems to be evidence to suggest that the rich countries are also producing more of certain kinds of scientists and engineers than they need. Neither the arguments nor their implications are entirely unrelated.

The main difficulty in determining the situation of those referred to as the educated unemployed in underdeveloped countries is that statistics on different types of graduates are not always easily available. However, in his aptly titled book, *The World Educational Crisis*, Coombs presents evidence pertaining to the Philippines, UAR, India, Burma, Latin America, and Nigeria which all points in the same direction – namely that these countries are producing graduates in both arts and sciences and especially in engineering, who cannot find satisfactory employment (Coombs, 1968, pp. 84–5). A recent study, *The Graduate Unemployment in India*, is the most comprehensive account to date, and a brief examination of its leading points will clarify the whole issue and give a good idea of the numbers involved for this huge and poor country. The authors, Blaug, Layard, and Woodhall, note that the phenomenon of graduate unemployment is not new in India, at least, and they point to the fact that between 1927 and 1937 ten commissions were set up in India to study acute unemployment among the educated middle classes. Indeed, the indigenous modern literature of India is preoccupied with this theme, as is much recent Asian and African writing. But it is not simply a question of an inadequate market being flooded with Arts graduates, though this is certainly part of it, for science and engineering graduates also experience high rates of unemployment, about 7 per cent, and have done so for many decades in India. This is, of course, crucially associated with the structure of the Indian educational system. The authors argue, in fact, that India is devoting too

41

much money and too many resources to university and secondary school education and not nearly enough to the primary level.

The consequences of this, if it is true, are profound. The decisions involved in making the Indian educational system more productive, in the economic terms of Blaug and his colleagues, are mainly political. Thus, we have here again a case in which the organization of science, expressed through manpower requirements, is significantly affected by political decisions. If the Indian government were to take the advice being offered by an increasing number of commentators and actually withdraw resources from the higher reaches of education, while making these resources available for the primary school sector, then it would seem to follow that the development of Indian science would be seriously affected.

This is not to say that Indian science would necessarily be adversely affected, for it might mean that all scientists and technologists and engineers produced in India would be able to find satisfactory jobs. But it would mean that the external characteristics of scientific-type careers might well change since official policy appeared to be dissuading students from taking courses in science and engineering. I am not positing an uncomplicated causal chain whereby government higher education policy will lead directly to certain easily identifiable consequences. Far from it. But I am suggesting that the reallocation of educational resources will set off a whole series of causal chains, the consequences of which might very well result in large and significant changes in the organization and practice of Indian science, in addition to the obvious effects of recruitment of technically skilled personnel.

This example from India, highlighting as it does the problem of scientific manpower in the underdeveloped world, can be adapted without a great deal of difficulty to the recruitment of scientists and engineers in the developed world and the ways in which this is influenced by political decisions. Indeed, the parallel is only too exact, for it is becoming increasingly clear that there has been serious overproduction of scientists and technologists in the West. Graduate unemployment has already struck Europe and America, although it will be some time before we can properly assess what has actually happened. Whatever the case, political decisions made with or without the wholehearted support of science advisory committees can, and do, exert substantial influence in shaping the development of science through the recruitment of scientific manpower. This is not, of course, exclusively a matter of the development of science. This is how history is made.

To put the matter in its most pragmatic context; if the government decides to go all out in order to achieve some difficult set of scientific and technological goals, then it will spare no effort, leave no stone unturned, allow no toes to remain untrodden on, to ensure that men, skills, and materials are made available. The many accounts of the Manhattan Project, the successful attempt to build an atom bomb that the American government undertook during the Second World War, provide ample testimony to this point. Hundreds of the country's most able scientists, technologists and engineers were literally taken over by the Project, massive funds were made available for certain types of research, extremely expensive equipment was commandeered or specially constructed.

The implications for science and technology of the Manhattan project are still working themselves out, more than twenty-five years after the dropping of the bomb, and they contain some curious paradoxes. The course of events in broad outlines has involved many complex factors. With the massive reallocation of resources to nuclear physics went a corresponding demand for manpower in this area and severe shortages of nuclear physicists and engineers were experienced in America in the early 1950s. In more recent years there has been a perceptible reaction against nuclear physics, and an increasing feeling that the major discoveries are more likely to emerge in the biological rather than in the physical sciences.

These developments are no doubt due in part to general changes in the career possibilities of physicists and biologists, in part to the cognitive challenges and styles of modern physics and modern biology, and in part to a host of other scientific and extra-scientific influences. One hypothesis – that, in the eyes of many young potential physicists, physics has been soiled because of its association with bombs, missiles and destruction, and that the ambitious 'atoms for peace' intentions of post-war nuclear science have not been fulfilled – bears special consideration here. In this connection, it is interesting to speculate about the future of the biological sciences. Their present flowering is not unconnected, as far as many of the practitioners are concerned, with the humanitarian implications of work in this field, and the fact that their work may contribute to human welfare in no way dissuades young people from pursuing careers in the biological sciences. However, the present quiet emphasis of many governments on chemical and bacteriological warfare (CBW) – as a 'clean' equivalent to a nuclear holocaust – may, if it is left to grow, succeed in turning away large numbers of biologists from work which could be used in this way. Already there are indications that this is happening.[3]

It is clear that many factors are intermingled in this sketchy account of some developments in American science in the last three decades. What this does show is that the 'obvious' supposition about massive government backing for one sort of science to the comparative neglect of other branches, is less than adequate. We might very naturally hypothesize that massive support would result in terrific manpower shortages in all other branches and that the area that was being funded to the hilt would have no trouble in attracting enough qualified personnel. This was not the case in American physics as a whole in 1951 and 1952, as can be seen from the fact that the greatly increased demand for R & D physicists on the outbreak of the Korean War did not stimulate anything like an adequate increase in supply. Figures from the American Institute of Physics employment register show that in these years the vacancies outnumbered those looking for jobs by five to one (National Manpower Council, 1953, p. 194). The pattern at the moment appears to be a not insignificant measure of unemployment among American physicists due in some measure to the factors cited above and also to a cutback in resources devoted to the space effort in recent years.

That maverick of sociological explanation – the self-fulfilling prophecy – comes into play at this point. Ever since the 1940s, and even before, the US government has produced many reports on scientific and professional manpower, indeed it would not be too far from the truth to observe that the US government has been almost obsessed with this subject over the past few decades.

The story has been one of recurrent crises, from the Second

World War and the rush to construct the bomb, the Korean War and the attendant draining-off of potential graduate students, the trauma of Sputnik which shocked American science policy-makers as nothing before or since, to the contemporary space programme which has eaten far into the stock of scientific financial and manpower resources. On each of these occasions the stock of scientific and technological manpower was considered to be too low and, as an extension of this opinion, the prosperity of the country would suffer because of this. The ideology of ever-increasing high-quality manpower is clearly expressed in an official publication of the National Manpower Council in the following unequivocal terms:

The United States has only about 6 per cent of the world's population. America's position as a world power, its ability to produce almost half of the world's output of goods, and its standard of living depend far more upon an advanced technology and the quality of its manpower than on the size of its working force. Underlying the high quality of the American labor force, which is a major reason for the country's remarkable productivity, is a large and complex educational structure which makes possible the training of the nation's scientific and professional personnel (National Manpower Council, 1953, p. 252).

In a very real sense this is a self-fulfilling prophecy, especially for a nation that starts out with the advantages of the United States. Define *progress* in terms of a scientific–technological society and the more scientists and technologists that are produced the more progressive will be the society. This not only instils a feeling of moral superiority but also deflects attention from those problems which are not solved directly by an increase in specialized manpower. But more of this later. What I wish to establish here is that scientific needs, and especially needs for scientific manpower, may be and often are, in fact, determined politically, and that this has repercussions both on the internal development of the particular sciences and on the relations between science and technology and the social organizations in which they take place.

This operates for scientifically advanced countries as well as for scientifically backward countries and, though the details vary considerably, the main point stands as an essential focus of the sociological study of big science. The arrangements that are made to meet the politically determined manpower requirements of science influence the development of the activities of science. However we view the matter, from the angle of the highly qualified researcher, who has to spend half of each day on routine jobs that could be satisfactorily carried out by a semi-skilled assistant, to that of the laboratory administrator who can afford to hire a battalion of bright men to follow up his and their every hunch, the answer comes out the same. In the situation of big science, as I have tried to show with respect to the funding of science, the provision of manpower has some definite extra-scientific characteristics which impinge upon and may have crucial consequences for the science that is done.

The material apparatus and the personnel of the institution of big science have been increasing at a high rate over the past decades. The numbers of scientists and engineers, it has been estimated, double every ten to fifteen years (Price, 1965, p. 7). If this continues, in the not too distant future we shall *all* be scientists and engineers. This situation has been parodied by one writer who has estimated that if the rate of discovery of sub-atomic particles and anti-particles continues on the same path as it has done from 1897 to 1962, then by the year 15,160 each physicist will have his or her own particle! (Freeman, 1962.) But not every physicist will discover an elementary particle, and the rate of increase of manpower and funds devoted to R & D has already begun to slow down. The talk is of cut-backs in science and technology, though it is most probably the case that the boom years of the mid sixties are at an end and that expenditures will level out. This new level, however, will still be enormously higher than the pre-1945 level, for the quantitative changes in the support of science and technology have led to qualitative changes in its relationships with the societies in which it exists.

Conclusion

The age of big science continues to unfold and its sheer volume of consumption and production sets much of the context of modern life. As I have tried to emphasize in this chapter, the scale and cost of science and technology, and the financial and human resources devoted to it, means that it is quite impossible to ignore as a social force. The other social structures, like the educational system, the economy, and government, are all related to science and technology in a variety of ways. They provide resources for it and receive resources from it. It is a one-sided, but not totally unrealistic picture of rich societies to see science and technology as the hub of a wheel, providing the focus for many of the most important social processes.

But the facts and figures, and the interpretations of some of them that have been offered, are marred by the *ad hoc* way in which they have appeared in recent years. The development of the field of science policy studies, particularly the work done in the last ten years, is both overwhelmingly systematic and overwhelmingly unsystematic. The masses of neat tables and complex formula that one encounters, especially from OECD, give a very strong impression that all is under control, that the reality of the data somehow corresponds to some other material reality. It is systematic in that the critic, however hostile, must pay tribute to the order created out of the chaos (often expressed clearly in the notes to tables); and unless he has the money, the time and the institutional connections, he cannot find out such figures for himself.

Unlike the intrepid anthropologist who may have the opportunity to go and discover what the Trobriand Islanders are *really* like, he who will dabble in R & D statistics is faced with an insurmountable task.

For the collection of R & D data is overwhelmingly unsystematic because most of those who do the collecting seem to have no clear idea of why they are doing it. This may, of course, be the result of theoretical reticence, but this is unlikely. Perhaps the sheer weight of data crushes the life out of any embryo hypothesis that may have originally fired the curiosity of the fact-gatherers. Nevertheless, there are still people who believe that 'the facts speak for themselves' and that we must first establish an 'empirical basis' before we can begin to speculate on the 'theoretical level'. This is true only in a very limited sense, for the concepts that we use, and the way that we use them in sifting and organizing our data, can themselves have important consequences for the possibilities of explanation. Certain problems, for example, are inexplicable in terms of the data we have, and it is often the case that the data determine what we consider to be problematic. If we do not ask important questions, then we cannot expect to get important answers.

It would be unjust to suggest that all the R & D statistics compilers are unaware of these problems. But awareness of the problems does not itself solve them. In fact, awareness may reinforce the belief that they are insoluble. I do not hold this view. The solutions, however, may emerge as a result of the penetration of the science policy field by the sociologist. Indeed, this book may be seen as an attempt to relate some of the work done in the sociology of science with science policy studies and the social organization of research and development. That this needs to be done, in order to confirm the progress of the study of the social relations of science and technology, is evident from the state of empirical unreality of much of the sociology of science, and the theoretical naïveté of much of science policy studies.

Success in this enterprise depends largely on an understanding of how science, as a social institution, works. And this is the task of Part Two.

Appendix

Basic Research and Applied Research

In 1963 an international conference set up what have come to be known as the Frascati standards for the measurement of research and development as a first step in the attempt to achieve some cross-national comparability for R & D statistics. Three types of R & D were distinguished in the *Frascati Manual*, namely basic research, applied research, and development.

An improved, new version of the *Frascati Manual* was published in late 1970. It distinguishes 'pure' from 'oriented' basic research, applied research, and 'experimental development'. However, it makes the point that 'The three categories of R & D may sometimes be carried out in the same centre by substantially the same staff. In real life, R & D activities do not necessarily fall into the three successive and distinct categories defined above. For survey purposes, artificial distinctions may have to be made . . .' (OECD, 1970, p. 11). In the brief remarks to follow, I shall try to point out some of the sociological consequences of these distinctions. For convenience I shall refer to the original and simpler distinctions. The later more sophisticated definitions do not differ substantially from them. These are defined as follows:

Basic research : Work undertaken primarily for the advancement of scientific knowledge, without a specific practical application in view.
Applied research : The same, but with a specific practical aim in view.
Development : The use of the results of basic and applied research directed to the introduction of useful materials, devices, products, systems, and processes, or the improvement of existing ones (ISY (1), p. 32).

These definitions are, generally speaking, in line with others that have cropped up in previous discussions of the subject, and they are similar to the definitions specifically offered by the National Science Foundation of America (NSF), a government-sponsored body whose function has come to be more and more concerned with the support of basic research in that country. The reason why I single out the NSF is that the American R & D effort far exceeds that of the rest of the world, both in absolute and in relative terms, as we have already seen.

The definitions of basic and applied research have important consequences for many problems in the sociology of science. For example, if the cry goes up in a society that more basic research is needed to achieve national goals, then the government might simply shift the meanings of the terms *basic* and *applied* a little and thereby be able to publish the next set of figures showing a transfer of resources from applied to basic research. This sleight of hand can also have important implications for the training of scientists and technologists, for the availability of non-governmental funds for different types of research, for the morale and productivity of research workers in different institutional locations, and for the flow of scientific personnel into and out of these locations.

On the surface, the definitions of basic and applied research accepted by the OECD appear simple and easy to operate. To determine whether a piece of research is basic or applied, all one needs to do is to ask the researchers 'Do you have a specific practical aim in view?' Another, and perhaps more practical method might be to look at the applications that scientists make for research funds, and to answer the question from these sources rather than asking the scientists direct. A third method might be to ask an expert panel for each field to rate the research projects being carried out according to this criterion.

Whichever method is used, it is clear that we might run up against a difficulty succinctly discussed by the French anthropologist, Lévi-Strauss, in his famous essay on 'Social Structure'. Here, Lévi-Strauss recalls a distinction made by the American anthropologist, Boas, to the effect that people may have 'conscious' or 'unconscious' models of the reality in which they live. These conscious models 'which are usually known as "norms", are by definition very poor ones, since they are not intended to explain the phenomena but to perpetuate them' (Lévi-Strauss, 1963, p. 281). He goes on to draw attention to a further distinction between the observers' (anthropologists') models and the participants' ('home-made') models. He is careful to remark that the bias or inaccuracy of any culture's 'home-made' models (in other words, the stories that people invent to invest their social activities with meanings that are acceptable to them) are extremely important pieces of information in their own right for an understanding of social life.

The relevance of Lévi-Strauss's comments on models of social reality to the basic/applied research distinction is immediate. Is this distinction, we might ask, merely a conscious model of scientific research which serves to perpetuate an unreal situation? Is it, in addition, properly to be interpreted as an observers' model, in the same way that visitors to a foreign country impose their own notions about the world on what they observe? Much of this boils down to the issue of whether the distinction between basic and applied research, as it has traditionally been drawn, is in any way *meaningful* to the scientists and others actually engaged in the research.

It is very difficult to ascertain the truth of the matter. There is no doubt whatsoever that the distinction is exceedingly widespread and convenient, and that it does seem to make sense of many scientific activities. There are several possibilities as to why this should be so: (1) the distinction in fact makes good sense, and realistically describes an actual state of affairs; (2) scientists and others working in science respond to inquiries in these terms because they do not wish to be distracted from their work by these extra-scientific problems, and are content to allow people who study their activities to continue to believe that the distinction is meaningful; (3) many scientists are perturbed by the distinction, which they consider to be both inaccurate and misleading, but no better alternative has either been suggested.

My personal inclination is to reject the first alternative. The main reasons for this are twofold. Firstly, the NSF and the OECD definitions of basic and applied research imply that the intentions of the researcher will determine the type of research he is doing. Therefore, if a researcher starts off with no specific practical application in view and, in the course of his work, one or more applications suggest themselves, then the research is transformed from basic to applied. If two men are working on the same project, either together or separately, and one has a specific aim in view and the other has not, then the research is basic and applied at the same time. If the sponsoring agency gives funds for a piece of research, having a specific practical application in view, and yet the researcher himself does not have such an aim, then how are we to classify the research?

Secondly, the distinction seems to suggest that research projects are unitary entities, things that we can circumscribe in terms of their operation and consequences. This is certainly not the case as far as many and perhaps all scientists are concerned. Much of the literature on scientists' views of their research, with application in mind or not, strongly conveys the impression that the nature of research is to step more or less blindly into the unknown. In addition, each piece of research begins with the potentiality of original discovery. In this light, the intentions of the researcher in terms of the applications of his findings are somewhat irrelevant. Further, where research projects have many aspects and step into the unknown at several points along the frontier of knowledge, it is quite possible that in certain respects the research can be classified as basic, and in other respects as applied.

Many of these criticisms of the basic/applied distinction can be brought against the research/development distinction, and one may be permitted a good deal of scepticism about the neat package that the OECD definition of development offers. The recent controversy over the American Department of Defense (DOD) Project *Hindsight* illustrates this well. *Hindsight* was basically an attempt to ascertain the 'economic measures of benefit . . . the payoff to Defense of its own investments in science and technology' (Sherwin and Isenson, 1967, p. 1571). The fact that the DOD had been spending about $300 to $400 million annually for research, and a further $1 billion for exploratory development in the 1960s, explains the felt need for measures of cost-effectiveness.

The *Hindsight* methodology consisted in identifying military 'Research Events' and tracing their origins back, over a twenty-year period. The results of the study (on a base of 710 Events) showed that 91 per cent were classed as technology, 8·7 per cent as applied science, and 'only 0·3 per cent of all Events were classified as undirected [basic] science' (ibid., 1574). The clear implication of this is that the DOD is wasting a lot of money on basic, that is, mainly academic research. It is along such lines that the debate developed in American science policy circles.

However, as one recent commentator has carefully argued, the real point of *Hindsight* is its 'inept, restrictive methodology' and that it was tolerated because 'it was a way of obtaining cost-effectiveness comparisons involving utilized research' (Kreilkamp, 1971, p. 64). Thus, the neat basic research, applied research and development packages are seen to be administrative and political conveniences and to ignore 'the real world of science policy' and the historical development of science and technology.

As I have noted above, some scepticism is expressed by the OECD investigators themselves. It is one thing, however, to be aware that the basic research, applied research and experimental development distinctions may not coincide with what happens in 'real life'; it is quite another thing to realize that the use of these distinctions in certain circumstances may distort reality. It is clear that the different levels of prestige and command of resources possessed by scientists is related, in some ways, to the labels by which their work is described, and that control of labels gives certain advantages to those who wish to shape reality.

I shall be returning to this theme now and again throughout the following chapters. My purpose here has not been to condemn these distinctions between different types of scientific activity as always necessarily useless or pernicious, but on the contrary to suggest some of the ways in which they might be applied.

NOTES

1. It should be added here that Wiesner, Dean of Sciences at the Massachusetts Institute of Technology, one of America's foremost scientific institutions, is careful to exclude 'basic research' and the work of the universities in general from these extra-scientific controls.

2. This is not a new phenomenon. Cipolla (1970) argues that the mobility of skilled workers and technicians in sixteenth- and seventeenth-century Europe was a most important factor in technological development, especially in the field of weapons.

3. A recent notorious case of this involved the University of Pennsylvania's Institute for Cooperative Research where, unknown to most of the members of the University, government contracts to the value of nearly one million dollars had been used to sponsor CBW research over a period of some ten years (Clarke, 1969, p. 174).

4. Particularly by Freeman (1969–70) for whose assistance in the OECD jungle I am most grateful.

Part Two
The Sociology Of Science

2 Approaches to the Sociology of Science

In Part I, I have presented some of the reasons why it is important to look at science and technology from a sociological perspective. Whether we like it or not, and (perhaps more to the point) whether we realize it or not, science and technology affect the lives of us all in a variety of known and still unknown ways. One of the major tasks of sociology has always been to investigate the consequences of social activities, both those that are intended and recognized by the people involved, and those that are neither intended nor necessarily recognized. These are often termed manifest and latent functions. In order to carry out such an investigation it is desirable to examine the ways in which the activities whose consequences we are interested in are organized. This means that in order to understand the impact of science on society, and also the impact of social forces on science, we must first consider the social organization of science.

This is, of course, an analytical device – an abstraction from reality – because the present organization of science consists the consequences, manifest or latent, of past activities. Thus, the very structure of this general type of sociological analysis is founded on the assumption that the organization of the present is a result of the organization of the past, just as the consequences of the present organization will be the future.

The arguments of Part Two rest on this common view of sociology, although I shall try to reflect some of the very different interpretations of social life that emerge from it. In the present chapter the main approaches to the sociology of science will be briefly discussed. Then a new approach, to be developed throughout the rest of the book, will be introduced.

Chapters 3, 4, and 5 are linked together as an extended evaluation of contemporary theory and research into the central problems of the sociology of science. My intention here will be to add support to those who are attempting to dismantle the old thinking and prejudices.

The Main Approaches

The sociology of science and technology is an umbrella which is shared by those sociologists who study science from a sociological perspective, and by others who also study science, from various perspectives, but with no real homes of their own. Thus, the writers from whose work I shall draw much of the information on and around science in this book are not only sociologists but also anthropologists, economists, psychologists, historians, philosophers, political scientists, educationalists, journalists, plus several working physical and biological scientists. We should not worry very much about the sometimes arbitrary distinctions between one sort of student of science and another – let it suffice to say that the sociology of science may benefit, and has benefited considerably, from the work of all of these practitioners when it has been directed towards the solution of problems concerning the organization and social consequences of science in society.

As might be expected, each of these specialists brings his own particular methods and skills to bear on such problems. It is, however, possible and convenient to separate out some of the main approaches to the sociology of science that have helped such scholars to organize their research and to interpret their results. Some of these approaches, not surprisingly, are linked to general theories of society, for as soon as science began to be seen as a social activity it began to be described and explained in similar terms to other social activities.

The first people to look at science systematically in a social context were Marxist writers such as J. B. S. Haldane, Joseph Needham, and, particularly, J. D. Bernal, all of whom were eminent scientists in England between the wars. Bernal, in his book *The Social Function of Science*, first published in 1939, expressed the essential arguments of this group in a manner and with a force that is still very relevant for the student of science today. Bernal saw science as the major tool in the transformation of the social and the natural world. Science, however, is not simply a social activity but also a practical enquiry and, Bernal claims, it can properly develop only where there is a union of theory and practice. In the pre-modern world this union was largely absent, and so the insights of the ancients had to remain mere speculation until the era of experimental science, when the experimental scientist, part craftsman and part theoretician, created modern science, in response to the material needs of his social situation.

For Bernal, the scientist is a worker, albeit with some peculiarities in his work-situation, and science in common with most social institutions is somewhat stunted in its growth in crudely capitalist societies. In science, as much as in any other single aspect of modern life, the contradictions of capitalism are apparent. This is noted by Marx in a speech delivered in 1856, where he draws attention to the 'antagonism between modern industry and science on the one hand and modern misery and dissolution on the other hand' (quoted in Bernal, 1939, p. 235). Over a century later, who is to say that the indictment is any the less relevant?

The Marxist sociology of science and technology, then, sets scientific activity clearly within the context of the Marxist theory of social change, and gives it an important place. And it was the potential of science and technology for human welfare that provided the focus for this and many other studies. The First World War had shown that science and technology were not merely hobbies for the rich and the inventive, nor were they simply marginal additions to the nation's history books: clearly science and technology were vital to national survival and prosperity.

In this atmosphere it was hardly surprising that scientists and others with various interests in science and its applications began to examine seriously the multitude of questions surrounding the social role of this traditionally neglected area. Government departments, prestigious investigating committees, the universities, and the growing voluntary associations of scientists, all contributed towards the debate, the core of which was the issue of the planning of science for the social good. The possibility and desirability of intelligent and socially beneficial science policy-making, the opposition to which declines year by year in *all* advanced nations, is the legacy of the Marxist sociology of science.

Sociologists in America, however, became concerned with the problems of the sociology of science from a quite different perspective. A long tradition, going back to Max Weber and beyond, had led to questions about the crucial institutional changes which were supposed to have shaped Western civilization. So, just as Weber himself had been concerned with the emergence of capitalism in predominantly Protestant societies, Robert Merton, in a lengthy monograph, asked whether science as a social activity was not also meaningfully and historically related to the Calvinist way of looking at the world (Merton, 1938).

Merton's conclusion, like that of Weber, was that the systems of ideas could be fruitfully related, though neither man – contrary to widespread belief – was rash enough to claim that puritanism *caused* either capitalism or science. In a series of papers, which continues to the present day, Merton has developed the modern sociology of science in a manner that concentrates attention on the way in which science as a system of social relationships operates in society. This approach emphasizes the social rules, the norms, of science and the rewards that are built into it in order that it should work efficiently.

This is the structural-functionalist approach, and is the one followed by most sociologists who study science. R. K. Merton is the most important proponent of this view and he is ably supported by many of his students who have themselves made significant contributions to the field. The basic premise of this approach is that scientists are organized into a social system and, like all social systems as analysed by the functionalists, the values and norms or rules of the system are such as to ensure that the system continues in roughly the same way as before. When things happen that might serve to disrupt the system, then mechanisms of social control, the teeth of the rules which are legitimated by the underlying values, are bared on the offending phenomena, and they are either destroyed or contained, or the system changes in some way to accommodate them. Thus, Merton points out, the virtual absence of fraud in science is explained not by the exceptional honesty of scientists (there is no evidence for or against this) but by the norm of 'disinterestedness', which holds the scientist at all times accountable to his colleagues and largely eradicates the possibility of cheating. Falsifying results is both too difficult to pull off successfully and abhorred by the scientific community, so that, as Merton comments, 'the dictates of socialized sentiment and of expediency largely coincide, a situation conducive to institutional stability' (Merton, 1963c, p. 559).

I shall return many times in the course of this book to the work of Merton and those influenced by him; but for the moment let it suffice to say that, in spite of the stimulus of this approach for the sociology of science, it has become more and more bound up with the internal workings of the social system of science, and less and less directly interested in the relations that exist between science and the social and political environment in which it takes place, though these relations (as I shall show) provide some of the most important underlying assumptions of this approach.

The third major source of information, if not insight, for the sociology of science, is the ever-expanding field of science policy studies, as is clear from Chapter 1. As I have already indicated, part of the momentum for the growth of these studies in the last decades can be traced back, at least indirectly, to the Marxist scientists who had argued powerfully that science must in some measure be planned in order that its maximum social benefit might be realized. This argument was not without its critics, even to the extent that a Society for Freedom in Science (prominent among whose members was Michael Polanyi) was active during the early 1940s to combat planning in science, or 'Bernalism' as it was sometimes called (see Rose, 1969; and Werskey in Barnes, 1972). Despite the various philosophical and sociological difficulties in the idea that scientific and technological change can be planned, science policy today is an important *fact* in the advanced industrial countries.

There are very good reasons why studies which concentrate on the numbers of scientists and technologists in different countries, on the financial and resources costs of science and related activities, on the anticipated and desired supply of qualified manpower, and so on, are the proper concern of the sociologist of science. Objections to this view would be both misguided and short-sighted; misguided because the alternative is that the sociologist should restrict himself to historical and survey material from which to make his generalizations about science. This is fine as far as it goes, though a sociology of science based on, say, seventeenth-century sources, as is Merton's early work, might turn out to be more relevant to seventeenth-century science than to twentieth-century science. The short-sightedness of the objection to science policy studies is, however, even more important, for the very categories used to measure science and scientists will tell us a great deal about how science is organized in our world. The assumptions that lie behind these measurements, and the comparisons among the countries for which they are available, will be further pointers to some significant issues concerning the place of science and technology in these countries. Science policy studies will provide essential empirical and ideological illustrations to any adequate contemporary sociology of science.

Finally, we may note the very large numbers of research reports that deal with scientists as such, rather than with science. These can hardly be dignified by description as a separate approach to the sociology of science, since they encompass a variety of approaches. Many of them, studying the scientist as an individual with special characteristics, are psychological in nature. Much work has been done on the notion of scientific creativity and the individual genius whose flashes of insight – on the tops of buses, in the bath, watching falling apples, while doing nothing at all – change the course of human history by revolutionizing science (see Taylor and Barron, 1963). While probably not demonstrably false, these explanations of scientific change are rather silly, and their superficiality serves to obscure the real complexity of the history and operation of science.

More to the point are those investigations of the types of people who are attracted to careers in science and their various social and psychological characteristics. In this connection, the issue of motivation is all-important. Many suggestions as to the forces that motivate men and a few women to pursue science and technology have been forthcoming, and a particular contribution of the sociology of science, in contrast to the less realistic psychology of creativity, has been to draw attention to the social sources of scientific motivation. Thus it is in the organization of science in particular social settings, rather than in the individuals concerned, that the sociologist looks for the motives that have produced scientists and technologists in some societies and not in others, at some times and not at others.

It would be quite misleading to suggest that these four ways of approaching science and technology are entirely distinct – I have labelled them as approaches mostly for reasons of convenience, and also to present in an introductory fashion some of the main problems that confront the sociology of science. We shall find that in this as in other sociological fields there is little actual purity of methods, and that in the present stage of its development the sociology of science and technology is experiencing an eclecticism that is not entirely unhealthy. It almost goes without saying that an approach which retains the merits and discards the limitations of previous approaches should be the goal of those who wish to systematize theory and research in the sociological study of science. Therefore, before coming to any conclusions about how the social institutions of science *really* work, we must examine the material conditions of the societies in which the scientific activity takes place and the nature of this activity, the norms and values of science and the ways in which they serve to maintain the social system of science, the political organization of science in countries at various stages of economic and social development, and the forces that motivate scientists to enter science in the first place, to stay there and to perform their tasks in a manner that ensures their continued participation and the success, however measured, of their enterprise.

What is needed, clearly, is a comprehensive framework that will both permit such a wide-ranging analysis, and that will help us to decide, once the separate factors have been analysed, which are of primary importance in the explanation of how science and technology work and the roles that they play in different societies.

A Comprehensive Framework for the Sociological Analysis of Science and Technology

The major problem in finding a comprehensive framework for the sociological analysis of anything is to ensure that the approach taken does not entirely prejudge the results of the analysis.

That is, if we decide to concentrate our attention on certain factors in a certain fashion to the virtual exclusion of others then, obviously, our results are prejudged to the extent that these other factors are pretty well ignored and will play little or no part in our explanatory scheme.

On the other hand, if we resolve to ignore none of the possible factors which might influence the operation of science in society, then the chances are that we will expand our account to such a length and complexity that at the end we will be no nearer to assessing their relative importance. Thus, there is a definite advantage to the Marxist and the Functionalist approaches to science that I have discussed which is not shared by other less systematic approaches. The Marxist and the Functionalist approaches tell us how to go about finding the answers and, in addition, the approaches themselves strongly suggest what the answers will be.

The Model Outlined

To clarify my position from the outset – I begin with a functionalist-type model for purposes of organization, and conclude with what may be termed a neo-Marxist position, for reasons which I hope will become clear.

The comprehensive framework that I shall use to organize the analysis of how science and technology may be sociologically studied takes the form of a model of social institutions proposed by the anthropologist Bronislaw Malinowski in his book *A Scientific Theory of Culture*, first published in 1944. I shall use Malinowski's model in much the same way as one might use a train. There are certain conditions attached to using such models, and to this extent one's actions are limited. On the other hand, buying a ticket and going on a journey does not commit one to the operating philosophy of British Rail, neither does it commit one to the social arrangements that make organizations like British Rail possible. In the same way, using Malinowski's model of social institutions does not commit me to the brand of social anthropological theory that he so powerfully expressed.

The model sets out the elements of any social institution that are considered to be important, and juxtaposes them in a most interesting fashion. It is particularly interesting with respect to science, viewed as a social institution; and instead of embarking on yet another interminable discussion on the definition of *social institution* I shall present the model and hope that the meaning of the concept becomes clear.

Malinowski identifies six elements in all social institutions and he organizes them diagrammatically as follows:

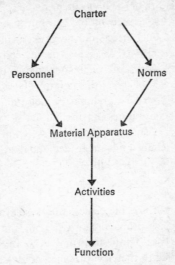

The definitions of these terms that Malinowski gives are clear and concise and I shall quote them directly. Charter is 'the system of values for the pursuit of which human beings organize, or enter organizations already existing'. Personnel is 'the group organized on definite principles of authority, division of functions, and distribution of privileges and duties'. Norms (or rules) are 'the technical acquired skills, habits, legal norms, and ethical commands which are accepted by the members or imposed upon them'. Material apparatus is 'a reserved portion of the environmental outfit in wealth, in instruments, and also a portion of the profits accruing from concerted activities'. Activities 'are embodied in actual behaviour' of the group. Function is 'the integral result of organized activities' (Malinowski, 1960, p. 53 ff.).

Science, Technology, and the Model

The first problem we confront – a problem which has bedevilled much work in this field – is to specify the continuities and discontinuities between science and technology. I shall begin with the assumption that the continuities and similarities are more important than the discontinuities and differences; and that to minimize the former and to emphasize the latter will lead us into more errors and will handicap our generation of explanations to a greater extent than the opposite procedure. The success of this book, then, rests largely on the payoff from this strategy.

Malinowski's model directs our attention at once to a set of factors which appear to be crucial for the understanding of how social institutions work. An examination of each of these factors for science *and* technology, at this point, will usefully serve two purposes. It will first be a preliminary indication of the nature and extent of the continuities and discontinuities between science and technology. Second, it will act as a sketch of the following chapters and hopefully guide the reader (and the writer) through the various arguments that follow.

Charter

The charter or purpose of science, the 'system of values' for the pursuit of which people organize or enter the institution, is of three general types. The first and most general of these charter-claims is embodied in the view that men study science as part of the quest for *knowledge for its own sake*. Thus we speak of the curiosity of the scientist and we note his single-mindedness in the search for solutions to the problems nature sets for him. This picture, however, may easily become over-romanticized, as frequently occurs in biographies and autobiographies of the great scientific heroes.

A somewhat more mundane though no less worthy charter is expressed in the view of *science for human welfare*, and though it is not necessarily antagonistic to the goal of knowledge for its own sake, it is often used in opposition to it. In discussions about the responsibilities of the scientist, for example, those who believe that science is (or should be) primarily a tool for alleviating human suffering and satisfying the needs of mankind tend to consider those who interpret science as primarily an intellectual pursuit to be socially irresponsible.

The third main charter-claim for science is that it, like many other activities, is mainly a job that people do, for salaries or profits. This is the extreme unromantic pole of the continuum

I have been describing. Science, in this account, is part of the occupationl and economic structure of certain types of societies. Once again, this view is not incompatible with the other two charters, but the different emphases are clearly important.

The charter-claims of technology overlap the last two of science. Technology for human welfare and technology as a job both serve as purposes for participating in technology and in values underlying the activity. The idea of knowledge for its own sake – though it has no exact equivalent – is largely covered by what has been termed the phenomenon of the 'sweet solution' to technological problems. This catches the notion of solving a problem because it is a problem, with the payoff in the satisfaction of the solution rather than the use to which the piece of technology may be put. As one mountaineer is reputed to have said on being asked why he climbed a particular mountain: 'Because it's there!'

Throughout the following pages, and particularly in Chapters 4 and 6, I shall be trying to identify these charters in different contexts and to draw out their consequences for the operation of science and technology and their relationships with the other major social institutions. As can be seen from the above, the overlaps between the charter-claims of science and technology seem more significant than the differences.

Personnel

We can make some large empirical generalizations about the personnel of science and technology at this point, which will be defined in later chapters. Scientists tend to work in universities and other similarly academic institutions, while technologists tend to work in industry. There are other workplaces, such as private research laboratories, government laboratories and research association facilities of one kind or another, though these, by and large, take up only a small proportion of R & D resources. Academic scientists tend to be highly qualified; almost all have first degrees and many have postgraduate qualifications. Industrial technologists, on the other hand, are less likely to have first degrees and unlikely to have postgraduate degrees. In fact, in many countries different paper qualifications for technologists have emerged, such as (in Britain), Dip.Tech., O.N.C., H.N.C., etc. These developments may well have the consequence that in the future technologists will have different rather than inferior qualifications from scientists.

A further difference between scientists and technologists is that the latter are much more liable to work in teams than the former, though with the growth of big science this too may be changing. It is probably true to say that there are now practically no independent scientists or technologists – the demands of modern science and technology alike force all their participants into organizations of increasingly larger size and greater complexity. As I have shown in the previous chapter, the supply of scientific and technological manpower creates difficult problems in poor and rich societies.

Lastly, much recent research strongly suggests that university scientists operate within a system of prestige and status whose main determinant is the publication of scholarly articles which are well-received by other members of the scientific community.[1] Industrial technologists, we are led to believe, operate more within a system in which administrative and managerial success is the basis of status and prestige.

The current literature on the sociology of science, then, tends to present a picture in which the personnel of science and technology are different in important respects. In Chapters 3 and 5 I shall examine the evidence for this view in some detail. It is to the next element of the social institution, the norms, that we must turn in order to penetrate to the heart of the matter.

Norms

The discussion of the norms of science revolves round the writings of Merton, and it is convenient and not entirely unrealistic to take his famous four institutional norms as the reference point for this sketch. These norms – Communalism, Universalism, Disinterestedness, Organized Scepticism (hereinafter referred to collectively as CUDOS) – represent the rules generated by the needs of science as an institution.[2] These needs must be satisfied if science is to survive and prosper, and so observance of these rules or norms is the key to scientific progress as a social process. Merton himself says little about technology in these terms, but it is reasonable to assume that, for a variety of reasons, technologists might be characterized by problems associated with their limited ability to live up to CUDOS.

A development from Merton's view, which can be termed the neo-Mertonian position, has emerged from the work of some of his ex-students and others influenced by his approach. Neo-Mertonianism tends to be rather individualistic in tone. It concentrates on such matters as the scientist's desire for recognition through publications; it expands Merton's theory of the role of originality in science into an interest in creativity; and it says a great deal about the reward system in science.

Other neo-Mertonians have looked into the situation of scientists and technologists in industry and have generally explained the norms of technology in two interrelated ways. First, the frustrated CUDOS syndrome appears. Then, as a response to this frustration, these technologists give up the attempt to be *real* scientists and switch to different, usually professional or managerial norms. Thus, as was suggested above, on this view the personnel of technology adopt an administrative status system and operate by the appropriate norms. These, the argument goes, are antagonistic to CUDOS, and this is said to explain the fact that certain types of technologists (mainly those who might be realistically called industrial scientists) have problems at work and low job satisfaction.

The next approach to the norms of science and technology – what I shall term 'anti-Mertonianism' – consists mainly in the attack on CUDOS as both empirically and theoretically unacceptable. CUDOS is more honoured in the breach than in the observance; scientists do not behave in this way; science does not need CUDOS to survive. An interesting variant of anti-Mertonianism is the celebrated essay of T. S. Kuhn (1962).

The position of the anti-Mertonians on the norms of technology – when one is manifest – is that technologists reject CUDOS. The important point here is that *industrial* technologists (and scientists) are said to reject the institutional norms embodied in CUDOS because they are deemed to be *academic* norms and inappropriate to the industrial setting. This leads us to the brink of the analysis of the norms of science and technology which, by and large, will be advanced in this book. For want of a better term, I label it the neo-Marxist approach.

The neo-Marxist view, which originates specifically with Bernal, refuses to consider scientists and technologists in isolation from their socio-economic position. Scientists and technologists, like other workers in advanced industrial societies, operate within the constraints of their work situations, and in terms of their economic interests. It is, therefore, the academic and the industrial situations themselves, rather than science and technology, that we must study in order to explain how different groups of workers act. We should therefore expect to find that the scientist and technologist in industry have more in common with each other than each has with his counterpart in the university, and vice versa.

Part Two of the book is mainly devoted to these problems. On completing that, I shall be in a position to modify the model of Malinowski, with which I started, so that it might more adequately accommodate the main arguments I have presented.

Material Apparatus

The material apparatus of science tends to be on a smaller scale than that of technology. Often the terms 'little science' and 'big science' are used to differentiate them. The facts that (a) these terms have gained very wide currency in the last decade; and (b) they rather beg the question about the relative importance of the continuities as against the discontinuities between science and technology, provide some useful support to my original assumption that the continuities are more important than the discontinuities. In the light of my remarks on norms, above, it may be added that most little science goes on in universities and most big science in industrial laboratories. It is not surprising, therefore, to learn that a far greater proportion of total R & D funds is devoted to technology than to science.

Activities

The activities of science and technology – in many ways the normal method of distinguishing between them – point up the continuity/discontinuity issue clearly. At the extremes, there is little difficulty. No one would call pure research in theoretical physics technology, nor would any call product development science. Generally, pure and applied research are considered scientific, and applied research and development technological. I have already argued that the basic/applied research distinction is a convenience (often with socio-economic consequences) and that this is yet another reason for emphasizing the continuities between science and technology, and minimizing the differences. My assumption here, then, is that at the edges it is easy to distinguish science from technology, but there is a significant area between these in which the distinction is not very useful.

A clear difference that we can identify, however, is that scientists very often have teaching responsibilities, whereas technologists very often carry out administrative and managerial tasks. This is, in any case, mainly a consequence of the facts noted above that scientists mainly work in universities and technologists mainly work in industry. I shall not be treating *activities* separately in the following pages; it is more convenient to subsume them in discussions of *personnel* and *norms* as and when appropriate.

The operation and interaction of all these elements have specifiable results. Science and technology as social institutions, that is, have consequences for the society of which they are parts, just as the elements of science and technology may themselves be considered as consequences of other social phenomena.

Functions

The function of both science and technology in modern societies is nothing if not to increase the economic and military capacities of these societies. Despite the stated intentions of some of those who decide the finances of science and technology, and many of those who actually work in them, the utilitarian consequence cannot be denied. There is, nevertheless, a claim that is often made with regard to certain kinds of science, especially (at present) high-energy physics, that science is a cultural activity and that it should be judged by its aesthetic rather than its economic results. We should expect this view to be held by those most sympathetic to the claim that the charter of science is the search for knowledge for its own sake.

At a time when science can cost a great deal of money and can utilize large numbers of highly trained people, it is perhaps relevant to question its imputed cultural function. It is no part of my argument to suggest that science should never have such a function, but I will most strongly insist that in a world of massive deprivation the utilitarian, where possible and where appropriate, should have higher priority than the aesthetic. Man, indeed, cannot live by bread alone. But there are too many men and women and children in this latter part of the twentieth century, who do not even have bread. Thus, there are added polemical reasons, in my opinion, for stressing the continuities between science and technology in terms of the functions they do and should fulfil in the world today.

The Science–Technology Continuum

In this outline of how Malinowski's model might help us to assess the continuities and discontinuities between science and technology, I have argued the case that they are on a continuum, and that this is a promising point of departure for a sociology of science. Though the social institution of science and technology might seem a rather abstract and remote thing, it is really all about how certain people (for example, scientists, bureaucrats) act in certain social situations (scientific research, laboratory management), and how these actions affect other people (for example, industrial workers, politicians, generals, the hungry) in other social situations (for example, threatened redundancy, economic crisis, war, famine).

Having introduced the model, I shall now go on to use it in the analysis of some of the major problems in the sociological study of science and technology. Some of these have emerged from my account so far, and others will be provoked by the very inadequacies of the model itself, as it now stands. The next three chapters will examine (in turn): the work situations of scientists and technologists as investigated within the framework of the orthodox Mertonian sociology of science; problems of the Mertonian norms themselves and other problems of the charters of science; and the theoretical and empirical destruction of the CUDOS.

1. For an interesting and detailed account of the operation of Scientific Communities, see D. Crane, *Scientific Communities and the Growth of Knowledge*, Chicago, 1971.
2. See Chapter 4 for a detailed discussion of CUDOS.

3 Science as Work

In Part One, I have tried to draw a picture of big science. I sketched the broad outlines of its material apparatus, in terms of money and projects, and of its personnel, in terms of manpower figures. There we saw that science in the 1960s has proved to be a costly business and that it utilizes the skills of large numbers of qualified workers. In this chapter I shall look at the personnel of big science as workers, in order to show how changes in the organization of twentieth-century science and technology have had important repercussions for those who work in them and for the work they do. If the sociology of science ignores these changes, then its reliability is open to question.

In adding more flesh to the bones of the social institution of science that I presented in the previous chapter, it will become more and more obvious that the different parts of Malinowski's model of an institution may only be kept separate in theoretical analysis. Questions about the activities of scientists and technologists will necessarily imply questions about the charter and the norms of science, and information about these scientists and technologists will serve as indispensable building blocks for the analysis of the charter and norms of science which follow on in later chapters.

Main Features of the Scientific Work-Situation
Scientists are to be found mainly in three types of employment, namely in academic institutions, in industry, and in governmental establishments.* They usually work in laboratories, have paper qualifications, and they are paid at a rate which is above

---

* In fact, most people with scientific training work as schoolteachers. In common with most other writers in this field, I exclude them on the grounds that they typically are not engaged in any sort of research or development activity.

the national average. The public stereotypes of the man in the white coat bent over the test tube or the absent-minded professor with a piece of chalk poised in front of a blackboard portray myths built up around essential kernels of truth.

These essential kernels of truth, however, have generally failed to accommodate other and more important facts concerning the ways in which science has changed, especially in the last fifty years or so. In this period, many scientists have become organization men to a greater or lesser extent, in the sense that they now work in teams within organizations requiring a high degree of bureaucratization, they often handle large sums of money, and they are often responsible for complex and expensive premises and equipment. This is *big science*. The lone scientist working industriously by himself with his own materials and apparatus is largely, but not entirely, a thing of the past. This is *little science*. One significant indicator of this fact is that the proportion of papers published in scientific journals having multiple authorship has increased enormously in the last several decades. In September 1964 the journal *Physical Review Letters* published a paper written by twenty-five people from six laboratories in five countries! This, then, is the age of big science, and although the little science of the past lingers on, and although it is still possible to produce important science with inexpensive equipment and only a few researchers, I am here concerned with the factors associated with the comparatively recent transformation from little science to big science.

These factors are directly reflected in the work situations of scientists and technologists and in the variety of career patterns which exist for them.

Place of employment, though probably the most important single predictor of the work situation of scientists and technologists, is not the only one. Many studies have been devoted to the *specialisms* of scientists and technologists. Chemists (Strauss and Rainwater, 1962; Paul, 1970), physiologists (Gerard, 1958), bio-medical scientists (Glaser, 1964), mathematicians and physicists (Hagstrom, 1965; Cole and Cole, 1967, 1968), engineers (Gerstl and Hutton, 1966; American Society for Engineering Education, 1968), and other specialisms have all been singled out for special and extended treatments. My purpose in this chapter is to generalize rather than to particularize, and so I shall, for the most part, emphasize the similarities rather than the differences between the various branches of science and technology.

Another aspect of the work situation that has been investigated concerns the *types* of R & D carried out. As I have commented on this in the Appendix to Chapter 1, and have expressed doubts about the validity of the distinctions between basic research, applied research, and development, I shall merely note that these distinctions between types of research have sociological consequences which will crop up from time to time in the following pages.

Last, and this differs from the other factors I have mentioned, in that it is an attitudinal variable, much work has been done on the orientations of scientists and technologists to their occupational tasks. One formulation of this is that some scientific workers are 'science oriented' and others are 'administration oriented'.

In what follows I shall concentrate mainly on the first and last of these factors – place of employment and orientation. The basic problem that is set by much of the literature of the sociology of science concerns the relationship between the social situation of the scientist, which will clearly include his training and his conditions of work, and the attitudes that the scientist has towards his work. As I pointed out in the last chapter, the current orthodoxy, represented by the Mertonian sociology of science, suggests that the institutional norms (on whose satisfaction the survival and progress of science depends) are easier to live up to in academic settings than in industry. (Government laboratories seem to occupy an intermediate position in this respect. Here I shall restrict myself in general to academic and industrial science and technology. In Chapter 5 I briefly report some research which compares the three types of workplaces.)

It is obvious that the situation of the theoretical physicist doing basic* research in a major university and who values his complete freedom to select problems, to publish what he likes, etc., differs from that of the industrial chemist developing some

---

* Although the criticisms of the basic/applied research and development distinctions that I made in Chapter 1 still stand, I have to use the distinctions in the following pages to present the argument. It is perhaps a good example of Thomas' self-fulfilling prophecy: if men define situations as real, they are real in their consequences. The distinction between basic and applied research may not always be real; its consequences certainly are.

product for the company on whose board he sits, and who approaches his research within an administrative framework which encourages him to spend time only on problems that appear commercially profitable, and not to publish results that will be of use to commercial competitors, etc. These are two opposite endpoints of a very long continuum, which includes those centres of higher education that are heavily subsidized to carry out service work for their industrial sponsors, as well as those laboratories of large firms whose research staff do fundamental research of critical importance (such as Bell Telephone where, to date, four Nobel prizewinners have carried out their prizewinning work).

The view that I shall put forward in this and the next two chapters is that it is not so much the scientific training of scientists and the necessity that the institutional norms be fulfilled that best explain how science works, but rather that it is the material demands of the work situation of different groups of scientists and technologists that best explains the operation of science. From this we may derive a series of hypotheses about the likely effects of science on other social institutions and vice versa.

In order to follow through this analysis, and at the same time to document some of the work in the field, let us begin examining some of the problems involved in explaining how scientists find their way into different work situations.

Recruiting Scientific Workers

Problems of recruitment occur when jobs fail to attract sufficient numbers or sufficient quality of workers, or both. In science and technology the usual form of the recruitment problem concerns the difficulty that industry appears to experience in enticing the brightest young scientists into its laboratories. The groves of Academe appear more congenial than the halls of Mammon to the freshly capped B.Sc., M.Sc., and Ph.D.

Why, it is asked, does industry fail to attract the numbers and quality of science graduates that it says it needs? Whether or not this is in fact the case, and many British Government reports together with much independent research seems to accept the view, it presents an interesting set of issues. These have relevance for the occupational choices of young people, the ways in which universities and colleges prepare science students for their working lives, and for the relative attractions of the different employment locations in which scientists might work.

On the surface this appears to be a fairly simple problem, and variables like the salaries and conditions offered in universities compared with those offered in industry have been examined, along with other variables like the sorts of research the young scientists would prefer to do and their pictures of these potential types of employment. The most plausible of the explanations suggested is that university scientists, in some manner or other, manage to imbue their students, especially those students who are most likely to attain the best degrees, with the idea that basic (or fundamental or pure) research is the most satisfying avenue for scientific talents, and that only in the university is one assured of the conditions for carrying it out. Thus, in spite of the documented lower salaries and less good facilities in universities as opposed to industrial laboratories,[1] the best graduates in science choose the former employment, and the rest of the young scientists go into industry only because they know that they will not get university jobs.

This is of course something of an exaggeration, but it is the opinion favoured by most of those who have written on the problem, and a little milder than the views expressed a few years ago by Mr Chambers (1964), one of the largest employers of scientists in Britain. It is quite true that scientists are far more likely to be engaged in pure research in universities than in either industrial or government laboratories. In their study of about 3,000 members of the American Chemical Society, Strauss and Rainwater (1962, p. 92) reported that whereas most of the academic chemists in their sample were assumed to be doing basic research, in industry only 11 per cent and in government only 36 per cent were engaged in basic research. Denis Pym, investigating British research chemists, found roughly similar results. Of the academics, 88 per cent were engaged in pure research, compared to 18 per cent in industry and 26 per cent in state employment (Pym, 1964, p. 32). Vollmer and his colleagues in a series of studies contrasted a university research laboratory with other industrial laboratories and found that, in the former, eleven out of fourteen faculty researchers were engaged in pure research (about 80 per cent) while in one of the latter, a nuclear industrial research organization, of the science researchers only 9 per cent were (5 out of 46) (Vollmer, 1964, pp. 21, 56). These trends are unmistakable. Most academic scientists are engaged in pure research; less than half of government scientists and very few industrial scientists are so engaged.

This factual finding is borne out in the volume by Mees and Leermakers, *The Organization of Industrial Scientific Research*, the second edition of which was published in 1950, thirty years after the first. It may be regarded as an authoritative statement, coming as it does from two of the most successful industrial laboratory executives in the United States. Not merely describing contemporary organization but reinforcing the standards they wish to maintain, they state that 'between 10 and 20 per cent of the laboratory work is devoted to fundamental research', the rest to various forms of applied research (p. 44). It is not often that we find such a close coincidence between the philosophy of an organization and what happens in practice – this is obviously a case where the charter and the function of this small-scale institution within an institution are in harmony!

Therefore, any student who is a potential working scientist, and who cares to peruse the evidence, will reach the conclusion that his teachers have been telling him the truth and that, indeed, if he wishes to do pure research, then he had better stay in the university. But why will he wish to do pure research, with the clear implication that the salary and physical conditions he will experience will be less attractive on the whole than in industry? And will the skills that he develops and the abilities he will demonstrate in carrying out such work be superior to those exercised in applied research and other forms of scientific activity? The answers to these questions must be mainly inferred from responses to questions about job satisfaction put to working scientists, though there is a little evidence of a more direct nature.

Many researchers have asked scientists and those about to enter careers in science for their views concerning work conditions in various settings. These questions often relate the freedom that the scientists will experience and have experienced in universities and in industry, and special attention is paid to problems of control over one's own work life and the autonomy that the scientist has in selecting research problems and carrying out research programmes. The evidence in the majority of cases points to the conclusion that university scientists do experience more freedom and autonomy and, generally, more job satisfaction than those in industrial or government laboratories. Further, the evidence shows that science students are not only aware of this state of affairs but actually assume that this will be the case, even appearing to use this information and these expectations in choosing careers.

Job satisfaction is a composite idea made up of different factors. Pym, in the research on British chemists I have already referred to, distinguished several sources of dissatisfaction experienced by his respondents: problems of manpower (insufficient supporting staff), facilities, organization and control, communications, status and advancement, and remuneration. The findings clearly indicated that academic chemists were considerably more satisfied than industrial scientists, with state scientists in between but much nearer to the industrial researchers in their level of satisfaction. This was especially noticeable where the organization and control questions were concerned. For the industrial chemists, from 195 people came a total of 449 complaints of which 202 were about organization and control, whereas 154 academic chemists had 310 specific complaints, of which only 49 were in this category. That is, nearly one half of all complaints of industrial researchers were concerned with organization and control, as against only one sixth from the academics (Pym, 1964, p. 33).

The findings of Strauss and Rainwater from their large sample of American chemists are similar to the British results. Strauss and Rainwater asked two questions that are of particular interest in this connection. They asked academic and non-academic chemists how characteristic they thought the following statements were of their work situations – 'I have ample opportunity to use my training and ability to best advantage' and 'I have considerable freedom to use my own judgement and initiative'. These statements were considered to be *very characteristic* by 60 and 82 per cent of the academics respectively, and in each case by fewer of the industrial chemists. Leaving aside the administrators, who are in a privileged position in industrial research laboratories, the full-time industrial scientists were at best between 15 and 20 per cent below the university workers in asserting that conditions did allow ample utilization of talents and freedom. For those industrial scientists below the Ph.D. level the differences were nearer 30 per cent (p. 112).

Students and their Expectations

That it is more often the abstract and analytical skills and training that are under-utilized by industry seems to follow from this evidence, because these characteristics are assumed to be more relevant to pure than to applied research, and it is pure research that is largely neglected in the industrial laboratory. Support for this view comes from some interesting studies on the preferences of science and engineering students for college curricula. The researchers, Krulee and Nadler, asked a series of questions of about 450 first-year students at a well-known American Technological University. Students in the science group, when asked about their choices for first position after graduation, ranked graduate school highest, both as the ideal and as the realistic first choice, followed by basic research as the ideal second choice, with applied research the realistic second choice. The mechanical engineering students, by comparison, ranked equipment design as their ideal first choice, with production work as their realistic first choice. Second, both ideally and realistically, was new product development, and applied research came third again as both an ideal and realistic choice. Thus, we may assume for all practical purposes that the science group in this sample (about 140 respondents), represents a potential university, basic-researching group, and that the mechanical engineers, about 90 in number, represent a potential industrial, applied research and development group. With this reasonable assumption in mind, it will be instructive to compare the views held by Krulee and Nadler's two groups.

When the students were asked to rank their ideal and realistic job expectations on a 10-point scale, the scientists and the engineers ranked roughly the same characteristics highly. One significant difference, however, is that while science students gave 'leave me free of supervision' fifth place as an ideal characteristic and sixth equal place as an expected one, the engineering students gave it seventh equal and tenth places respectively. This means that the science students considered themselves actually to have a fair chance of being free from supervision in their jobs, whereas the mechanical engineering students considered it the most unlikely characteristic of any work they could realistically expect to do.

That this is related in an indirect fashion to the different types of research work that the students seem to expect to be doing is reflected in the role they give to 'good grounding in basic theory' as a quality essential for success in their chosen fields. The scientists put this at the very top of their list of qualities (but equal to 'hard work'). The engineers on the other hand place 'ability to express yourself' first, 'practical knowledge of facts in your field' second, 'hard work' third, and 'theory' a rather poor fourth. Thus, whereas the scientists in this sample tended to emphasize theoretical skills and to feel fairly confident about job autonomy in their future careers, the engineers ranked administrative and pragmatic skills most highly and tended to expect little job autonomy in their careers.

Krulee and Nadler make a very pertinent comment on this state of affairs in remarking on the theoretical content of many courses:

... it is not surprising that many students are uneasy about the increasing emphasis on analytical skills, nor that they expect that insufficient time will be given to the development of their administrative abilities ... The faculty would appear to plan as if the desirable outcome were the only alternative and to ignore some less desirable possibilities that the students evaluate as highly realistic (Krulee and Nadler, 1960, p. 158).

Thus are created university and industrial scientists!

The results of researches on British science students provides further elaboration of this process whereby the young potential scientist picks up information about the sorts of experiences he is likely to have in university and industrial research laboratories. A great deal of interesting and relevant information is provided by two studies carried out by Donald Hutchings and published in monograph form in 1963 and 1967. The first, *Technology and the Sixth Form Boy*, is of wider scope than its too limited title suggests, and the second, *The Science Undergraduate*, follows up the findings of the first on a sample of over 2,000 students of science and technology at five English universities.

Technology and the Sixth Form Boy is a study of nearly 1,500 schoolboys in science sixth forms, and Hutchings sets out to test the widespread hypothesis that the brighter students prefer careers in pure science, whereas the less bright ones choose applied science, mainly engineering and technological subjects. This hypothesis is clearly borne out by the English evidence where brightness is measured by A-level success, though it is notable that the pattern is somewhat different for certain other European countries. What is at issue here, however, is why this should be so, and Hutchings very properly examines the attitudes of the boys towards pure and applied research, and, by implication, careers in the university and those in industry. The distinction between 'pure' and 'applied' appeared to be significant to the boys, the first being identified with the scientist, and the second with the technologist, while research itself seems the preserve of the scientist and the technologist is left with 'routine practical work'.

Hutchings comments that 'pure' and 'research' 'seemed to connote something magical and idealistic and both were attached firmly to the scientists . . . An overwhelmingly large number of boys stated a preference for "pure research" as a career and this was always equated with pure science . . . Research seemed to be favoured for its independence, variety, rewarding results . . . reasons for choosing engineering and technology were often materialistic' (Hutchings, 1963, p. 34).

Of the 1,423 boys in the sample, 580 had chosen to study pure science and 293 had chosen engineering (applied science). The desire to do research was the main reason, by far, why those who had chosen pure science had done so. In fact, two thirds of the total sample included research as one of their top three career choices. Of course, not everyone who wishes to do research is able to do it, and this is especially true where 'research' is equated with 'pure research' in its university context. Hutchings reports that 'many boys said that they were "not good enough" to do research and had therefore chosen applied work. There seemed to be general agreement among the sixth-formers that the "best brains" were needed for research and that, therefore, to be doing research was to be "at the top".' Not only was this so but university research 'was almost always preferred to research in a government department or in industry: the reason for this was usually given as the greater independence of university researchers; but the dreaming spires of university life seemed always to be before the boys as an ultimate goal' (ibid., p. 40).

This attitude was so strong that 53 per cent of the English boys who had chosen pure science considered that the study of various technologies was not appropriate to universities, which are concerned with fundamental scientific ideas, though the view was rejected by a majority of the sixth-formers in the total sample.

The carry-over of these phenomena into the university by the science students, after having experienced to some extent the reality against which previous expectations could be measured, was investigated by Hutchings in *The Science Undergraduate*. The sample consisted of 1,233 students of pure science and 791 engineering students, the applied scientists. Among the former were 117 women (9·5 per cent) and among the latter only 4 women (0·5 per cent). A notable feature of this work is that it is careful to distinguish *among* the pure and applied sciences, in this case maths, physics, chemistry, and zoology, as contrasted with civil, mechanical, electrical, and general engineering, as well as *between* pure and applied science. This detail does not, it is true, alter the general conclusions that are reached, but it does indicate that there are important differences between subjects within the pure and applied groups.

The demand for research places leading to higher degrees in the university was very strong in this sample – as Hutchings says, 'a very common remark was, "If I get a good enough degree, I hope to stay on and do research"' (Hutchings, 1967, p. 9). In fact, over 70 per cent expressed this view. Let us look at the breakdown of those who wished to do Ph.D. degrees by subject and by class of degree expected. Not surprisingly, in light of the evidence I have already reported, a greater proportion of pure science students intended to do research for the doctorate than applied science students, 54 to 25 per cent. These figures conceal some large differences: for example, about 60 per cent of physicists and chemists wished to do Ph.D.s, while only 35 per cent of mathematicians so wished, this latter figure being comparable to the 31 per cent of electrical engineers in the same category, as contrasted to only 17 per cent of general engineers (exclusively Oxbridge) who intended to take the Ph.D. On the other hand, nearly 60 per cent of all applied scientists expressed the intention of taking some post-graduate qualification with one of the professional institutions as opposed to only 3 per cent of the pure scientists, and with the civil engineers the proportion seeking this course was almost three out of every four.

In England, a first-class or very good second-class degree is usually essential if the student is to obtain a place to do research and financial aid to support him. It is therefore all the more interesting to learn that of the 64 per cent of students who hazarded a guess as to the class of degree that they would achieve, well over half who did not expect to earn firsts or top seconds still intended to do research. Of those expecting the better degrees, 88 per cent of the predicted firsts and 77 per cent of the predicted upper seconds intended, definitely or probably, to do research. Reteroactive validation of these intentions – reality testing – is provided by an analysis of past trends in numbers of science graduates continuing to do research degrees. This shows that most pure science students with first-class degrees stay on to do research, while less than half of applied scientists with firsts do so. Further, about a quarter of those with degrees lower than upper seconds manage to stay on to seek research degrees, and more pure than applied scientists in this category succeed in this respect.

Although Hutchings does not explain this seeming paradox, one important contributory factor may be suggested: many students who do not get very good degrees are offered assistant-ships which often lead to registration for higher degrees, and so in some ways, certainly financially, the man with the first-class degree is less well off than his fellow researcher with a lower second or a third-class degree. (Degree results, however, do not appear to be particularly good guides to research success, as, indeed, A-level results are by no means sure indicators of good degree results.)

Students who had definitely decided to do research were questioned about their research intentions, and, as Hutchings explains, 'the most striking single fact to emerge from the students' interviews was the almost complete lack of ideas about future postgraduate research' – only 2·5 per cent (19 out of 763 students) had even 'fairly specific plans'. The fact that the other 97·5 per cent were speculating, with varying degrees of vagueness, must make us a little wary in interpreting the figures Hutchings gives about their preferences for pure and applied research.

These are as follows: of the 493 pure scientists in this sub-sample, 66 per cent intended to do pure research, while only 12 per cent of the 288 applied scientists wanted to do pure research. Within these totals, 80 per cent of the chemists, the largest single subject group in either total, opted for pure research, with the proportions of the other three pure science groups (maths, physics and zoology) doing likewise being all in the 51 to 59 per cent range. As for the applied scientists, of the 88 per cent choosing applied research, 92 per cent of the civil engineers did so, the electrical and mechanical engineers both had proportions in the high eighties, and the general engineers 75 per cent. The two most deviant groups, the zoologists, of whom a bare majority chose pure research, and the general engineers, of whom one in four opted for pure research, were unfortunately represented in this sample by rather small numbers, 41 and 20 respectively, and so it is difficult to draw any strong conclusions from this particular aspect of the study. It is possible that in the case of the zoologists the fact that over a third of the original sample were women, and that the general engineers were exclusively from Oxbridge, both doubtless important variables, influenced these research decisions. The information is not available to allow us to comment further on this.

On this sample of science undergraduates, then, the same sorts of conclusions emerge once again about research experiences and conditions in universities as compared with those in industry. To quote Hutchings's summary which condenses the results of the students' ratings of various phenomena related to scientific research:

. . . research in universities was thought to be much less restricted than in industry, with greater freedom to choose the problem of study and much less pressure to produce quick results. Industrial research was characterized by applied problems, team-work rather than individual work, and concerned more with refinements of known techniques than with new discoveries. The benefits of industrial research included more up-to-date equipment, better physical conditions, more technical assistance and greater financial support (ibid., p. 59).

Unfortunately, Hutchings does not tell us of the differences between the pure and applied science groups in their assessments of university as against industrial research – it would be rather surprising if they were insignificant. Indeed, the main criticism that can be levelled against these studies is that they are too short. For example, it would be interesting to learn of the breakdown of the various responses on *all* the variables selected to differentiate the groups, and not simply on some, apparently idiosyncratically chosen. One wonders why we are given the characterization of research workers by year of study alone, and not by the pure/applied and subject distinctions.

The problem that has run through my account so far is the general one of explaining why university science has the characteristics and the reputation it has and why industrial science has other characteristics and quite a different type of reputation. The forces operating on teachers and students and industrial personnel in science that influence them to validate many of the impressions they receive from various significant others, are both internal to their own institutional situation and external in terms of the general societal demands made on them.

As we have seen, the images of science and technology are largely defined on the basis of *where* the scientific activity is carried out, rather than the *type* of scientific activity that is performed. Universities are places for basic research and pure scientists. Industry is where technologists carry out applied science. The workplace and its tradition constrains the science that can be performed. It is a short step from this position to the argument that the *real* scientist who finds himself in industry will be unhappy, not simply with respect to the low job satisfaction reported by Strauss and Rainwater, and Pym, and others, but profoundly frustrated because his work situation prevents him from living up to the institutional norms of science.

Let us now turn, therefore, to the imputed dilemmas of the industrial scientist.

Scientists in Industry

Several sociologists of science have developed sets of theoretical constructs which are supposed to represent clusters of characteristics pertaining to the typical university scientist and the typical industrial scientist. These constructs are seen as either polar types of opposite extremes located on the same continuum, such as 'professional *vs.* organizational' scientists, 'science oriented *vs.* administration oriented', and sometimes even 'scientists *vs.* technologists'. The present status of these constructs in the sociology of science is fluid, for as more information has been accumulated about the characteristics of scientists doing different types of jobs, it is often difficult to remain convinced that a previously plausible classification continues to be useful.

The current image of the industrial scientist is of one who has severe problems, specific to his position as a scientist in a non-academic setting. This is not simply a case of university scientists being more satisfied with their work lives, but also (as many writers suggest) that there is something inherent in industrial situations that causes people trained as scientists to experience certain strains and pressures. This is easily amplified into the implication, expressed by Hutchings's pure science sixth-formers, that somehow universities alone are the proper place for *scientists*, and that almost by definition those who might appear to be scientists, but who work in industry, are really a sort of second-class citizen, called *technologists*. Nevertheless, those who go into industry are not always willing to relinquish the title of scientist, and they are not always prepared to be technologists. They consider themselves to be scientists who happen to work in industry.

This situation is analysed by Simon Marcson in his monograph on *The Scientist in American Industry*, published in 1960 under the auspices of the Industrial Relations Section of the Department of Economics at Princeton University, a study of a research laboratory of a large corporation, disguised by the name Pacific Electronics Company (PEC). The research staff of this laboratory numbered 449, of which over 60 per cent of the professional staff were directly engaged in research; nearly 30 per cent were technicians; and the remainder were in managerial or supervisory positions.

Marcson operates on the assumptions that:

By education and by professional training, research chemists or physicists are usually concerned with research achievements which will bring scientific recognition . . . scientists develop such needs as recognition, involvement, and self-realization, which in time come to define their goals . . . In short, the scientific community and the business community have different ideas about what is valuable and worth while (Marcson, 1960, p. 5).

No evidence is given for these broad statements, but, on the basis of such unproved assumptions, the author sees fit to erect an argument that purports to analyse the inevitable strains that the scientists in industry will experience, and to suggest some remedies. From the interviews that he conducted with some of the scientists and managers in the PEC laboratory, Marcson does report some indirect evidence bearing on this point, but this leads on to further difficulties involving the distinction between basic and applied research, nowhere defined. The view that is put forward leads one to suspect that the company hires young scientists on false pretences (assuring them that they will have some freedom to choose their own research projects, whether basic or applied), that it proceeds to teach them how to behave in industrial research organizations (by establishing hierarchical chains of authority and interfering with their research), that it does this so successfully that most scientists eventually adapt (even to the extent of redefining scientific research itself), and that administrative skills and practices become of primary importance in the conduct of the laboratory. This conduct 'sets research in a predetermined direction. It provides an over-all controlling system for the direction research will take. It even does more than this. It influences and controls the research results' (ibid., p. 115).

How are these remarkable management triumphs accomplished? Before giving Marcson's answers, it is imperative to reiterate that these triumphs of management over the original expectations and attitudes of the scientists can be seen as remarkable only if the scientists actually held these expectations in the first place, which is by no means certain. As there is no direct evidence on this point, we can only note the assumptions on which Marcson is operating, which are those of the Mertonion sociology of science, briefly presented in Chapter 2. (As I shall argue in the next two chapters, Merton's conclusions about the norms of science are both contingent and sometimes false.)

The whole issue as it is presented can be seen as an attempt by the management to give the illusion that the industrial laboratory is equivalent in important respects to university laboratories, while in reality ensuring that the scientists work as much as possible on commercially useful research rather than research of doubtful commercial value though of obviously pure scientific value. For example, many industrial laboratories, including PEC, were given 'university-sounding titles', and the laboratory attempted to convince the university recruit 'that he will be located in a work situation somewhat akin to the departmental organization of the university' (ibid., pp. 39–40). As one scientist stated: 'There are people in the general research section who are given the privilege of working on non-commercial projects. However, there is the illusion when you are hired that this is the general case for all. One believes because one wants to.' (ibid., p. 57).

Two major attitudes to work emerge from these scientists, though there are grounds for suspecting that they actually emerge from previous theoretical (and some empirical) studies and that Marcson simply impresses them on PEC. These are the professional orientation and the company orientation, and it is hypothesized that scientists in industry with the former experience more severe strains and frustrations than those with the latter orientation. The company positively encourages the company orientation, not surprisingly, by several methods, the most important and effective of which is embodied in the prospects for promotion it offers. In PEC there were two primary means for advancement, the administrative ladder and the professional research ladder, with the former route providing considerably higher salaries and much greater freedom of action within the limits of the laboratory organization. (In a note, Marcson informs us that after the completion of his study, and perhaps as a result of it, a new position of 'Fellow, Professional Staff' was introduced in the company, permitting senior scientists to remain in research while commanding higher salaries.)

To be successful in industrial terms, therefore, the obvious course is for the professional scientist to adopt a company orientation and so to advance up the administrative ladder. In Marcson's words,

. . . top laboratory management . . . are not only former practising scientists, but also scientists who have undergone changes in their views about research. Early in their careers in industrial research they shared the concern of the scientist about basic research on significant questions. Now they view the company's product interests as of equal importance (ibid., p. 41).

Further, it is concluded that even for the large number who stay in scientific research as such and do not move into administrative positions, 'the scientist in the industrial laboratory changes from having a major interest in basic research to having one in applied research' (ibid., p. 71). Far from offering convincing evidence from other studies as to the general applicability of these statements, Marcson has little direct evidence to support his views in a satisfactory manner from the PEC laboratory.

Executive and colleague authority are postulated as the two systems of authority, analogous to the two types of company and professional orientation, that might be used to ensure the proper functioning of industrial scientists. The success or failure of the industrial research laboratory is determined by the ways in which compromise between these authority systems is achieved. Thus Marcson argues that 'the management of scientists requires extensive training and expertness in the adequate development of indirect techniques of control' (ibid., p. 137). The reader might be forgiven for a moment's hesitation at this point, wondering if he has by some chance stumbled on a quotation from a volume of instruction directed at persons whose duties involve the care of dangerous patients suffering from grave psychiatric disturbances. This is the human relations approach to industrial affairs with a vengeance!

The point of all this research is, of course, financial, and relates to profits. University scientists, by and large, do not have to show an economic return on the capital invested in their research,[2] though the returns in prestige and national pride resulting from scientific and technological triumphs cannot be underestimated today. Industrial scientists, on the other hand, are generally under commercial pressures to justify the existence and continuation of their research. A complaint that one comes across time and again in the literature on scientists in industry is that research funds are available for commercially viable but scientifically uninteresting projects, and (as a corollary) research funds are often cut off when a project reaches its most scientifically important stage because it is no longer commercially viable. There is little doubt that this latter condition is the cause of much frustration to some industrial scientists.

This has led some researchers to postulate that such scientists are less productive and/or less creative than they might be in situations in which they were free to follow their own interests in an unrestrained manner.

Now, on the basis of what has been said, it is not difficult to see that university trained scientists working in industry might consider that scientific creativity is often incompatible with productivity in the commercial sense intended by industrial managers, even research administrators who are themselves part-time scientists. This is the focus of many pieces of work, some of which are conveniently collected together in Barber and Hirsch's volume of readings, *The Sociology of Science*. There are also many other American studies, as well as some European researches, which attempt to explain the situation of the large number of scientists who work in industry.

In his article 'Nine Dilemmas in Industrial Research', Herbert Shepard outlines the most obvious problems that industrial laboratories, interested fundamentally in proving their commercial utility to the parent company, face in their dealings with research scientists. The dilemmas identified are as follows: company needs *vs.* scientific needs, 'cosmopolitan' *vs.* 'local' scientists, publication *vs.* secret research results, company time *vs.* research time, delegated or shared authority, project or functional groups, research management as fulfilment or regression for the scientist, and two others regarding the positions of non-professional and professional workers that defy brief reference.

Shepard concludes his paper, published in 1956, with a plea for more empirical research on research, by the laboratories themselves, and he makes the telling point that the unwillingness of laboratories to experiment with the social correlates of research organization is indicative of these very dilemmas that they face.

Of all these dilemmas in industrial research perhaps the most sociologically interesting is that of the 'Cosmopolitan' scientist in an industrial laboratory full of 'local' scientists. The local/cosmopolitan split highlights some of the complex consequences that result when science is applied for profit. The distinction was first introduced in quite a different context by the ubiquitous Robert Merton who, noting its close relationship to Tönnies's famous *Gemeinschaft/Gesellschaft* distinction (actually translated by Zimmerman as localistic and cosmopolitan), put it to good use in a discussion of community influentials. The year after Shepard used local and cosmopolitan to distinguish types of industrial scientists, the terms were developed by Alvin Gouldner in a two-part article which is a model of sociological research, both for its theoretical and its empirical sophistication.

Cosmos and Locals

Gouldner identifies three variables that can be used as criteria for distinguishing between locals and cosmopolitans, which he convincingly deduces from previous research reports. These variables are loyalty to the employing organization, commitment to professional skills, and reference group orientations. Thus, for our present purposes, the scientist in industry who demonstrates high loyalty to his company, low commitment to specialized scientific skills, and who does not consider the wider scientific community as his main reference group, would be classified as a local. On the other hand, the industrial scientist who has no particular loyalty to his company, who has high commitment to scientific skills and who uses an outer group, the scientific community, as his main reference group, will be classified as a cosmopolitan.

In this study Gouldner is at pains to emphasize that these are what he terms 'latent social roles' in the sense that the three criteria are not explicitly established in any organization in normal circumstances, although they might often be informally very important, for example, where promotion was concerned. He also points out that the criteria may well be related and not entirely independent from each other, and that we should expect extremes as well as intermediate types, as is confirmed by the fact that out of a total of 125 people interviewed, staff members at a small American college, 29 were extreme cosmopolitans, 43 were extreme locals, and the remaining 55 were intermediate, though tending a little to the local end of the scale.

In the second part of the study, in response to some of his findings, the author argues that six types of academics, four locals and two cosmopolitans, emerge from the data. I will not give the details of Gouldner's interesting discussion as it is not entirely relevant to the problems of scientists in industry, though the fact that the original dichotomy now becomes a six-fold classification most certainly is. The lesson we must learn is that when the evidence does call for the multiplication of types or concepts then we must be bold. In this case, as we shall see, there appears to be good justification for thinking that there are more than two types of scientists, in and out of industry, and that to restrict ourselves to the cosmopolitan/local distinction would be to fail to appreciate some important differences within each of these.

A further contribution to this debate is provided by Glaser, whose examination of data on 332 research staff working in a governmental medical research laboratory in the United States suggests that highly motivated scientists are both local and cosmopolitan. In a collection of research papers brought together in his book, *Organizational Scientists*, Glaser goes on to separate out three types of highly motivated research scientists, namely basic research local–cosmopolitans, applied research local–cosmopolitans, and adaptive local–cosmopolitans. In this analysis the additional factor of the goals involved, those of science as such and those of the organization employing the scientists, is taken into account and the cross tabulation of this factor with level of motivation of the scientist gives the three types quoted. Being adaptive local–cosmopolitans 'is the way in which the successful supervisors round out their professional careers as high-prestige people in a high-prestige organization in the world of science' (Glaser, 1964, p. 125).

Be this as it may, the same problem besets this as previous work: can we assume that we already have sufficient knowledge of the goals or norms of science? Are the assumptions made about the intrinsic antagonism between science and utility sufficient to convince us that the ways in which commitment to science and the motivation of scientists are measured truly reflect the realities of the situation in modern science? I shall offer some detailed comment on these points in the next two chapters; for the moment let it suffice to say that we must tread through the findings of such research with great caution.

This caution is further encouraged by another study reported in the *American Journal of Sociology* for 1964–5 by Goldberg, Baker, and Rubinstein. The researchers investigated an industrial laboratory in order to test the legitimacy of the local/ cosmopolitan distinction and its developments for the investigation of research scientists. It is important to note that the laboratory studied by Goldberg and his colleagues was mainly devoted to product development, manufacturing and technical service, in contradistinction to the laboratory analysed by Glaser, which was mainly devoted to bio-medical research. (Other investigators, of course, have studied other types of research establishments.)

Goldberg et al, in fact, present empirical evidence to show that, for their laboratory at least, the researchers 'varied in the extent to which they sought after personal gratifications in general, whether these came from the organization or the profession' (Goldberg, 1964, p. 710). This totally unsurprising result leads the writers to suggest that laboratories might differ somewhat and that we need to explain why they do.

The matter is nicely summed up in a paper by Colin Fletcher which reviews the whole history of the use of the cosmopolitan/local distinction in research on scientists. On the basis of his own study, Fletcher concludes:

. . . the thresholds or tolerances of the cosmos thesis have yet to be established. Conceivably both conceptions of cosmos can be fruitful. Cosmos may be applicable unidimensionally in the study of academics in academic organizations. It may also be applicable multidimensionally for the study of scientists in industry. In universities there is no great pressure to conform to its norms and manifest organizational loyalty. Professionals in industry are expected to see their success as part of the firm's success (Fletcher, 1969, p. 20).

Freedom and the Problems of the Professional

An important dimension – perhaps the most important dimension from the point of view of the industrial laboratory administration – is the relationship, if any, between freedom and creativity.[3] The assumptions about which I have expressed some doubts in the last few pages bear strongly upon this. If one believes that creativity and scientific performance are highest under conditions of maximum freedom, then it is reasonable to argue that in laboratories where freedom of the scientific staff tends to be limited, creativity and performance will be adversely affected. It is a short step from here – bypassing another key assumption that all scientists desire to be as creative as possible – to the position that industrial scientists are unhappy and frustrated. The resolution of this unsatisfactory state of affairs that is suggested, by and large, is that industrial scientists aspire to administrative positions.

But the situation is never as simple as this. In a very detailed series of research projects, Pelz and Andrews (1966) show us how complex the world of the research and development laboratories can be. Such variables as coordination of research effort, colleague contact, variety of research interests, age, research climate and teamwork, appeared to influence the relationships between freedom and creativity. Perhaps, at this point, one should raise a major problem in any attempt to relate anything to creativity or scientific performance, and that is: how do we measure creativity and/or performance? Pelz and Andrews used two measures: (1) evaluation by peers and supervisors, and (2) scientists' own reports of outputs (papers, patents, reports). Two general qualities were assessed, contribution to knowledge in the field and overall usefulness to the organization in which the scientist worked. 'Without evidence of strain,' they say, 'judges would evaluate approximately 50 scientists on two dimensions in less than an hour' (Pelz and Andrews, p. 262). A scientist per minute may be highly efficient in terms of research economy, but it inspires little confidence in the independence and value of the measures.

The weakness of this methodology – however carefully it may attend to detail – connects directly with the main point on which I have been insisting. Just as the demands of the work situation affect scientists in a variety of ways, they may also strongly influence the understanding of what constitutes creativity or high scientific performance. The very definitions of these phenomena may indeed vary quite dramatically from one workplace to another. The orientations that scientists have towards their work are clearly linked with the criteria for success.

As I have suggested, the notion of the scientist as a professional – whether in the university or in industry – provides the framework for many of these discussions that I have been charting from the comparative safety of the critic's observation post. Indeed, two of the major studies of industrial scientists, Strauss and Rainwater's *The Professional Scientist* and Kornhauser and Hagstrom's *Scientists in Industry*, both published in 1962, take the idea of the scientist as a professional as their organizing theme. A glance at the table of contents of the latter book will suffice to make the point: none of the seven chapter titles contains any specific reference to science or scientists, every one of them contains a specific reference to professions or professionals. In Britain we find a similar emphasis: Prandy's research on metallurgists and other scientists and technologists is entitled *Professional Employees*, while Gerstl and Hutton's study of engineers is subtitled *The Anatomy of a Profession*. (One might be forgiven for suspecting that some of the imputed anxieties and difficulties pertaining to status and prestige existing among different groups of scientists had rubbed off on those who had studied them.)

This is not the place to enter into a discussion of what a profession is (even the experts seem to have given up trying to settle this question) or of the place of the professions in modern society (the latest research seems to indicate that fairly soon we will all be professional!). However, the place that the scientist accords to his profession, and the differences that exist among scientists in this respect, are relevant to this whole problem of the scientist in industry, as conceived by the sociology of science. This takes us back to the issue of how satisfied scientists in various forms of employment are, and to questions of status and prestige that are undoubtedly as important to scientists as to anyone else.

Compared to the scientist in industry or government, the university scientist is in a relatively unambiguous position with respect to status and prestige. Universities are, generally speaking, high status organizations and those who work in them will benefit from the status and prestige of the university, irrespective of their particular jobs. Further, the number of people who have any sort of contact with a university, although growing, is probably fairly small, and so it is unlikely that many people – the public at large – will be aware that there are many low prestige and low status jobs at universities. Industry, on the other hand, is much more within the experience of the majority of the population, for though many people might never have been inside a factory (and many fewer still inside an industrial research laboratory), the notion of what a factory is like, even if this notion is not particularly accurate, is part of our general culture. Thus the scientist in a university enjoys the status and prestige of his setting, while the scientist in industry must either identify with management or workers for some measure of his status and prestige, or he must carve out for himself a separate niche. The available evidence seems to suggest that one of these niches is that of the professional, and the implication is, as I have indicated several times in the foregoing pages, that where the industrial scientist chooses a professional orientation he may do so in opposition to an identification with the management and the company employing him.

One of the most powerful statements of this view is that made by Kornhauser and Hagstrom. Kornhauser stresses the need for a wide definition of professionalization to accommodate the changing circumstances brought about by the dual processes of the professionalization of organizations and the bureaucratization of professions. This is a very reasonable position, and four criteria are offered to describe the conditions that any worker must fulfil if he is to be considered a professional. Firstly, he should have some specialized competence with considerable intellectual content. The other three conditions are really elaborations on this; he should have extensive autonomy in exercising his competence, he should have a strong commitment to a career based on his competence, and he should have influence and responsibility in the use of his competence.

Thus, Kornhauser argues, given these four conditions of the professional, goals, controls, incentives, and influence, we find built-in strains between the work establishments of industry and the very idea of professional work (Kornhauser, 1962). The curious thing about this argument is that if we forget for a moment that it is the scientist who is the object of the study and think of this discussion in terms of the lawyer, the doctor, the accountant, the trained manager in industry (now most certainly a professional in his own right), then a very different perspective begins to form. Now we see the so-called professional orientation in its more usual context, as opposed to the amateur, as characteristic of the man who is trained to do a special job and who wishes to be free of interference while he is doing the job.

There is, of course, an element of this in the descriptions of scientists, pure scientists, that is contrary to the image of the man engaged in scientific pursuits with commercial aims. But there is a much stronger element in the traditional view of the scientist as a man who would never think of science as a profession, and for whom the thought of science as a profession would be almost analogous to science as something one does for financial gain. This is the gist of the distinction that Max Weber implicitly made in his famous essay on 'Science as a Vocation' (1958). Weber started off by speaking of the careers of scientists in the universities, but quickly moved on to say to his audience: 'But I believe that you actually wish to hear of something else, namely, of the *inward* calling for science', and he proceeded to examine the sometimes mystical implications of this phenomenon (Weber, 1958, p. 134 and *passim*).

It is perhaps relevant to speculate on how many industrial scientists and technologists experience this '*inward* calling for science' and what it consists of. And it is equally relevant to wonder why the questions which would provide some empirical foundations for these speculations are so rarely asked. The sociology of science in the United States seems so thoroughly saturated with the assumptions about norms and values to which I drew attention in Chapter 2, that even when apparently contradictory findings emerge, practically no one ever suggests that the original assumptions might be wrong and that the social system of science might have changed in important ways since the seventeenth century.

Conclusion

In this chapter I have begun to suggest that some of the work experiences and orientations of scientists and technologists are constrained by the hard realities of their places of work. Certain consequences flow from the fact that some scientists work in an academic environment and others work in an industrial environment. The next two chapters will present what has been termed the orthodox Mertonian version of the norms of science: the assumptions on which a great deal of the work done in the sociology of science presently rests. This will be compared with some current debates in the history and philosophy of science concerned with 'scientific revolutions', and my intention will be to highlight the operations of and the relations between the charter and norms of science.

I shall examine the logic and the plausibility of R. K. Merton's account of the norms of science very closely and I shall try to show that it is, at best, a partial account of one part of modern science in a particular type of society. This will necessitate consideration of the charter of science, for it is clear that the norms of an institution cannot be entirely independent from its purpose. Indeed, the particular merit of the institution model of Malinowski is that it forces us to see that the elements of a social institution are interconnected. On the basis of what has already been said about the material apparatus, the personnel, and the activities of big science, we may begin to see some of the patterns of these relationships emerging.

Then I shall go on, in Chapter 5, to review some of the specific empirical evidence against the Mertonian account of the norms and values of science, and to show how it affects our understanding of big science. Thus, for those who are interested in such distinctions, Chapter 4 will be mainly theoretical and Chapter 5 will be mainly empirical. In the former we shall be dealing with the views of sociologists and philosophers who largely – but not exclusively – are concerned with how scientists should behave and with explanations of the imputed actions of scientists, whereas in the latter we shall be dealing more specifically with sociological research, reporting on how scientists actually do behave and the attitudes they hold.

NOTES

1. There are indications that this may be changing, at least with respect to salaries in British universities for chemists (see *Financial Times*, 26 October 1971, p. 12).

2. One of the consequences of Project *Hindsight* may well be an increased political pressure on universities for just such accounting procedures (see above, pp. 52–3). This is certainly one factor in the current debates surrounding the Rothschild Report in Britain.

3. For the largely unsatisfactory attempts to explain scientific creativity, see Taylor and Barron, 1963.

4 The Norms and Values of Science

It will be recalled that the model of the social institution provided by Malinowski postulates that the charter of the institution – 'the system of values for the pursuit of which human beings organize, or enter organizations already existing' – is the source from which the other elements emerge. Through the personnel on one side, and the norms on the other, the charter permeates the institution and, via the material apparatus and the activities, we arrive at the function. As I have already indicated, the view of the sociology of science that is being put forward in this book suggests certain modifications of both the elements and the structure of Malinowski's model.

The 'activities' and the 'personnel' of the institution of science, and indeed of any institution, are difficult to distinguish, and I can see no useful purpose in keeping them apart. They have generally been discussed together in previous chapters and from this point, for convenience, I shall refer to them by the single term 'staff'. The 'staff' of an institution, thus, refers to the personnel and its activities. This, I believe, simplifies matters without loss of definition.

The structure of the model and the relations between its various elements present a more difficult problem. The logic of my argument so far implies that it is quite unrealistic to conceptualize the social institution of science in terms of a one-way flow from charter to personnel to material apparatus. My emphasis on the work situation and workforce, largely the material apparatus and the staff of science, suggests that these factors may have more autonomy than Malinowski allows. Therefore, rather than assert some definitive set of relationships between these factors, I shall at this stage in the analysis draw attention to the possibility that each of these elements – staff, material apparatus, charter – may have relative autonomy and a measure of independent causal influence on the results of the scientific enterprise.

Bearing this in mind I shall, in the present chapter, examine in some detail the major interpretations of the charters and norms of science with a view to improving upon the inherited model of the social institution of science.

The Charter-Claims of Science

There is no widespread agreement as to the charter or purpose of science, neither among those who practise science nor among those who study science. The lowest common denominator of all the accounts reveals that science is concerned with *knowledge*, although some people might question even this. The sociology of science, therefore, as the title of this book indicates, is concerned with 'organized knowledge'. While not denying the importance of the epistemological questions this raises (and which I shall touch upon in the second part of this chapter), one may still share a little of Fritz Machlup's (1962) hearty empiricism on the subject. At the very least we may safely understand the charter of science as the purpose for which knowledge is sought; and of the many possible purposes, three stand out.

Knowledge may be sought for its own sake, for the sake of something or someone else, and (although it could be considered as a variety of the second, however much some people may shudder at the thought) knowledge may be sought for financial gain, as a job, in the form of wages or profits or both. In the following I shall concentrate on the first two of these charter-claims. The third will come into the next chapter.

In the first place, then, knowledge has been said to be sought for its own sake. This view conjures up images of the ideal type of pure science and the entirely disinterested researcher who gives no thought to the consequences of his work outside the solution to particular sets of cognitive problems. This charter-claim is frequently associated with the view that science is (or should be) a cultural enterprise, like music or painting, and that any uses it might have – as music soothes customers in supermarkets and paintings decorate the homes of the rich – are extraneous to its real purpose. This view can also shade into the 'cathedral-building' rationale that expensive science, such as high-energy physics, is a monument to our way of life just as cathedrals signified the cultural advance of feudal Europe. Often, this is linked to the notion of the ivory-towered academic, scientist and/or scholar, labouring away in isolation, thus providing one stereotype for the popular imagination. This is not always entirely favourable, for the image can slip into one of a dilettante who is playing with something dangerous and insufficiently understood. The evil consequences of science and the picture of scientists as irresponsible seekers of knowledge for its own sake is a recurrent theme in much twentieth-century science fiction.

The main alternative to knowledge for its own sake is that the purpose of science is to collect and to further knowledge for the sake of someone or something else. There are three possibilities that spring immediately to mind. The first is that irrespective of the charter of *science* the scientist does what he does for his own individual satisfaction. It is important to note that even if this is the case, it does not necessarily follow that the charter of science is the individual satisfaction of the scientist. And further, given that most people do many things for individual satisfaction, among other motives, it is hard to see why this should be a distinguishing feature of scientific activity.

The second possibility is that the purpose of science is knowledge for some social group or collectivity. We have in our time seen the phenomena of science for the nation, for class, for party, for race, and for humanity itself. This latter goal, science as knowledge for the sake of mankind, is extremely widespread, and it has even been institutionalized in such international agencies as UNESCO. I shall be devoting some attention to this ideal in the last chapter.

The third possibility, which is really a very special case of the second, is that the purpose of science is to gather knowledge for the sake of the scientific community. This view, which is implicit in much of contemporary sociology of science, presupposes the notion of the scientific community as a system of social relations in which certain roles, patterns of rights, duties, and expectations are played out by scientists, and as a consequence what we know as *science* is sustained and grows. On this view, the emergence and progress of science depends on the proper articulation of sets of scientific roles.

None of these opinions on the charter of science excludes any other in a strict sense. It is quite possible to hold, as do most scientists in all probability, that the purpose of science is both to gather knowledge for its own sake and for the sake of humanity, to choose the two most popular options. Further, it is helpful to regard the matter within some socio-historical perspective, for it will not be difficult to obtain evidence that some scientists emphasized knowledge for its own sake at some periods, especially when the fruits of some particular piece of work have proved catastrophic; and similarly it is not difficult to extract quotations from the writings of scientists and others during periods of national emergency to show that the charter of science concerns knowledge for the sake of nation or state or race. But again, many would argue, science is being analysed in terms of how people, and often non-scientists, use and abuse it – rather than in terms of what science *is*. This is a perfectly proper criticism, and it is precisely to answer it that I am attempting to modify Malinowski's model of the social institution. The function of an institution, therefore, is the actual result of the organized activities, and this may be in contrast to the purpose or charter of the institution.

It must be clearly stated that there is no necessary reason why the charter and the function of any social institution should be in conflict. It was Malinowski's point that between the charter of an institution and its function, a great deal of social activity occurs. The physical device of interposing personnel, rules, apparatus, and activities between charter and function is a vivid illustration of the truth that intentions and results may be related in a variety of complex ways. This notion, of the unintended and unrecognized consequences of social action, which has been a component of social thought at least since Kant, prompted Robert Merton to write an early paper on the subject (1936) and a later, more famous essay on 'Manifest and Latent Functions', first published in 1949 (Merton, 1963c, Ch. 1). In this essay, Merton argued that the peculiar talents of the sociologist are best directed to an analysis of the latent functions, i.e. the unintended and unrecognized consequences of some social unit for the system in which it operates and for other systems with which it is in contact. Marion J. Levy, in her book *The Structure of Society*, published in 1952, further refines this by distinguishing between functions which are intended but unrecognized and those which are unintended but recognized.

The lesson of all this has been learned by sociology generally, and the type of analysis that distinguishes between the intended and the unintended consequences of social action is now commonplace. But few writers make the point so clearly as Malinowski does in showing, contrary to the drift of his general theory one might add, that it is the crucially sociological variables that intervene between charter and function and that mediate in the relation between intention and result.

These results for science are of two main types. The first type is what we might subsume under the heading of internal results, such as theories or facts or hypotheses or such like. The second type are external results, which would include, particularly, the effects of science on society, to use a well-worn but still useful phrase. (It goes without saying that the workings of other social forces, particularly the economy, the political system, education, and the military, have important effects on science.) One way to cut short any discussion in the sociology of science, and in my opinion to reapportion responsibility, is the strategy of denying that the effects of science have anything whatsoever to do with *science*, arguing instead that they fall in the realm of technology. Indeed, as my account of the distinction between pure and applied research and development in previous pages has shown, there is in some circles a strong tendency to restrict the meaning of *real science* to pure science with perhaps a little applied research thrown in, especially where the latter turns out to have fundamental implications. Much applied research and all of development work can therefore be excluded from *real science*. In this case, then, all the applications of science, that is, technology, can be neatly separated out from science itself. This view, one may hypothesize, will often be associated with that definition of the charter of science that concerns the pursuit of knowledge for its own sake. (The latter part of Chapter 2 deals with these matters.)

I shall be dealing with the implications of these positions for the control of science and the possible futures of modern societies in Part III, but let me state here and now that to limit *science* and its results to the internal aspects, with the consequences that I have described, cannot be shown to be wrong. It can, however, be shown to be quite unrealistic.

This is mainly due to the fact that science has changed in important ways, and if it was true and realistic at one time to restrict the results of science to internal affairs, then it is not so today. Even in past centuries scientists have been known to ensure that their findings were not broadcast in order to prevent their abuse. A famous case is that of John Napier, the great Scottish mathematician and inventor, who is reputed to have taken secret plans of weapons of destruction to his deathbed rather than let them fall into the hands of those who would use them for evil purposes. This, and similar examples, are brought together in John Nef's powerful account of the relations between war and human progress, *Western Civilization since the Renaissance*, which argues that many scientists saw clearly that war was inimical to progress and that science and technology only prospered in times of peace. These scientists refused to contribute to war efforts or, more usually, attempted to use their skills to limit or moderate wars, and they exhibited what we should now call a sense of social responsibility in science.

This can only become fully established when science itself becomes fully established in a society; that is, as a result of the process of the institutionalization of science and technology in society.[1] This is the great change in science and its social relations to which I refer when I assert that it is no longer realistic to restrict the results of science to internal affairs. The results of science become critically external when science and technology are societally institutionalized. In terms of the model of the social institution that I am using, this means that science and technology become institutionalized when the charter, staff, norms, material apparatus and function of science can be identified through their linkages with other social institutions, and especially with the so-called core institutions of any society like the economy, the family, the educational system, and the political system.

To speak of the linkages between one institution and another is of course a convenient shorthand. What we really mean is that one element in the institution is linked to an element in another institution. For example, when we come across attempts to explain the motivations of scientists by means of reference to the examples set by their teachers, this boils down to the relationships between the staff of the educational system and their norms as they are linked, in a causal chain in this case, to the staff of science and their norms. Another example is the link between the material apparatus of science and the charter of the political system, which has already been discussed with relation to the American machinery of R & D contracting, and so on.

If one were to spell out the actual, probable, and potential links between the institution of science and all of the other important institutions in even one major scientific–technological society, a library of volumes would be needed. Here I have emphasized only a few of these connections from a sociological perspective. This, then, is the rationale for looking beyond science in order to see how its charter measures up to its function.

We must exercise great care in speaking of the charter or the function or the norms of science, for it is likely that these vary to some extent among the sciences and they may vary within one science at different stages in its development.* Indeed, there is a good deal of evidence to suggest that sciences do pass through stages of development, particularly in terms of the popularity of a new field measured in the power it has to attract graduate students and prestigious practitioners, in terms of the legitimacy of the problems that it sets up, as perceived by those in adjoining areas, and the truths that appear to be acceptable (i.e. enshrined in textbooks) at particular times. All of these factors, both within a science and among sciences, might make us feel that all statements about *science* as a unity, including those made in previous pages of this book, are of very doubtful validity. But this would be a counsel of desperation, and a more satisfactory attitude is to accept the risks involved, to correct overstatements where the error is immediately apparent, and to hope that critics will continue the operation from the vantage point of their special knowledge.

All this having been said, I should like now to plunge into an examination of the norms of science and to use this as the most

* As a necessary corrective to the massive and crude generalizations in which we speak, it is arguable that there is no *science*, but there are many sciences and the number and types of sciences are in almost constant flux. This is largely a consequence of the nature of big science in the modern world, for as the pace of scientific advance increases and new methods and techniques are constructed, the breakthrough of this year may provide the basis of a new science for the next decade, and a new technique may find successful application in a traditional area and generate yet another science.

fruitful route to an understanding of the ways in which the functions of science, in terms of internal and external results, are related to the charters of science.

The Norms of Science[2]

The norms or rules of any institution, in Malinowski's formulation, encompass the technically acquired skills and habits, legal and ethical commands, accepted or imposed and often embodied in texts and regulations. This characterization is, of course, very wide indeed, and it would involve an almost impossible command of the operating details of science if it were taken literally. This is not to suggest that these details can be entirely ignored for, as I have argued all along, we need to know the broad differences, at least, between the various sciences in order to make any plausible generalizations. The ways in which we modify generalizations are as important as the generalizations themselves.

Bearing this in mind, I shall present and discuss the major accounts of the norms of science, beginning with the general views expressed by Merton and Parsons and some other American sociologists, and continuing with the dispute between Kuhn and Popper about how science actually progresses (an argument with important sociological as well as philosophical implications). In the next chapter I shall examine the results of some empirical researches on the norms and values of chemists, bio-medical scientists, mathematicians, and physicists.

The point of this review of the literature will be to show how the charters of sciences can be seen to be transformed through their norms into social functions for science itself or for the societies in which it operates, or both.

The Mertonian Norms (CUDOS)

The first attempt to spell out the norms of science explicitly belongs to Robert Merton and is contained in his essay 'Science and Democratic Social Structure', first published in 1942. In this short paper he speaks of the ethos of science which is made up of four sets of norms – universalism, Communism, disinterestedness, and organized scepticism, what I have already referred to as CUDOS.

Universalism, much discussed by Merton's teacher Talcott Parsons in his general sociology, refers to the impersonal character of scientific results. As Merton vividly says, 'the chauvinist may expunge the names of alien scientists from historical textbooks but their formulations remain indispensable to science and technology' (Merton, 1963c, p. 553). It is important to note that universalism refers not only to the basis on which scientific results are evaluated but also to the opportunities to produce results. As Merton says: 'Free access to scientific pursuits is a functional imperative.' (ibid., p. 555)

Thus universalism, as opposed on the one hand to ethnocentrism and on the other to particularism, truly characterizes the scientific attitude. Immediately we can see why Merton is at pains to point out that the norms, and particularly universalism, are institutional imperatives for science, in the sense that any deviation will contribute to the destruction of the institution. It appeared quite clear in 1942, when he wrote that the Nazi rejection of non-Aryan science, especially Jewish (Einsteinian) physics, incomplete as it was, resulted in certain problems for German science, and Merton concluded that where social forces make universalism in science difficult then science itself will, in the long run, suffer.

When reprinting his paper in 1949, Merton had another excellent example of the importance of universalism for the progress of science, namely Soviet biology. In 1948, at a famous meeting of the Lenin Academy of Agricultural Sciences of the USSR, there took place a debate which brought out into the open a controversy that had been brewing for many years in Soviet biological science between the so-called Mendelism–Morganism school of genetics and that of Michurin and Lysenko, two Soviet scientists.[3] The point at issue as far as this debate is concerned is that the former school denies that acquired characteristics are inheritable, and the latter affirm this. It is not irrelevant to point out that the inheritance of acquired characteristics, if it were shown to be possible, would be helpful though not absolutely essential for the Marxist theory of social change. Thus, this was more than simply an esoteric argument between two groups of mutually incomprehensible scientists.

Briefly, the verbatim report of the meeting indicates that out of the sixty or so speakers who contributed to the debate, only six spoke up directly against the Michurin–Lysenko view, and of these, three reported at the end of the conference that they had changed their minds, and intended to support fully the theory to which they had so recently been converted. In the words of one of these three, Professor I. M. Polyakov (later secretary of agriculture to the Central Executive Committee of the USSR Academy of Sciences):

The Michurinian trend of science, headed by T. D. Lysenko, is a broad and profoundly scientific popular movement, a movement which helps us to proceed more swiftly along the great road of triumphant building of Communist society. It is in this trend that Soviet biological and agricultural scientists must work (Lenin Academy, 1949, p. 624).

I do not quote these words to demonstrate the depths to which science can decline in totalitarian societies – there are references enough in the report to 'the great teacher Stalin' to inform us in this respect – but, on the contrary, to point out that the norm of universalism is more complex and has more implications than might at first sight appear. For if we were to replace in the above quotation the term 'Communist society' by, say, 'a just society', or 'a better world free from hunger and misery and war', then we should still be violating the norm of universalism, in one of its aspects. For universalism is held to exclude any extra-scientific criteria in the prosecution and evaluation of scientific work.

Merton, and at greater length his student Bernard Barber in *Science and the Social Order*, argue that only in a democratic society can science operate properly, for only in a democratic society will there be a sufficient degree of freedom from particularism and ethnocentrism. Therefore two main points emerge from this norm of universalism which leave us with unanswered questions. In the first place, what are the consequences for science as a social institution if its first norm seals it off, as it were, from the world in which it exists? Secondly, is it in fact the case that democratic societies alone provide the social structure for the maximum progress of science?

If science is considered to be a purely intellectual exercise, and many people do approach it in this way, then the norm of universalism is and must remain absolute. In these terms only scientific considerations are ever relevant to scientific work. This would mean that medical science, for example, would advance at an even greater rate than it does at present, for the norm of universalism would ensure that no squeamish, unscientific rules prohibiting crucial experiments on human subjects would obstruct this advance. On this argument, democratic societies, concerned with the rights of the individual and minority groups, appear to place in the way of scientific progress obstacles that could be and have been removed by totalitarian societies. Thus, as far as the norm of universalism is concerned, in some respects, only in non-democratic societies, like Nazi Germany and Stalinist Russia, is scientific research truly unfettered. (In other respects it is obviously well and truly fettered, but this is not the point at issue here.)

Therefore, we must clearly recognize that there is a similarity in principle, in terms of science considered as a purely intellectual exercise, between the Michurin biologists in the Soviet Union after the Second World War rejecting certain genetic experiments that seemed to conflict with their view of the world, and the contemporary rejection by British scientists of experiments on human subjects that would conflict with their view of the world. Each is a violation of the norm of universalism, each pays supreme attention to extra-scientific considerations. The difference, however, is considerable. For whereas non-Marxist scientists would disapprove of the violation of the norm in the Soviet case, they would, presumably, approve wholeheartedly of the violation in the British case. In short, both the Soviet and the British case violates certain norms, but the latter reinforces other norms – those of humanity.

This is the reason why it is inadequate to study science, for our purposes, as a purely intellectual pursuit. We must continually be aware of the ways in which science is *not* self-contained, and, as I have indicated, a concentration on the institutional norm of universalism, paradoxically, can obscure them in certain circumstances.

Nor are Merton's other three norms of science entirely free from this difficulty. The second norm is labelled 'Communism', to denote the fact that there is common ownership of goods in the scientific community. Reflecting the more cautious times in which he wrote, Bernard Barber in 1952 renamed this 'communality', dropping the original Mertonian term 'because of its political and ideological significance' – itself an interesting comment for the sociology of the social sciences (Barber, 1962, p. 130, note 7).

There are two main aspects of the norm of communality. The one is science as public knowledge and the other is the rejection of secrecy in scientific matters. Let it be immediately and categorically stated that much, if not most, of contemporary science is carried out under conditions of formal or informal secrecy, and that one has to restrict the notion of public knowledge in describing modern science in such a way that private knowledge will appear to be just as accurate a description.

Secrecy and Communication

There are two contexts in which science operates in secrecy, and they are now and then interdependent. The context of national security, especially in time of war (hot and cold), has made substantial inroads into the norm of communality in science. As will be noted later, when I come to discuss the actual values and norms that scientists are found on empirical investigation to hold, whatever the status of this institutional rule at one time in the development of science, it is now more honoured in the breach than in the observance by scientists working for their country's security.

The second context is that of industrial or commercial interest. It stands to reason that in a society whose economic organs are organized for individual rather than social profit, enterprises that devote large amounts of money and manpower to research and development of a scientific and technological nature will be unwilling to allow their competitors access to any results that could conceivably be commercially exploited. Thus, the logic of a free enterprise capitalist society would dictate that secrecy of useful industrial research is necessary for the companies involved. True, we are always hearing that a closed laboratory door keeps out more than it keeps in, but the enormous growth of industrial espionage in recent times attests to the fact that those responsible for the control of industrial research are unconvinced by the adage.

Present trends do not suggest that industrial or defence research and development is declining with respect to the usually freely accessible university and institute research, and so we may expect that as far as secrecy is concerned science will become less rather than more communal. Even in 1952 Barber would have been guilty of excessive idealism for claiming that:

> Only in times of extreme crisis, when defeat in war threatens not only science but liberal society itself with destruction, will scientists accept the restriction of secrecy. And even then they accept it only in limited areas and only temporarily, as a 'dire necessity' in the interests of sheer survival in order eventually to restore the customary morality of science. In times of peace, the requirement of secrecy . . . arouses moral conflict in many of the scientists who participate in research under this condition (Barber, 1962, p. 131).[4]

In the 1970s, though the moral conflicts remain, the secrecy increases to such an extent that it becomes an expected part of some branches of science and is even built into the career structures of the many scientists involved (cf. Committee on Science, *AAAS*, 1969). For example, it is rumoured that in recognition of the importance of publishing papers for advancement in a scientific career, special journals, restricted to those who have security clearance from the authorities, have been set up in the United States. And this curious but not untypical fact leads on directly to the second aspect of the norm of communality – the interpretation of science as public knowledge.

Whereas the supposed prohibition of secrecy is the negative aspect of communality, science as public knowledge is the positive imperative to scientists that they should make their results public, or, more realistically, available to other scientists. The main medium through which this ideal has been realized is the scientific paper published in one of the 50,000 or so scientific journals that have seen the light of day since about the middle of the seventeenth century when the first scientific societies began to produce them. At present there are about 30,000 scientific journals, publishing about half a million papers annually, and nearly 300 journals given over to abstracting material from this vast store of material (Price, 1963, pp. 8–9). Thus it cannot be denied that, on the surface at least, scientists appear to be making every effort to ensure that their knowledge is public. (This is, of course, a special use of the term *public*. As far as the general public is concerned most scientific papers might as well be written in code or not published at all. I shall be dealing with the important issue of the popularization of science in Chapter 6.) One might even be forgiven for reflecting that scientists are showing excessive zeal in the fulfilment of this particular norm.

But this is only the surface of the matter, for when we dig a little deeper we find that, apart from the problems of restricted research, which have been discussed above, the process of scientific communication is not as simple and straightforward as it at first appears.

It is important to note that the 'crisis in the scientific literature' has been apparent for some time. We have been in the midst of a publication explosion for years. Bernal, writing in 1939, was already very much aware of the worsening situation in scientific publication, so much so that he reprinted as Appendix VIII of *The Social Function of Science* a report on an American 'Project for Scientific Publication and Bibliography'. It is ironic that the subject has spawned its own burgeoning literature, as is evident from the recent Ciba Foundation symposium on *Communication in Science*. As Lord Todd, the Cambridge chemist, says in the introduction to this volume:

. . . the other day, I had a look at the array of current chemical journals received by me personally. There were 24 journals given over to publication of scientific papers each appearing at least once a month (and a few of them even more frequently), in all of which papers relevant to my interests as an organic chemist appear regularly, as well as the usual group of assorted general scientific periodicals of more casual interest. Of course, I cannot read them all – and still less can I cover the others which are taken by our library. (To tell the truth, I cannot really keep pace even with the two abstract journals which cover my interests.) At a rough estimate if I spent all my waking hours reading (including week-ends) it would take me about a year and a half to read one year's journals in my own subject (Todd, in Reuck and Knight, 1967, p. 5).

There are two current explanations for this phenomenon of the continued growth in the number of scientific papers being published every year. Bernal suggested an explanation in terms of the economic pressures which forced scientists to go for bulk rather than quality of publications, which was, he claimed, 'dictated by the need of establishing priorities, itself an indication of the unnecessary struggle for existence that goes on inside the scientific world' (Bernal, 1939, p. 118). This is an early expression of the view – heard in almost every university – that the researcher must 'publish or perish'. The second explanation, suggested by Merton and elaborated by some of his students, acknowledges the enthusiasm of scientists for publishing their work and their jealous guarding of priority, but sees in this, far from the unwilling participation of scientists in an exploitative economic relationship, a confirmation of the institutional norms of the social system of science.

The Mertonian explanation is characteristically complex and based on much erudite history of science, though, as I shall demonstrate, it may fruitfully be seen as an example of the more general functional theory of stratification as expressed by Davis and Moore (in Bendix and Lipset, 1966). Put in its simplest terms, Merton's argument states that the many priority disputes in which scientists have often and ungraciously become embroiled (Galileo, Newton, Cavendish, Watt, Lavoisier, and Freud are only a few of those Merton mentions), cannot simply be explained by their egotism, for modesty and disinterestedness are strongly characteristic of scientists. In fact, in the original presentation of the four norms of science, disinterestedness is the third, but even there it appears as more of an adjunct to communality than a norm in its own right. Its translation into practice, Merton (1963c, p. 559) says, 'is effectively supported by the ultimate accountability of scientists to their compeers'.

The link between these norms of communality and disinterestedness, against the background of science as public knowledge, is clearly the value placed by the scientific community on original knowledge and priority in its discovery. Thus, even though scientists are enjoined not to consider their inventions or discoveries as personal property and to do all in their power to inform their colleagues of the work that they are doing, the overwhelming value that original knowledge has for the scientific community ensures that each scientist will fight tooth and nail to defend his priority through the medium of swift publication. It is not merely the tidy minds of the editors of scientific journals that account for the fact that the dates on which papers are *received* by the journals are affixed to many of them. The large numbers of letters journals, in which communications are printed almost immediately on receipt, bear witness to the same thing.

Thus, Merton continues, the social system that values originality and rules that one's work should be freely available to others naturally encourages scientists to publish articles, if not simply to make the latter more convenient then also to obviate the slightest possibility that any speck of originality will be lost. Having made his case as to the relationship between publication, priority, and the social system of science, Merton is careful to reiterate that all of this is epistemologically quite irrelevant but sociologically (and perhaps psychologically) crucial:

. . . scientific *knowledge* [he asserts] is not the richer or the poorer for having credit given where credit is due: it is the social *institution* of science and individual men of science that would suffer from repeated failures to allocate credit justly (Merton, in Barber and Hirsch, 1962, p. 468).

The implication here is clearly that if due credit were not as a rule given to scientists then they would become less and less willing to act out their scientific roles, their adherence to the institutional norms would decline, and science as a social institution would collapse. To generalize the point about priority, we may say that, in terms of this approach, the recognition that publishing scientific papers brings from the scientific community provides the institutional motivation that keeps the journals well filled and science progressing.

Science and Stratification
Sociologists will recognize this form of argument as a special case of the general structural–functional framework that Merton himself, Talcott Parsons and others have been developing as a major part of American sociology in the last few decades. Literally thousands of pages have been written on the problems of attempting to explain the existence of something in terms of the functions it is supposed to fulfil, in this case explaining the existence of priority disputes in terms of their purported confirmation of the value of originality in science. However, the explanation offered by Merton goes further than this in suggesting that the persistence of the institution of science depends on the proper allocation of credit, and recognition is the expected reward of the scientist who does valuable work. The more valuable the work is, i.e. the more original it is, the more credit will be given. This naturally leads us to inquire about the ways in which rewards are actually distributed in science, a topic with which I shall shortly deal.

This is, as I hinted above, the scientific (in the occupational rather than the methodological sense) case of the general functional theory of stratification. This theory, briefly, asserts that rewards in society are allocated on the basis of the functional importance of the tasks that people carry out – the doctor earns more than the shop assistant because of the need to motivate the former to undertake more training and a more responsible position in society. If the shop assistant earned as much as the doctor, and had as much prestige and status in society, the argument goes, then most people would prefer to take the easier occupational route. The differential rewards are explained in terms of the function that they fulfil in motivating people to prepare for and carry out difficult tasks. There is more to the theory than this but, in my estimation, these are its core ideas, and in spite of the fact that it has been heavily attacked from many directions, it still survives surprisingly well. In a nutshell, then, Merton's view is that if it were not for the fact that scientists got sufficient rewards then no one would bother to do science.[5] They keep trying, and there is substantial evidence that scientists do work very hard, because they know that the institution of science will ensure their rewards if and when they come up with original work.

One has only to state the argument in these terms to realize that it has nothing to do with science as knowledge, as Merton points out, but everything to do with science as a social activity. But, as Merton fails to point out, the theory deals with science as it is organized within a particular social order, and *not* with irreducible characteristics of science as a social activity in any social order. Again, as was the case with the norm of universalism, Merton is seen to be evaluating science as a social institution in liberal-democratic society, and claiming or inferring that in this type of society science operates and progresses in its most satisfactory manner. Once again there is sufficient evidence to indicate that he is, in some important respects, mistaken.

In what ways, then, is a considerable emphasis on priority and publications detrimental to the progress of science? In the first place, arguing about priority is a waste of time, valuable time that might otherwise be spent on scientific work. It also tends to poison personal relations between scientists and between groups of scientists to such an extent that direct competition may be engaged upon in the form of a race to the solution of some problem, which leads to duplication of work and inefficient use of resources. The most celebrated case of this in recent times has been documented by Watson in his personal account of the discovery of the structure of DNA, *The Double Helix*. The book is a racy story which tells how Francis Crick and Watson in Cambridge, with the experimental help of Maurice Wilkins and Rosalind Franklin in London, had beaten Linus Pauling in California to this discovery.

It is somewhat far-fetched to argue that it was the competition with Pauling that motivated those working in England – the impression that the narrative gives is that some of the participants were more concerned with ensuring that their work remained secret till formal publication than others. In this respect we may contrast Watson's candid comment that Wilkins wasn't the type to keep something about his work back from the Cambridge team, with Watson's own letter to a friend announcing the breakthrough. Watson himself says: 'We would prefer your not mentioning this letter to Pauling. When our letter to *Nature* is completed we shall send him a copy' (Watson, 1968, pp. 76 and 217 ff.). In the event, the correspondent told Pauling who, in Watson's phrase, effectively conceded the race. There is in all of this affair an unmistakable mixture of a fear of exposing ideas to premature criticism and a fear of having one's ideas taken over by a competitor.[6] The sociological explanation that we are asked to accept by Merton and others is that these circumstances are to the benefit of science, to such an extent that the institution would fail to survive if the need for competition of this sort, and the stimulus of the promise of certain types of rewards, were absent.

As I noted above, the clue to all of this lies in the inferred need of scientists for recognition and the ways in which the institution of science distributes its rewards. Merton himself is not so naïve as to think that it is the need for recognition that distinguishes scientists from other people and that this need tells us how science works in the way it does. This explanation, which is put forward by other sociologists who acknowledge great debts to Merton (see Hagstrom, 1965; Storer, 1966), would be not only simplistic but also theoretically unacceptable to him in terms of his continual emphasis on the institutional and not the individual sources of the norms of science. As he says:

It is not only the institution of science, of course, that instils and reinforces the concern with recognition; in some degree, all institutions do. This is evident since the time W. I. Thomas included 'recognition' as one of what he called 'the four wishes' of men. The point is, rather, that with its emphasis on originality, the institution of science greatly reinforces this concern and indirectly leads scientists to vigorous self-assertion of their priority (Merton, 1962, p. 454).

This is an admirable statement, and full of sociological insight, but the objection to it is one that I have been hinting at all along with reference to Merton's norms of science. The objection is that the analysis is intended to apply to science as a social institution universally, in all societies – whereas, as I have argued, it appears to hold good only for science in certain types of societies. In other words, in advanced capitalist societies characterized somewhat by *laissez-faire* individualism and the profit motive (in ideology if not entirely in fact), scientists and other professional workers may be convincingly portrayed in Mertonian terms. This hardly proves, as Merton argues, that advanced capitalist (or for that matter, advanced communist) society is the best sort of society for the prosecution of science. The hypothesis that science as a social institution would break down in a society where these norms were ignored is a separate matter. The evidence presented in the previous pages suggests that in spite of widespread deviance from the norms in certain circumstances, science has not broken down either in the East or in the West. (We shall see, in the next chapter, that much the same comments may be applied to academic and industrial science, too.)

There is, then, no apparent reason why science could not operate rather differently, nor why different institutional norms might not motivate scientists differently in a society whose system of stratification differed in important respects from twentieth-century Western societies. In addition, it is clear that in a society where socio-economic differences did not automatically entail higher and lower status, prestige, and more or less material possessions – in a word, where differentiation of roles did not imply differential rewards – science, like many other social institutions, might operate very differently. How, then, are the norms and the rewards related in modern science?

The 'Reward System' in Science

Merton's position on rewards in science is that the organization of the institution ensures that those who deserve them (i.e. those who produce original work of high quality) are seen to get them, and the promise of rewards is always present for those who may one day do so. To test this view, S. and J. Cole (1967), using 120 university physicists as a sample, have examined the relationships between the quantity of a scientist's scholarly output as against its quality. They found that, generally speaking, those who published a great deal were also likely to have their work deemed of high quality, as measured in this case (as it very often is) in terms of the number of times that it is cited by other scientists. For the moment I shall merely note this – though I shall return to discuss the notion of the quality of scientific work later. The Coles claim that the 120 physicists that they studied fell into four natural groups, namely the *prolifics* (33 per cent) who produce many high quality papers; the *mass producers* (12 per cent) who produce many but low quality papers; the *perfectionists* (18 per cent) who produce few but great papers; and the *silent physicists* (37 per cent) who produce very little and that of indifferent merit. The main hypothesis is that each of these four groups is rewarded differently by the social system of science for its contribution or lack of it to the common pool of original knowledge.

There are three main forms of recognition in science, the authors claim, and these constitute the reward system. Thus, we may immediately note that the study is *not* a test of the hypothesis that recognition is the reward for successful scientists, for this is assumed, but rather of the hypothesis that there are different sorts of recognition with which different producer types are rewarded. These rewards relate to: (*a*) honour, (*b*) occupation, and (*c*) reputation.

Honorific rewards, such as Nobel prizes and memberships of prestige scientific societies, are fairly numerous in science nowadays, though only a very few are considered to be so highly prestigious that they are known to most scientists. In addition, the evidence of this study suggests that physicists who win these very highly prized rewards tend to monopolize most of the prestigious honours. This fact, long part of the folklore of science (with its opposite – that scientists never get proper recognition in their own times) has been formalized elegantly by Merton into the 'Matthew Effect'. This effect refers to the phenomenon whereby famous scientists get more fame and lesser scientists remain unknown, even to the extent that their actual contributions to science may be underestimated. As the Gospel According to St Matthew has it: to him that has shall be given, from him that has not shall be taken away. The sociologese account of the Matthew effect, by Merton, is as follows:

. . . the Matthew effect consists in the accruing of greater increments of recognition for particular scientific contributions to scientists of considerable repute and the withholding of such recognition from scientists who have not yet made their mark (Merton, 1968, p. 58).

That this is not entirely unknown to scientists themselves is demonstrated by the quotation that Merton presents from a famous man of science (unfortunately neither the name of the man nor the source of the quotation are given) who states the dilemma of whether or not to add his name to a student's article (ibid., p. 59). If he doesn't then no one will read the paper, if he does then the student will get less than his proper credit. The reward system in science, or rather in university physics research, reaches its zenith in the most prestigious honorific awards which, by their nature, are decidedly scarce and, seemingly, much more likely to be won by a comparatively small group of scientists than to be evenly distributed among all those scientists who might appear to be deserving on the basis of their contributions.

A larger source of rewards, the second on the Coles' list, is membership in top-ranking university departments. There are all sorts of reasons why this should be considered as part of the system of rewards, for it implies and is implied by other aspects of the system. On the one hand, given that part of the criterion of a top-ranking department is the presence of top-ranking people and facilities, one would expect that the second rank of scientists (those without the highest honorific rewards just mentioned) would gain by association in such departments. This gain, or reward, might be just as important in terms of the attention that their work will receive by virtue of its prestigious birthplace as in terms of the intellectual stimulation derived from famous colleagues.

On the other hand, given that the Matthew effect appears to operate to some extent for departments as well as for men (see

Zuckerman, 1967, pp. 29–33), the aura of present success may predispose the scientist in the high-ranking department to anticipate future success and thus smooth the way to later eminence. This last point is not to be understood as an argument against individual creativity but rather as a suggestion that might profitably be taken into account when we look at the social context of scientific discovery.

The third kind of recognition the Coles note is, they consider, the most widespread. This is the reward of attention from colleagues, particularly citation, wherein one scientist reads the work of another and mentions it in his own publications. In this study the authors use a weighted measure of citations, i.e. older papers count for more when cited than more recent papers, and as this is the way in which they decide on the quality of scientific papers, it is as well to bear the fact in mind.

On the assumption that these three forms of recognition constitute the reward system in science, the authors go on to consider whether or not this system operates properly in the sense that it rewards high quality contributions better than low quality ones. To do this they present data on how each of the four groups of physicists fares as far as these rewards are concerned. The results are most informative.

Basically, the point that comes through the statistical tables is that quality of research, whether accompanied by quantity of publications or not, is recognized. Whereas nine out of ten prolifics and perfectionists had at least one honorific award, only about four out of every ten of the silent and mass-producer physicists had one award or more.

The results on the membership of top departments further suggested that quality rather than quantity of research is all-important. An independent ranking of the top ten American university physics departments was used to show that 77 per cent of the perfectionists and 58 per cent of the prolifics – both high quality types – belonged to top departments, while less than 30 per cent of the low quality mass producers and silent physicists belonged to these departments.

Further, as we might expect, those who have published a great deal of high quality research, the prolific physicists, are best known to their colleagues. The writers asked nearly 1,300 physicists to indicate whether or not they were familiar with the work of each of the original 120 physicists, and this was called the 'scope of reputation'. The prolifics were best known; over two thirds of them were known to their fellow physicists. The most interesting pair of figures is for the perfectionists and the mass producers in so far as 55 and 29 per cent respectively were known to their colleagues. Thus mere exposure in terms of number of publications seems less important for building up a reputation than the quality of these publications. And only 5 per cent of the silent physicists were known by their fellows.

One difficulty should be pointed out here, and this refers to the problems involved when we try to measure phenomena which might not be entirely independent of each other. For example, on the surface it would appear that the more material one has published the more likely one is to be known to the relevant community. Thus the high quantity producers are in fact known to a greater extent than the low quantity producers, of the same quality papers. But, as was emphasized, the perfectionists were twice as well known as the mass producers, suggesting that quality was all-important. Given that quality is measured in terms of citations, then it is possible, indeed likely, that those whose work is of high quality but who produce little work will be mentioned as often as, or more often than, those whose many publications are of low quality. Thus if we look at the number of times that a man's *name* appears in the scientific literature, either in his own papers or in footnotes to the papers of others, then we might find that on this measure of 'quantity', which depends on the quality of publications, it follows that the high quality physicists will have the greater exposure and will therefore be better known than their low quality fellows. Which is indeed the case. The impression that the Coles give of the community of physicists carefully sifting through the mass of scientific papers and arriving at some consensus on the high quality contributions is thus only partly true. What appears to happen is that, within a very complicated process in which many variables are at work, the sifting process occurs long before the ordinary scientist opens his copy of the journal. Roughly, in the main, eminent physicists who are themselves much exposed to the spotlight of their colleagues themselves expose the work of other eminent physicists, thus reinforcing the possibility that eminent men will command most of the attention of the community of physicists.

The Matthew effect, for these and other reasons, operates throughout the whole system of rewards in science, and not simply in the allocation of Nobel prizes and other honours (see S. Cole, 1970).

It is therefore only half true to say, as do S. and J. Cole:

. . . it appears that the reward system in physics operates to give all three kinds of recognition primarily to *significant* research, whether this is found in the work of high producers or low. Here quantity of published research seldom makes for equivalent recognition. To this extent, the reward system of physics approximates the often expressed norm that excellence of research is what truly matters (Cole and Cole, 1967, p. 387).

To repeat: it very much looks as if the useful notion of quality of research, as measured by the number of citations that a man's work receives, is being backed up by what is presented as an independent measure of reputation, where this measure of reputation is linked in an important fashion to the consequences of the process of citation. This interpretation is somewhat supported by the evidence that the Coles give on 'reputational visibility' – a measure of whether a physicist had been heard of, though not actually read. Here, the perfectionists were still about twice as well known as the mass producers, a result which is quite consistent with the notion that high quality and low quantity producers have as much or even more exposure through the footnotes of others than the low quality and high quantity producers.

But all of this, my criticism as well as the study of physicists itself, is rather speculative and suggestive, in the sense that our information about these matters is sparse. This impression is reinforced by a later article by the same authors, on the same 120 physicists and their 1,300 fellows, specifically on the visibility of the 120 and the awareness of them manifested by the 1,300. In this piece the authors isolated the important factor of research speciality within physics – elementary particles, nuclear, atomic, molecular, and solid state. It was found that specialists influenced the degree of visibility of the physicists, so that 'reputation for work done in so-called "hot fields" can more easily permeate the boundaries of speciality than work in less prestigious fields' (Cole and Cole, 1968, p. 402).

The Coles conclude this study with a series of qualifications which could be appended to many studies in the sociology of science and which, while not necessarily throwing doubt on the validity of the particular studies, do seriously limit their scope of general application. They say:

This is the case for physics. It remains to be seen whether these conclusions hold for other scientific disciplines and even the humanities . . . It seems probable that different results might obtain in disciplines that are not as highly institutionalized as physics . . . We must also point out that we have been dealing solely with physicists in graduate departments of physics. This population is itself an élite group. It is likely that had we sent our questionnaire to physicists teaching at undergraduate colleges and to those working in industry, we would have found greater differences in knowledge (ibid., pp. 412–13).

And, one might add, not just in knowledge.

These studies of rewards in science, therefore, are deficient in two respects. First, as the Coles point out, they refer only to academic science. Second, they give us no reason to believe that even academic science would collapse if the reward system operated in some other way. The basic assumptions of Merton's sociology of science are that originality and priority in discovery must be seen to be rewarded if the institution is to survive, and that the different forms of recognition that these rewards take, and their efficient allocation, are directly related to the institutional norms. These assumptions are not tested in any way, either by Merton or by the Coles, nor, to my knowledge, by anyone else working within the Mertonian framework.

The nearest that Merton comes to questioning his own formulation of the norms of science is in his elusive paper entitled, significantly enough, 'The Ambivalence of Scientists' (Merton, 1963a). Here Merton outlines, for a start, *nine* 'institutionally defined pairs of norms' and notes 'the tension that can be generated by potential inconsistency within each pair' (ibid., p. 78) – thus the ambivalence of scientists and his explanation of 'deviant behaviours of scientists' as 'normal responses to a badly integrated institution of science' (ibid., p. 81). But in this paper, instead of turning his considerable critical powers on to his own theory of science, he chooses, yet again (see Merton, 1961; 1962; 1963b), to discuss the problems of multiples and priorities!

The existence of the norms of universalism, communism and disinterestedness, therefore, have not been demonstrated, and their consistency and ability to create an integrated scientific institution leaves many unanswered questions hanging in the air. The brunt of my argument so far has been that these norms, and the form of social organization of science that they imply, have a limited though important connection with science as such, but have a very great deal more to do with science as it is carried out in advanced capitalist society. I have argued that these norms have a place in science in so far as it operates in this wider society, and that the functionalist view, that the very persistence of the institution depends on the fulfilment of the norms, relates only, if at all, to this wider social framework in which the institution of science, like all other institutions, works, partly autonomously and partly under certain constraints.

The fourth norm that Merton put forward in his original account of science as a social institution is 'organized scepticism', which he correctly characterizes as 'both a methodological and an institutional mandate' (Merton, 1963c, p. 560), and this marks a very important boundary between the sociological and the philosophical accounts of the scientific enterprise. This boundary has been hotly attacked and stoutly defended, especially in recent years, and I shall devote the rest of this chapter to the most important battles for this territory.

The Sociology of Knowledge and the Philosophy of Science

As far as the institutional mandate of organized scepticism is concerned, there is little further to add beyond what has already been said in the discussion of the other three norms, particularly that of communality. Allowing his colleagues easy access to the fruits of his work is not incumbent on the scientist for fun – it is the most direct fashion in which the scepticism, or criticism, of the scientific community can be organized. The methodological importance of this norm is to do with the *standards* on which the criticism is organized, its content, its permissible boundaries, the criteria of evidence for and against scientific views.

This is the point at which the sociology of science might be seen to stop and to step aside in favour of the philosophy of science. Sociology, it might be said, has meddled far enough in this area, and must not cross the line which separates science as the system of knowledge and science as the social artefact. In short, we are asked to believe that nothing we can find out about the social organization of science could have any effect on the scientific or epistemological nature of science. Merton himself makes precisely this point in his discussion of Stalinist and Nazi science, commenting that 'the criteria of validity of claims to scientific knowledge are not matters of national taste and culture. Sooner or later, competing claims to validity are settled by the universalistic facts of nature which are consonant with one and not with another theory' (1963c, p. 554, note 4).

This is a view that is at present being questioned in some quarters and it is of particular interest and importance for the sociology of science, not least because it poses some problems that have rarely been properly faced. These problems concern the differences and similarities between scientific knowledge and other types of knowledge, and they strike to the very heart of that many-faceted doctrine that is known as the sociology of knowledge. I cannot here do more than state crudely the main point of this doctrine: it suggests that the validity of our knowledge (in the form of theories about the world, and values and beliefs that we might hold) is relative to, and/or dependent upon, our socio-economic condition. Briefly, whereas this idea is widely accepted for social or political theories, it is widely questioned with relation to the theories and laws of science. Merton's norm of organized scepticism suggests not only that the findings and explanations of scientists are made public but also, as I have noted, that there are certain standards – the methodological rules – that govern the ways in which scientific work is evaluated.

Parsons, recommending Merton's general approach, amplifies this point into 'the basic norms of scientific knowledge ... empirical validity, logical clarity ... logical consistency ... and generality of the "principles" involved' (1951, p. 335). One must immediately record the tentativeness with which Parsons presents these norms of scientific knowledge, but whatever emendations the philosophers of science may make to them, his intentions are clearly to set off scientific from other types of knowledge. Thus he distinguishes existential belief systems from evaluative belief systems and argues that each of these has empirical and non-empirical components. Science, in this scheme, is therefore the existential (or cognitive) empirical belief system and philosophy is its non-empirical cognitive counterpart. On the other hand, there are also evaluative types of belief systems, empirical and non-empirical, which he identifies as ideology and religion.

Notwithstanding the rather curious implications of this classification of belief systems, it has the very real merit of comparing and contrasting the ways in which men arrive at and organize their views about the world. Thus, parallel to the utility of looking at science as a social institution, Parsons is looking at scientific knowledge as one of the possible types of belief system. I mention this fact, which holds irrespective of the viability of this particular classification of belief systems, in order to show how it counteracts the extreme view of some positivists that only scientific knowledge (or, more accurately, a statement that is scientific in one sense or another) is meaningful, and that all other statements are meaningless. The relationships between the types of belief systems further testify to this focus of interest. Parsons is careful to distinguish non-empirical beliefs from scientifically inadequate empirical beliefs, which is to say that the other three types of belief systems are not simply cruder sciences, but are systems of beliefs on their own terms, terms quite different from those of science.

One crucial difficulty here concerns the use of the term *knowledge*. Parsons generally restricts it to refer exclusively to empirical knowledge, the fruit of scientific investigation. He briefly discusses, under the heading of 'the problem of knowledge', the necessity for the logical closure of the system of scientific knowledge and leaves us with some hints about the relations between non-empirical knowledge (so-called) and 'the grounding of empirical knowledge' (ibid., p. 360). This takes us to the very borders of epistemology and Parsons declares that this is a border that he will not cross, in so far as its technical philosophical aspects are concerned. But this is a very hazy border, and one along which the sociologist of science must wander, for it is part of our business to inquire whether the social organization of science has any relevance whatsoever for the standards by which scientists actually *evaluate* scientific

E

knowledge and the explanations of phenomena which flow from the structures built out of this knowledge. Parsons has been an interesting guide this far, but it is to others that we must turn for directions from this point on, and it is of no little interest, as we shall see, that our new guides, pointing us in opposite directions, to some extent appear to be leading us back into the uneasy world of scientific and other belief systems from which we are beginning the expedition.

But I anticipate – though in the interests of psychic well-being. Our new guides are Popper and Kuhn and their controversy is of great interest and relevance for the future development of the sociology of science.

Popper and Kuhn

The origin of the present argument over the nature of science is to be found in the magisterial work of Karl Popper, *The Logic of Scientific Discovery*, which was published in German in 1934–5 and reissued in an expanded English version in 1959. This is an historically informed attempt to substantiate the anti-inductivist hypothetico-deductive model as the correct logic of science.

I do not wish to become involved here with the detail either of Popper's position, which has continued to evolve over the years, or of those positions that his work has consistently opposed. It is perhaps enough to say that he considers the progress of science to be a matter of the formation of hypotheses which are deduced from bodies of theory, and attempts to test them against the empirical evidence that the scientist collects in order to ascertain how far the original theories can be held to be falsified or corroborated by the results of experiments. The rough guide to the merit of scientific theories is the number and range of potential falsifiers which may be deduced from them in the form of empirically testable hypotheses. This is all beautifully summed up in the title of a collection of some of Popper's most important essays – *Conjectures and Refutations*. The upshot of these philosophical investigations into the nature of scientific discovery was that the previous emphasis on the verification of scientific theories and/or hypotheses characteristic of positivists and inductivists became counterbalanced by Popper's view which stressed falsification and, it may be added, a rather more exciting picture of the development of science.

However, both Popper's deductivist and his opponents' inductivist accounts of science remained firmly what I have previously termed 'internalist' views of science. Science for them is entirely an intellectual production, an inhabitant of the world of ideas, perhaps the most honoured inhabitant of what Popper has called 'the third world'. To keep the record straight I shall repeat the point with which I opened this discussion. There are, in my opinion, no clinching reasons why science should be regarded exclusively in internalist terms, whereas it is at least realistic to take the social context of any activity in which people take part into account in any effort to understand its processes and the ways in which it changes. The assumption on which any sociology of science is built, indeed the rationale for the whole enterprise, is that, like education and religion and politics, science as a belief system and science as a set of social relationships are not totally unrelated, and that each influences the other in patterns that may be discerned and explained. That is to say, as I have suggested, that the work of the sociology of knowledge does not stop at the gates of science, as the internalists assume, but continues into the very structure of science, as the sociologists of science assume. The difference between these two approaches is that the internalist philosophers of science would never be in a position to know whether or not, in fact, their assumption was correct, whereas the research programme of the sociologists of science will eventually reveal their value or limitation.

The emergence of T. S. Kuhn into the limelight, with the publication of his book *The Structure of Scientific Revolutions* (1962), the influence of which can hardly be overestimated, brought all of these matters into the open – out of the footnotes and into the textbooks, one might say. As with Popper, I shall only give the barest idea of Kuhn's position as outlined in his book. Perhaps it is useful to note immediately that Kuhn wrote a paper for a symposium on the history of science at Oxford in 1961, about the time of the publication of *The Structure of Scientific Revolutions*, and the title he chose for it was 'The Function of Dogma in Scientific Research'. His use of the term 'dogma' appears to me to be extremely important to his account of science, and the fact that he did not continue to use it to any great extent, and that he replaced it with other terms, has led to some confusion in the debate that his work initiated and to much arguing at cross-purposes.

Kuhn sees the development of science in two stages, roughly normal science and science in crisis. Normal science, which is characterized by what he calls a 'paradigm', is what is happening when the scientific machine is ticking over smoothly. The paradigm sets the limits of the problems to be solved by the scientific community and it determines the standards that will be acceptable for the solutions that the members of the community offer. Then, for one of a variety of possible reasons, a crisis develops within the normal science and, if the crisis cannot be successfully resolved by means of the old paradigm, a scientific revolution will take place and the old paradigm will be ousted to be replaced by the new paradigm.

A crucial part of Kuhn's thesis is that scientific paradigms are often relatively incomparable, or, to use the more technical phrase that has become one focus of the debate – competing paradigms are incommensurable. It is only fair to note that, contrary to the evidence of some random remarks that have been picked up by his opponents, Kuhn has never asserted that all competing paradigms are absolutely incommensurable in the sense that there is never any point of contact between them. On the contrary, he has always been at pains to point out that whereas between one pair of theories there may be a fairly clear choice, i.e. a high degree of commensurability, between another pair there may be much less of a choice with respect to the existing evidence, because the theories address themselves to different sets of problems into which are built different standards for the acceptability of solutions, i.e. a high degree of incommensurability. Given that paradigms may be commensurable, then the choice between one paradigm and another may be made on the basis of scientific reasons, or, to represent Kuhn more accurately, reasons acceptable to the scientific community operating under the paradigm that prevails.

There has been a curious inability on the part of Kuhn's critics to grasp this point, an inability that has led one of them to accuse Kuhn of wishing to portray science as a series of irrational choices and another to characterize Kuhn's account of scientific progress as the victory of mob psychology!

What, then, one might ask, are these reasons that scientists might have for adopting one paradigm and rejecting another? The answer that Kuhn gives appears in a volume of essays largely devoted to the debate I am now reviewing, and it is disarmingly simple.

... good reasons for theory choice ... [Kuhn says, are] reasons of exactly the kind standard in philosophy of science: accuracy, scope, simplicity, fruitfulness, and the like. It is vitally important that scientists be taught to value these characteristics and that they be provided with examples that illustrate them in practice ... such reasons constitute values to be used in making choices rather than rules of choice. Scientists who share them may nevertheless make different choices in the same concrete situation ... the relative weight placed on different values by different individuals can play a decisive role in individual choice. More important, though scientists share these values and must continue to do so if science is to survive, they do not all apply them in the same way. Simplicity, scope, fruitfulness, and even accuracy can be judged quite differently (which is not to say they may be judged arbitrarily) by different people. Again, they may differ in their conclusions without violating any accepted rule (Lakatos and Musgrave, 1970, p. 262).

On the surface it would therefore appear that Kuhn and Popper are largely addressing different problems and that when they do face the same issues then their answers are not wildly disparate. As Kuhn himself has written directly about this, it is as well to follow his course and to evaluate his claims against those of Professor Lakatos, who appears to have taken up the cudgels in support of Popper and, indeed, to have developed substantially the Popperian position in response to the perceived challenge.

Enter Lakatos

Kuhn begins by saying that his own previous analysis of the problem of incommensurability between scientific theories is very relevant to his debate with the Popperians, but that here as elsewhere the breakdown of communication occasioned by it is only partial and never complete. This being so, it is possible to identify three points at which differences have arisen between his position and that of the Popperians. First, he notes 'the perceived difference in our methods: logic versus history and social psychology; normative versus descriptive' (Lakatos and

Musgrave, p. 233). Kuhn counters this by claiming that in his work and in the work of his opponents 'the descriptive and the normative are inextricably mixed'. But this assertion has an unfortunate ambiguity about which sociologists, historians, philosophers – to mention only a few – have argued for centuries. It can mean that the views we are discussing are sometimes of a normative kind and sometimes of a descriptive kind, that these writers sometimes state what scientists ought to do and sometimes state what scientists actually do. Or, on the other hand, it can mean that Kuhn considers that, try as we may, we can never keep the normative and the descriptive apart, and that every description of scientific procedure has an inbuilt value-judgement, and that every prescription about the procedures scientists ought to follow has an inbuilt description in it. This is clearly a contemporary version of the debate to which Max Weber contributed so influentially at the turn of the century and which has continued to the present day in the social sciences. Because Kuhn uses the expression 'inextricably mixed' I should tend to the opinion that he stands on the latter rather than on the former side of the ambiguity. But if this is the case then he appears to contradict himself a few sentences later when he argues that Lakatos's position is social-psychological, and not wholly normative as claimed, because of its 'repeated reliance on decisions governed not by logical rules but by the mature sensibility of the trained professional'. If the social-psychological and the normative are inextricably mixed then the point loses its force, for we shall not be able to distinguish as clearly as Kuhn seems to do between logical rules and the mature sensibility of the trained professional.

The second point of disagreement, which Kuhn reduces to cross-purposes, and the third point, may in this discussion be fruitfully telescoped together. They involve the notions of normal science, paradigms, and scientific revolutions. And this takes us back to the notion of 'dogma' which, as I pointed out previously, Kuhn dropped in favour of normal science and paradigms. In spite of all of his efforts, Kuhn has not convinced his opponents that normal science or the paradigm is not, in some senses, dogmatic. The difficulty, in my view, stems from the sociological naïvety of both Kuhn and the Popperians, but of the two in this respect the former is the more realistic. This is all quite independent of the intrinsic inadequacies of the concept of paradigm and the account of the shift from one paradigm, or normal-scientific tradition, to another. Kuhn has in fact recognized some of these inadequacies to the extent that he has adopted the term *exemplar* in place of paradigm.

The issue, as far as one can tell, for all parties is now revolving around the ways in which scientists should and do cope with scientific problems and puzzles. Lakatos, carrying the Popperian torch, but with his own new high-octane fuel, considers that science is a matter of permanent revolution, everything is tentative; whereas Kuhn considers that normal science is not at all like this and that, apart from the crises which from time to time lead to revolutions and new paradigms (or exemplars), scientists are content to work away within a fairly settled context where the fundamentals are not questioned and puzzles rather than problems arise. Where the Popperians see scientists as ideally rational beings whose purpose is to set up their work in as vulnerable a manner as possible, Kuhn sees scientists as often defending their theories with dogged determination, putting obstacles in the way of the critics, and – in some extreme cases – preferring to die with their old paradigms rather than submit to the victory of new ones. It is permanence in revolution against tradition-crisis-revolution and tradition again.

But even here the differences may not be as great as at first sight they appear. It is in an important point, in which Lakatos indicates his departure from his original Popperian position, that the thin end of the Kuhnian wedge enters. Lakatos says: 'The main difference from Popper's original version is, I think, that in my conception criticism does not – and must not – kill as fast as Popper imagined' (Lakatos and Musgrave, p. 179). Once we have accepted this modification which Lakatos has roughly described as the difference between dogmatic and methodological falsificationism, we see clearly that not simply any refutation of any hypothesis will immediately lead to the destruction of any theory, however well-founded. For this purpose Lakatos has introduced the distinction between progressive and degenerating problem shifts or research programmes, on the criterion that the former 'leads us to the actual discovery of some new fact' (Lakatos and Musgrave, p. 118).

The differences now take on a new perspective. Lakatos

appears to be saying that there are two types of science, the progressive and the degenerating, which brings him closer to Khun.

> Thus [Lakatos exclaims] the 'dogmatism' of 'normal science' does not prevent growth as long as we combine it with the Popperian recognition that there is good, progressive normal science and that there is bad, degenerating normal science, and as long as we retain the *determination* to eliminate, under certain objectively defined conditions, some research programmes.
> . . . Where Kuhn sees 'paradigms', I *also* see rational 'research programmes' (Lakatos and Musgrave, p. 177).

It is not accidental that Lakatos's comment that Kuhn is working in a social-psychological framework as opposed to his own normative framework occurs in this passage.

The suggestion that there are two types of science is further reinforced by Watkins as follows:

> I believe that it [the idea of Normal Science] is of considerable sociological importance. A sociologist investigating the scientific profession as he might investigate, say, the medical profession, might do well to use it as his ideal type. But I shall consider it from a methodological point of view, and methodology, as I understand it, is concerned with science at its best, or with science as it should be conducted, rather than with hack science (Lakatos and Musgrave, p. 27).

And he concludes that normal science and/or the paradigm is an untenable idea for the best science, though the unconsidered 'hack science' might conceivably find a use for it.

The difference between progressive and degenerating science, between best and hack science, lies as always in the reasons that scientists have for holding on to one theory and for rejecting another. Lakatos, in a characteristically vivid outburst, betrays no doubt whatsoever that Kuhn has abandoned all rational standards in his account of scientific revolutions.

> There is no particular rational cause for the appearance of a Kuhnian 'crisis'. 'Crisis' is a psychological concept; it is a contagious panic. Then a new 'paradigm' emerges, incommensurable with its predecessor. There are no rational standards for their comparison. Each paradigm contains its own standards. The crisis sweeps away not only the old theories and rules but also the standards which made us respect them. The new paradigm brings a totally new rationality. There are no super-paradigmatic standards. The change is a band-

wagon effect. Thus *in Kuhn's view scientific revolution is irrational, a matter for mob psychology* (Lakatos and Musgrave, p. 178).

A search of the literature, and not merely the psychological literature, reveals no definition of crisis that remotely resembles 'contagious panic'; nor does Kuhn anywhere speak of totally new rationality – it may be noted that he is in no way obsessed with the old rationality, let alone any new variety; and finally the charge of mob psychology is a Popperian invention that has a basis in Kuhn's writing that hovers between slender and non-existent and tending to the latter. To these charges Watkins adds the final accusation that Kuhn's portrayal of the conversion from one paradigm to another is analogous to religious conversion and that the crisis in science corresponds 'to a period of . . . schism, confusion and despair, to a spiritual catastrophe' (Lakatos and Musgrave, p. 33).

Kuhn can, I believe, be defended against these excessive and wasteful criticisms merely by perusing the text of his *Structure of Scientific Revolutions*. Until Lakatos gives us the source of his semantic shift from crisis to contagious panic it is impossible to answer his point. Contagious panic is certainly one response to crisis. Perhaps it is the typical response of philosophers when their theories are attacked – it is quite often the case when socio-logical and political theories are assaulted.

Where Watkins speaks of 'spiritual catastrophe', Kuhn, whom he is supposed to be reporting, goes out of his way to *deny* that 'new paradigms triumph ultimately through some mystical aes-thetic . . . [Kuhn's view is in fact that] rather than a single group conversion, what occurs is an increasing shift in the distribution of professional allegiances' (*SSR*, p. 157).[7]

Far from Kuhn insinuating that each paradigm operates under a totally new rationality, or that there are no super-paradigmatic standards, the following is the case. Kuhn says explicitly that 'within the new paradigm, old terms, concepts, and experiments fall into new relationships with one another' (ibid., p. 148). Further, the question that Kuhn considers scientists do and should ask when confronted with competing theories (although lacking in sophistication as he admits) is nevertheless to the point. The question is: 'which of two actual and competing theories fits the facts *better*?' (ibid., p. 146). If fitting the facts, naïve as it is, becomes a matter of mob psychology and irrationality then we had all better start to think again! But even here Kuhn adds that fitting the facts or the ability to solve problems 'are neither individually nor collectively compelling' (ibid., p. 154) in paradigm choice. Other considerations like neatness, suitability, and simplicity are brought into the evaluation of one paradigm over another. I shall return to this shortly.

Kuhn's analysis of theory-choice does not imply that all rationality is thrown to the wind, but that of the many methodological rules that all scientists are trained to obey, at one time some are applied in one way and at another time they are applied in another way. At one time one rule is superordinate and at another time another rule is deemed more important. This is presumably why Kuhn is so annoyed with Lakatos for his 'rational reconstructions', because Kuhn's whole project is a matter of painstaking research into what scientists actually do in periods of normal and crisis science, a matter of finding out which rules were considered most important and how they were applied in each case. For Lakatos, the project involves laying down rules about how scientists should act and bemoaning the facts when they do not act in the prescribed fashion.[8] That this happens frequently is presumably a corollary of Lakatos's pet thesis 'that most scientists tend to understand little more *about* science than fish about hydrodynamics' (Lakatos and Musgrave, p. 148, note 1).

There are two sorts of science for the Popperians then, progressive and degenerating science, good science and bad science, best science and hack science. But the second of each of the two pairs, although it may be what scientists do in the course of scientific activity, and an accepted part of scientific practice, is plainly not *science* at all. It is something quite different, and if it gets mixed up with real science, then our civilization is in danger. The only thing that staves off anarchy and irrationalism, it seems, is permanent revolution! For Kuhn, on the other hand, the two sorts of science, normal and revolutionary, both worthy of our attention, simply characterize types of scientific change and share the essentials of logic and method without which science as a whole would not survive. And it is precisely in these rules and in the variety of their application that we find the good reasons for science to progress in one way within a paradigm or exemplar and in another way through crisis and revolution.

Sociological Challenges – Real and Imagined

In this account I have mainly been concerned to reinforce Kuhn's defences against his Popperian critics, and thereby to illustrate some of the implications of this important controversy for the sociology of science. These implications are, at present, rather more potential than actual, for Kuhn's *intentions* in this connection are not altogether clear. It will help to distinguish two stages in the argument. First, in my view, Kuhn is clearly justified in his claim that science and scientific progress can be approached sociologically with interesting results, and the Popperians are clearly wrong in asserting that these attempts by Kuhn make science a 'religion', or scientific change a matter of mob psychology, spiritual catastrophe, or any sort of undiluted 'irrationalism'. We must hope that this part of the argument is over and that the shifts in Kuhn's positions, especially with respect to his revamped paradigms, are matched by explicit recognition by the Popperians that much of Kuhn's analysis can at least coexist with much of their own analysis. When Musgrave (1969, p. 94) complains that the sociology of science obscures hard won distinctions, by which he presumably means those characteristics of the victory of falsificationism over verificationism, he is displaying the Popperian inability to understand that the idea of a sociology of science is not necessarily antagonistic to a well-established philosophy of science, though some versions of the sociology of science certainly are. (It is clear that the Mertonian sociology of science – holding as it does that the sociology of knowledge stops short of scientific knowledge – could be an important ally of the Popperians, if they only realized it.) It is too early to say whether or not Kuhn's social psychology of science constitutes such a threat, but at present it seems to be quite compatible with much of the revised Popperian position as represented by Lakatos's sophisticated falsificationism. This would appear to be Kuhn's view, also.

The second stage in the argument, however, is much more problematical. This concerns the actual sociology of science that we might expect to follow, not only from Kuhn's work, but also from the new developments in the Popperian philosophy of science.

That Kuhn himself considers some of his work to be sociological is entirely beyond doubt. It is worth quoting him again on this point, for it indicates the way in which his proto-sociology of science may indeed turn out. He says:

Some of the principles deployed in my explanation of science are irreducibly sociological, at least at this time. In particular, confronted with the problem of theory-choice, the structure of my response runs roughly as follows: take a *group* of the ablest available people with the most appropriate motivation; train them in some science and in the specialities relevant to the choice at hand; imbue them with the value system, the ideology, current in their discipline (and to a great extent in other scientific fields as well); and, finally, *let them make the choice*. If that technique does not account for scientific development as we know it, then no other will. There can be no set of rules of choice adequate to dictate desired *individual* behaviour in the concrete cases that scientists will meet in the course of their careers. Whatever scientific progress may be, we must account for it by examining the nature of the scientific group, discovering what it values, what it tolerates, and what it disdains (Lakatos and Musgrave, p. 238).

Far from being irrationalist, this research programme clearly recognizes two important realities. It recognizes that there is, as Polanyi says, 'no accepted theory of scientific knowledge today' (Polanyi, 1967, p. 533). The attempt of the Popperian philosophy of science to provide one is of the greatest value, but it is by no means universally accepted and its defence of rationalism, especially, becomes more threadbare as time goes on. The realities of the philosophical situation alone, therefore, would force us to look outside the logic of science for a fuller understanding of its progress.[9]

The second reality which Kuhn recognizes is the crucial significance of the socialization of the scientist, particularly the ways in which the young scientist picks up values and norms of science in the course of his training and his work. In his 'Postscript' of 1970, he draws attention to 'the manner in which a particular set of shared values interacts with the particular experiences shared by a community of specialists to ensure that most members of the group will ultimately find one set of arguments rather than another decisive' (p. 200).

Michael Polanyi's criterion of *plausibility* illustrates this well. The trained scientist has to judge between what is plausible and implausible, reasonable and unreasonable, the breakthrough and the blind alley. Education consists in transmitting the ability to notice some things and to ignore others (see Polanyi, 1964, p. 96;

Barber, 1962; and Barber and Fox, in Barber and Hirsch, 1962). While many factors are said to enter into the scientific process, for example exactitude, systematic importance, intrinsic interest of subject matter (Polanyi, 1967, p. 542), falsifiability (Popper, 1961), simplicity (Goodman, 1967), accuracy of prediction, number of different problems solved (Kuhn, 1970, p. 206), and so on, there is no overwhelming evidence that any one of these (or even combination of these) always works best. Putting all one's eggs in, say, the basket of simplicity, may give excellent results some of the time for some scientific specialism, but it may lead to catastrophic errors at other times for other sciences.

Thirty years ago, in a little-noted article in an American philosophy journal, Thelma Lavine made some unusually interesting comments on these problems. Noting that the traditional non-Marxist sociology of knowledge stopped short at the door of science, Lavine argues forcibly for a sociology of cognitive norms. In spite of her terse prose, the message is clear: 'it is the specificity of interaction and adjustment of separate demands, mental, existential, and social, which furnishes the key to the understanding of concrete cognitive adequacy' (Lavine, 1942, p. 353, italics in the original). As the mental, existential, and social demands vary, so does the relative importance of the norms of science vary, and these variations are related to the training the scientist receives, the social context within which he is carrying out his work, and the social meaning that the enterprise has for him.

Indeed, the greatest weakness of Kuhn's formulation is that it makes the progress of science too exclusively a matter for the scientific community, and neglects to consider the factors external to the scientific group itself which may have a considerable bearing on its theory-choice, and much more besides. Factors such as war and revolution, economic boom and recession, religious revival and the spread of secular ideology, clearly affect the charter, staff, and material apparatus of science (as they affect other social institutions) in many ways.

Nevertheless, Kuhn's suggestions do provide the sociology *and* history *and* philosophy of science with many interesting and researchable hypotheses. For example, do we know what constitutes a group of the ablest available people, what is the most appropriate motivation for them, how they are trained both in science as such and in their specialities, what is their value system, the current ideology of their discipline – this type of provocative phrase, of course, makes philosophers of science see red (a nicely ambiguous phrase, in this context). Who, in fact, makes the decisions in science as to theory-choice? This is the choice of which Lakatos has accurately said 'the pragmatic meaning of "rejection" [of a programme] becomes crystal clear: it means *the decision to cease working on it*'. Has anyone ever systematically attempted to find out why certain scientists at certain times stop working on some project and start working on another? The doctoral researches of graduate students are obviously of importance here, but the study of these matters is in its infancy.

If we regard Kuhn's thesis in this light, then it can be seen that it contains a host of suggestions and a battery of possibilities that would keep sociologists of science busy for years.[10] In the foreground of this vast research programme is the lack of information about much of this area; but the framework suggests that we look at how scientists are trained, which types of people go into the training process and how they emerge, the norms and values that guide their scientific choices, and how they interpret these norms and values in terms of the forces exerted on them by the communities to which they belong. These are the details that must be filled in, in order that we may properly begin to assess the problems that remain, for the moment, in the background of the sociology of science. These are the problems that have remained unanswered throughout the years of discussion around the sociology of knowledge. The debate in the history and philosophy of science between the Popperians and Kuhn, and more importantly the current scepticism about the role of science and technology in the modern world, have highlighted the failure of the sociology of knowledge to come to grips with that most distinguished of all its objects – scientific knowledge.

In short, in my view, the present task of the sociology of science involves the study of science as a social institution, as I outlined in Chapter 2 with a view eventually to explaining the ways in which our picture of science, thus constructed, has a bearing on scientific knowledge, the intellectual productions of scientists. This, in a sense, is the 'social philosophical' task of the sociology of science, and it is entirely possible that all our investigations will reveal that there is no patterned relationship between science as a social institution and science as a set of intellectual productions. But we cannot know this before we have done the work, before we have filled in the foreground.

In an interesting contribution to a recent symposium on *Scientific Research and Politics* (Dencik, 1969), Wiberg makes a useful suggestion which would help us to trace the connections between the ideologies and the conclusions of scientists. For example, where two scientists started off with different ideologies and came to different conclusions about the same piece of scientific work, then we should be forced to investigate the exact natures of both these types of differences. On the other hand, where ideologies differed yet conclusions were the same then we should have 'a more valuable . . . intersubjectivity' (ibid., p. 77).

We can develop Wiberg's idea, in terms of my previous discussion, and distinguish between charters (the forms that 'scientific' ideologies take), *findings* and conclusions, for it is clear that scientists often agree about the 'facts' but draw different conclusions from them. A table to illustrate this may be constructed as follows:

		Findings			
		Similar		Different	
		Conclusions		Conclusions	
		S	D	S	D
Charters	S	1	2	3	4
	D	5	6	7	8

Cases 1, 4, 5, and 8 are unproblematic in so far as our 'rational expectations' are that (given they are working on the same problems) scientists who make similar findings will draw similar conclusions; and that different findings will lead to different conclusions, irrespective of charter differences. Case 5 would be most satisfactory in the sense that scientists with different charters draw similar conclusions from similar findings. For example, Soviet communist biologists opposed to Lysenko and Western bourgeois geneticists did draw similar conclusions from similar findings, in the 1930s, 1940s, and 1950s. That is, the different charters did not 'interfere' with the scientific findings-conclusion process.

Case 2 suggests that someone is committing a logical error or simply misunderstanding the evidence, or perhaps that different technical norms, such as I have just been discussing, are involved. Cases 3 and 6 provide the strongest suspicion that charters (and the particular scientific ideologies that flow from them) are at work. Case 3 might cover some of the schools of geology in circulation in the nineteenth century before and just after Darwin published *Origin of Species*. Geologists starting off from similar theologically influenced charters could come up with quite different findings and yet draw similar conclusions which were consistent with Biblical assertions. On the other hand, for case 6, controversies about the supposed relations between race and intelligence often occur when people with different ideologies (e.g. southern conservatives and northern liberals in the United States) do studies that produce similar findings, and the researchers draw different conclusions consistent with their own ideologies.

Case 7 suggests that the particular conclusion in question – perhaps the statement of a law of nature or a very well-founded physical constant – is so important to the scientific enterprise that neither divergent ideologies nor contradictory findings will shake it.

These few examples are intended to illustrate rather than to demonstrate the potential utility of this way of looking at the relations between the charters of science and scientific conclusions. I have excluded material apparatus, staff, and norms from the scheme in order to be able to present it in a manageably simple fashion, but it can be seen that a more complex table would give us even more opportunity to trace out the factors involved in the production of scientific conclusions. This 'social philosophy of science' that I have mapped out briefly covers the overlapping territory of the sociology of knowledge and the philosophy of science. It is a question of theoretical practice (in its commonsense usage) whether this territory is entirely barren or whether something may grow in it.

The 'social-philosophical' task of the sociology of science is not the same as the polemical task that has run through my account in this chapter, though it is related to it in a variety of ways. I shall conclude this discussion of the values and norms of science with some remarks on this polemical task.

The Political Sociology of Science

The present state of science and technology is coming more and more under critical public scrutiny. Part of this is a disillusionment with science, the extent of which is still not adequately documented, and which is not restricted to a lack of confidence in the abilities of scientists and technologists to control or even be aware of the potential effects of their intellectual and material productions. It also extends to a sometimes vague and often ill-informed opposition to the activities of science and technology, and an evaluation of scientific knowledge which implies that it is in some unspecified manner anti-humanitarian or diabolical or contrary to the 'real' values of man. At this level, then, the philosopher of science is plunged into the political arena to defend science against this type of attack. And it is here, paradoxically, that the Popperians join forces with sociologists of science like Parsons and Merton and Barber, in an attempt to tie science, more or less, to a particular form of society, in Popper's case the 'open society' and in the case of the functionalist sociologists of science, liberal democratic society.

As I have already criticized Merton on this count in some detail, I shall restrict myself here to a few remarks about the Popperian political sociology of science. Lakatos is absolutely unambiguous on this score. 'The clash between Popper and Kuhn,' he asserts, 'is not about a mere technical point in epistemology. It concerns our central intellectual values, and has implications not only for theoretical physics but also for the underdeveloped social sciences and even for moral and political philosophy.' The ultimate stigma follows: 'Kuhn's position would vindicate, no doubt, unintentionally, the basic political *credo* of contemporary religious maniacs ("student revolutionaries")' (Lakatos and Musgrave, p. 73). Thus it must be opposed not simply in the spirit of a philosophical debate, though there is no lack of spirit in this debate, but almost (we may surmise) as a moral and political duty.

This zeal contrasts strangely with what can only or at least best be described as the liberal *style* of Popperian philosophy of science. For example, Lakatos draws attention to Popper's point that often we have one hypothesis 'up our sleeves' while falsifying another, and adds that, on his argument, we *must* have one (ibid., p. 119). Never destroy before you are in a position to rebuild. A good liberal principle and one bursting to the seams with common sense, except that *some* people *never* seem to be in a position to rebuild and so some theories, institutions, and relationships appear to be eternal!

Again, in emphasizing an argument of Popper, Lakatos indicates the liberal style of the school. Popper argues that it is impracticable to challenge all one's assumptions at the same time – criticism must be piecemeal (ibid., p. 131). It is not entirely irrelevant to note that this is the philosophical parallel to Popper's influential sociological thesis of the necessity for a piecemeal analysis of social change. Holism, whether philosophical or sociological, is the culprit that will lead us into errors. The consequence of this piecemealism might be that nothing will ever *really* get changed by people who believe in this sort of procedure, for there are no clear rules as to the conditions under which it is proper to begin to question some of the previously most fundamental assumptions of one's science or, for that matter, one's society.

All of this seems to be quite contrary to the spirit of the Popperian research programme, and so it is. I am simply drawing out some examples of what I have termed the liberal style of the philosophy of science and showing their consonance (or perhaps 'elective affinity' might be a bolder and more suggestive way of describing the connection) with certain liberal traits in social and political thought. And it is of some interest to note that in this respect the Popperians and the functionalists share the same orientation towards the role of science and the possibility of scientific knowledge in liberal, democratic societies.

Parsons puts this in a peculiarly apt manner. In his discussion of the institutionalization of science in the West, a discussion which follows Merton most of the way though always in a wider socio-cultural context, he shows how the cultural complex of science and the humanities, organized initially through the universities into professions, integrates science into Western society. This means that scientists and their work are generally legitimized as a part of the ongoing social structure, and this place of science in a form of society is not only explained in terms of the traditions that led up to its present position but is also to some extent guaranteed by the fact that:

the scientist shares the status in the universities with the other key groups who are primary culture bearers and on terms such that the values of science come to be inculcated in the value-system of society generally through the education of its primary élite elements (Parsons, 1951, p. 342).

Science survives and thrives, then, through sociological as well as purely cognitive means. The fact that science can be a beautiful and profoundly satisfying activity is not, by itself, sufficient to ensure that it does survive and thrive. Parsons's view, which I share, is that science must become institutionalized, and its occupational roles must cohere within a broader system of supporting roles. And just as it is bound to be misleading to investigate how this system of roles and norms operates in the wider society without due concern for the dimension of power – roughly, the political organization of society – we cannot fully understand how the social institution of science works without looking at its distribution of power. Internally, with respect to the production of knowledge, we have seen that a purely cognitive picture of science leaves much to be desired; and externally, I have suggested that the organization of the societies in which science is carried out may have more than a little influence on the science itself.

The political sociology of science, then, is an attempt to confront the realities of power with the epistemological needs of science. In this chapter I have not answered many questions, but I hope that I have succeeded in formulating the problems clearly and indicating how they might be investigated.

In the next chapter, Part Two of the book is concluded with some empirical evidence against the Mertonian orthodoxy, some variations on the theme of the work situations of science, and a modification of the social institution model to generate some hypotheses for the version of the sociology of science being developed here.

1. I discuss this more fully in Chapter 6.

2. Many of the arguments in the rest of this chapter have been influenced by the recent works of Mulkay, Dolby, and Barnes (see Barnes, 1972); King, 1970, and particularly Martins, 1972. My paper in Halmos, 1972, gives further details.

3. For a full account, see Medvedev (1969). In an unusually interesting paper Mikulak (1970) discusses the persistence of Lamarckism in Marxism and the Russian tradition.

4. Edward Shils entitled a book on this general topic, *The Torment of Secrecy* (1956). However, as the secrecy has increased, the torment appears to have decreased.

5. This, of course, highlights one of the greatest difficulties of the theory. 'Sufficient' means, here, 'enough to provide adequate motivation to take up a particular occupation'. Those at the top are hardly likely to permit a test of this falsifiable hypothesis. The theory, thus, misses the point of the reality of stratification and privilege in modern society (see Tumin, in Bendix and Lipset, 1966).

6. Another example of the dysfunctions of this type of competition in science is discussed by Collins (1971) in a most interesting study of the development of the CO_2 Laser.

7. This critical epidemic is obviously catching. Popper, in one of his rare direct appraisals of Kuhn's work says: 'I admit that an intellectual revolution often looks like a religious conversion' (Lakatos and Musgrave, p. 57).

In the Postscript to the new edition of *SSR*, Kuhn addresses himself to this problem – though it is difficult at this stage to see exactly how he intends to solve it (Kuhn, 1970, esp. pp. 191–8).

8. This view has curious similarities to some aspects of the structuralism of Lévi-Strauss, especially with respect to his models of social structure (Lévi-Strauss, 1963, Ch. xv).

THE NORMS AND VALUES OF SCIENCE

9. Indeed, the whole conception of a philosophy of science which seeks to find guarantees for scientific knowledge may be entirely misconceived. For provocative elaborations of this view, see Bachelard (1968); and Althusser (1969).

10. The most fruitful analysis to date is that of Herminio Martins, especially his discussion of paradigm span, parity, autarky, univariance, and independence (Martins, 1972, pp. 19–32).

5 The Real Worlds of Science

In Chapter 3 I presented some of the different findings that sociologists and others have made about the ways in which scientists are recruited into various scientific occupations, and the 'orientations' to science that they were supposed to have had. The upshot of my criticisms of many of the conclusions drawn by those sociologists working within the framework of the Mertonian sociology of science, and particularly in terms of its unhappy consequences for the industrial scientist, was that it was unrealistic to assume that the values and norms of *academic* science were necessarily the values and norms of *science as such*. In the Mertonian view, industrial scientists faced inevitable frustrations as scientists and so tended to choose administrative and commercial outlets. The alternative position that I suggested was that the demands of the work situation – academic or industrial – constrained the values and norms of the scientists involved in a variety of patterned directions.

Chapter 4 looked in some detail at the Mertonian norms and at the values and norms of science postulated in current debates. Two main conclusions resulted. First, the Mertonian account of science appears to be seriously deficient when confronted with some of the contemporary realities of big science. It does not even hold to any great extent for academic little science, far less for industrial big science. Second, both the Mertonian–Parsonian and the Popperian theories of science have some significant connections with more general theories of society. In this sense, then, we may begin to speak of the political sociology of science, and we can begin to realize the political functions of similar work in the sociology and philosophy of science. Only in the work of Kuhn, I argued, do we see a serious attempt to get to grips with the problems that the natural sciences throw up for a sociology of knowledge. In this there are strong convergences between

Kuhn and the Marxist view of science, and from both of these sources emerges the neo-Marxist sociology of science that I am trying to advance in this book.

The present chapter augments these themes in three main ways. In the first place, it presents some evidence which goes part of the way to destroying the assumptions on which the Mertonian approach rests. Next, it develops the analysis of the influence of the work situation on the norms and values of science. Third, it reintroduces the model of the social institution with which I begun the argument of Part Two, and shows how it can be modified and strengthened to guide us in our attempts to improve our understanding of the social institution of science.

Some Actual Values and Norms of Science

There are two curious facts about studies of the actual values and norms of science. One is that so few researchers have tried to find out what norms and values scientists hold by asking them directly. The other is that two of the most direct studies on the subject were published in a strange place – from the point of view of most sociologists. Let us take the first fact first.

As has already been indicated, most of the work in the sociology of science done by Merton and his closest associates has been of an historical and analytic kind. It is not that they are methodologically opposed to survey studies on attitudes and beliefs, for the Columbia University Bureau of Applied Social Research (one of whose most prominent leaders Merton has been for many years) has carried out extremely important survey research. There is no obvious reason why Merton and his colleagues did not mount a project to ascertain whether or not scientists actually held the norms with which the social institution of science was supposed to motivate them; and if they did hold these norms, how much deviation from them actually occurred. As I suggested in the last chapter, it might be expected that few scientists – even of the purest academic variety – would be able entirely to observe the norms as specified.

It might be argued that such research was deemed unnecessary because these are institutional norms but, of course, this does not get us very far. Institutional norms require to be observed to some extent by the people in the institution, especially if the very persistence of the institution is predicated on the successful operation of the norms. The institutional avoidance of institutional norms, about which Merton has written in the context of 'reference groups', finds no place in his sociology of science.[1] In his paper on 'The Ambivalence of Scientists' (1963a) Merton recognizes some of these problems in principle though, to me at least, his ambivalence on these issues more than matches theirs!

There seems nothing for it, then, but to try to find out what scientists think about the values and norms of science. It is not to the major sociological journals, however, that we turn for the published results of such research. It is to a journal which, from the point of view of most sociologists (even sociologists of science), is both rather obscure and not easily obtainable.

The Evidence of West and Krohn

In the *Institute of Radio Engineers Transactions on Engineering Management* of June 1960, S. West published a paper entitled 'The Ideology of Academic Scientists'; and in September 1961 Roger Krohn followed this with a piece under the title of 'The Institutional Location of the Scientist and his Scientific Values'. What these two papers do, in spite of their inherent weaknesses, is to throw doubt on the traditional picture of the norms and values of science that Merton and others had built up within the structure of their general and powerful sociological theory.

West begins by noting, quite properly, that few attempts have been made to ascertain whether scientists do actually hold the values often imputed to them and held to be essential to scientific progress. From a mixed list of eleven of such values he sifts out six central principles, namely freedom in research, impartiality, sufficiency of evidence, absence of bias, diffusion of information, and group loyalty. Questions constructed around these six values were asked of fifty-seven university scientists with Ph.D.s, M.D.s, or both. Even on such a small sample the results are provocative.

In response to questions probing the role of freedom in research it emerged that, for most of the scientists, this meant largely the freedom that they had to choose their own problems. Nearly half asserted that an unlimited choice of problem was either indispensable (14) or quite necessary (13) to them. A further eight thought it merely desirable, and the rest (22) were willing to accept limitations of one sort or another to their freedom to choose the problems that they would investigate. That this is not simply a matter of coming to terms with an enforced reality is suggested by the fact that the five researchers who indicated tolerance of the lowest amount of freedom were in fact working under conditions of higher freedom.

The next five values were investigated in a different form. Five cards with brief descriptions of the values were handed to the scientists and they were asked, with respect to each, 'Under what circumstances would you *not* wish to follow this principle?' The responses, some of which were very long, were analysed into themes for each principle.

Impartiality about facts, the principle that the scientist should express no judgement about the desirability of their consequences, was upheld without exception by 19 out of the 57, whereas only 12 respondents agreed that conclusions should in all cases be suspended until the facts assured reasonable certainty. On absence of bias 12 out of the 57 said that they would only consider the characteristics of scientific statements in evaluating them – most of the remaining 45 admitted that direct or inferred characteristics of the scientist involved would play a part in their estimation.[2]

One might mention in passing the Velikovsky affair in this latter context (see De Grazia, 1966). In 1950 Immanuel Velikovsky's book *Worlds in Collision* was published in the United States by the eminently respectable Macmillan Company. On the basis, seemingly, of popularized accounts of Velikovsky's physical and astronomical theories, which were published in some large-circulation magazines, many scientists simply refused to take him seriously. It would be too easy to explain the apparent breaches of the norms of science, manifested by the treatment Velikovsky's work received from the scientific community, with simple reference to the Kuhnian analysis I outlined in the previous chapter. It could be argued (in fact it has been argued, to some extent) that Velikovsky was outside the paradigm of astronomy and physics of the time, and thus he was rejected without much discussion of the substance of his views by the custodians of this normal science. But this is probably an unnecessary hypothesis, for the problem does not arise in the first place if we conceive of the possibility that organized scepticism and universalism are not really norms of the scientific community at all.

West provides an extreme case of this which could, no doubt, be generalized to other topics at other times. He reports:

In the seventeen interviews in which the 'flying-saucer' controversy was introduced as a concrete example, either by the respondent or by the interviewer, there were five respondents who asserted that they would not accept reports of such a phenomenon, no matter who made the observations (West, 1960, p. 58).

The point is *not* that these five (and the others unrecorded) are a disgrace to science and should be drummed out of the scientific community forthwith, but that all scientists probably feel the same about some things and that an account of the norms of science that denies this and links the survival of science to these norms is mistaken. As an essential rider to this it may be added that these same five scientists or their heirs may one day be quite prepared to accept evidence about flying-saucers, and, just as there are good reasons for being dogmatically opposed to this phenomenon today, there may be good reasons at some point in the future for changing one's mind. Rationality, as was argued in the last chapter, is not all of a piece, and there are good reasons for theory choice in many cases which are nicely balanced by other reasons for an alternative choice. The social and/or cognitive norms that govern these choices are, of course, of particular interest and concern for the sociology of science.

The question about the diffusion of information, not surprisingly, largely provoked references to the military significance of scientific knowledge. Of the 40 scientists in the sample who mentioned it specifically, 11 wished to impose conditions of partial or delayed access to such information and 27 advocated completely controlled access. Only 2 out of the 57 scientists, therefore, made a point of saying that there should be full and unrestricted access to scientific information of military value. Again, there is no moral judgement stated or implied here. The thing to note is that the evidence from this small sample hardly supports the existence, let alone the strength or ubiquity, of the norm of communality.

The last value in this connection is group loyalty and, though it has little bearing on my previous discussion, it is interesting to note that only 11 out of the 57 scientists were prepared to give complete support to their fellow scientists over all other groups.

From all of this, then, it is clear that many of the scientists in this particular study do not support the traditional norms of science to the extent that we could be confident that these norms *now* influence the activities of scientists, even if they did at some period in the past. West goes even further than this in an attempt to ascertain the relationship between support of the norms and research behaviour as measured by number of papers published and motivation as judged by peers. No significant relationships were found. In conclusion, noting the case of a dishonest attack by an eminent statistician on a weak colleague, West writes: 'It seems undesirable, therefore, to regard the classical morality of science as more than fortuitously associated with productive research' (ibid., p. 62).

Krohn, in his study, starts off from a rather different position. Whereas West was sceptical that the traditional norms of science were in fact operative and set out to test their existence, Krohn accepts the traditional values and sets out to show how they vary from one institutional location to another. He asked a series of questions of about 50 industrial and university scientists and about 40 scientists working in government laboratories. He formulates a set of hypotheses derived from the general view that:

the change in the location of science will be accompanied by three major changes in scientific attitudes and values:

(1) A change from the conception that research is properly conducted by individuals to the ideal that it belongs to large-scale, formally organized, research projects.
(2) A change from the traditional conception of the scientist as an independent intellectual to the notion of the scientific professional.
(3) A change from the justification of research by the value of knowledge for its own sake to its justification by its utility in the achievement of general human welfare (Krohn, 1961a, p. 133).

Krohn constructed eight attitude scales to ascertain if there were any significant differences among the three groups of scientists. Three of the scales were aimed at their conceptions of science, another three at the nature of the scientific role, and the last two at organizational features of scientific research. The findings were structured in terms of two sets of comparisons –

university and industrial physical and biological scientists made up the first, and university and government bio-medical scientists the second. The results leave little doubt that university scientists demonstrate more allegiance to the inferred traditional norms than their colleagues in industry and government.

The greatest differences between university and industrial scientists were on the knowledge–utility scale on the nature of science and the freedom–bureaucracy scale on research organization. The former implies the third of the major changes referred to above, while the latter refers to the first. The comparisons of university and government scientists, however, produced rather less clear-cut results and if anything the government biologists were nearer the traditional values than the university biologists. There were no particularly significant differences between the medical scientists in the two settings.

These apparently puzzling results were more thoroughly discussed in another paper by Krohn under the title of 'Science and the Practical Institutions' (1961b). The thesis of this paper is that where scientists become attached, through the development of their particular branch of science, to the practical institutions like medicine, then they will move farther and farther away from the traditional values of science, the academy and the life of the intellect. This was borne out by the responses of regular university scientists, basic and clinical medical scientists on the attitude scales. Professional training and other practical ends, implicit in the practical institutions, were said to account for the significant differences in scientific values found between the groups.

The research of both West and Krohn, therefore, suggests the possibility that the values and norms actually held by scientists vary from one type of employment to another, a view which is not necessarily incompatible with the Mertonian account. It also suggests more than this, however, for it calls into question (a) the fact that science as such needs the Mertonian norms; and (b) that even most scientists act according to these norms most of the time.

The door is opened in this manner to a more thorough scepticism about Merton's sociology of science. Before I go on to discuss further work which throws more doubt on it, it may be interesting to look at what can be termed a rearguard action in defence of the orthodoxy. In 1965 Warren Hagstrom published his book *The*

Scientific Community, an attempt to modify the Mertonian scheme so that it might better use some new developments in sociological theory and deal with some contemporary aspects of the social organization of science.

Neo-Mertonianism in Defence of Orthodoxy

In contrast to West and Krohn, Hagstrom paints a rather impressionistic picture, though it may be fairly stated that his methods are, in principle, no less viable than the small samples and limited scope of their researches. In about ninety unstructured interviews the author sought to establish the relationships that existed between a man's colleagues and the sort of work that he did, in short, how the scientific community (whose existence is to some extent assumed and to some extent inferred from the patterns of the interview responses and supporting evidence) operates to ensure that science progresses and that scientists are adequately motivated. Thus, although as we shall see Hagstrom develops in an original direction, the underlying structure of his argument is firmly within the theoretical tradition of the Mertonian sociology of science. This is not to minimize the differences between the original formulations of Merton and Hagstrom's own contribution, which are considerable, but to emphasize that they both appear to hold on to certain assumptions about the social organization of science which no data appear to challenge and all data, however superficially dilatory, appear to support.

The twist that Hagstrom gives to the theory derives from certain notions about the exchange of gifts suggested by the French anthropologist Marcel Mauss. This is summed up thus: 'The organization of science consists of an exchange of social recognition for information' (Hagstrom, 1965, p. 13). Scientists give gifts in the form of scientific papers to the scientific community, which rewards the giver with scientific prestige in the form of citations to the work of the scientist, prestigious prizes and awards, membership in high-ranking institutions, and – perhaps the greatest accolade of all – eponymy, the process whereby the name of the scientist is given to what he has discovered or invented or indeed to the age on which he stamped his mark. Boyle's Law and Planck's constant are examples of the former; Newtonian and Darwinian eras are examples of the latter. The way in which Hagstrom's simple observation is integrated into a general explanatory outline for the sociology of science is clearly summarized and bears quoting at some length as it embodies many of the ways in which the social system of science operates. Hagstrom writes:

The thesis presented here is that social control in science is exercised in an exchange system, a system wherein gifts of information are exchanged for recognition from scientific colleagues. Because scientists desire recognition, they conform to the goals and norms of the scientific community. Such control reinforces and complements the socialization process in science. It is partly dependent on the socialization of persons to become sensitive to the responses of their colleagues. By rewarding conformity, this exchange system reinforces commitment to the higher goals and norms of the scientific community, and it induces flexibility with regard to specific goals and norms. The very denial by scientists of the importance of recognition as an incentive can be seen to involve commitments to higher norms, including an orientation to a scientific community extending beyond any particular collection of contemporaries (ibid., p. 52).

The first thing to be noted about this statement is the importance attached to *recognition*. The theory revolves around the need of scientists for recognition from their fellow scientists and the consequences that this has for the social institution of science. As I have already pointed out in the previous chapter, Merton himself has commented that the need for recognition appears to be an element in all social activities, and that the important fact to understand is that in science this is closely linked to originality, with important consequences as shown.

This emphasis on recognition can be challenged from two directions, namely from the Popperian critique, which concentrates almost exclusively on cognitive factors and argues that scientists are motivated by and respond to intellectual challenges; and from the direction that I have suggested in many places throughout this book – that the organization and development of science are not independent of the social structures in which they occur. In a society where the sort of recognition that Hagstrom and others speak about is so closely connected with prestige and material rewards and various types of power, this account of the social system of science may have some credence. But this does not necessarily mean that this is the best, far less the only society in which science can thrive. And further, even if recognition of the type that Hagstrom describes is vital for the scientists he has studied, it by no means follows that *all* scientists in all settings share this characteristic. One way around this latter objection is to deny that certain categories of people who clearly work in science are scientists at all. This is, in fact, what Hagstrom does, and the manner in which he does it renders his work less than useful for the understanding of the majority of those who work in science.

In discussing the channels of communication through which the scientific community operates he singles out 'published articles and books, and papers read at society meetings. This [he says] is the most important channel of communication from the standpoint of the larger community. Those who do not contribute at all through this channel cannot be considered scientists' (ibid., p. 43). Therefore, with one stroke of the pen, Hagstrom defines away a significant objection to his theory of the scientific community, and a not insignificant portion of the scientific workforce. Pelz and Andrews (1966, p. 273), for example, in their studies on scientists working in the National Institutes of Health in the United States, specifically note the number of individuals in their sample who produced no papers or reports. A survey of American physiologists carried out in the 1950s reveals that in the three-year period prior to the investigation one in nine bacterial and one in eight plant physiologists doing research had published no papers (Gerard, 1958, p. 134). And lastly, Cotgrove and Box, in their study of British industrial scientists to which I shall shortly return, report that in a five-year period the majority of their sample had not published a scientific paper (1970, p. 156).

None of these examples is definitive. The evidence on reports to meetings of scientific societies is not available but we are justified in assuming that large numbers of scientists who work in industrial laboratories do not participate in this type of activity either. Hagstrom would deny the title of scientist to them and significant numbers of others who are in government and university and private research laboratories. It is noteworthy that he mentions neither patents nor unpublished technical papers in his list of six channels of communications. Patents and technical papers are probably the most important and widespread means of communication used by scientists in industry. Hagstrom in the

course of his book discusses the problems that priority disputes pose for the sociology of science; patenting, however, is
ignored.

This, then, is a major weakness in the account of Hagstrom in
particular and the Mertonians in general. Sometimes by definition, and at other times merely by implication, large sections of
modern science are excluded from the analysis. This procedure
has two main implications. In the first place they commit the
fallacy of generalization from unrepresentative samples. But this
is really quite a minor fault and one that can be easily rectified by
simply relabelling the enterprise. What Hagstrom and Merton
are doing, therefore, is not so much 'the sociology of science' as
'the sociology of élite science' or 'the sociology of academic
science' or perhaps even 'the sociology of pure science' –
though, as I have previously indicated, this latter concept is
probably not very helpful.

It is very far from my intention to denigrate this work *per se*.
Indeed, Harriet Zuckerman's research (1967 b) into the scientific Nobel prizes, Merton's own labours in scientific creativity
and originality, the psychological studies of Terman (1954),
and Roe (1953; 1965), and Eiduson (1962), on outstanding
scientists, have shown beyond doubt that this special area in the
sociology of science can be most fruitful and interesting. And it
would be quite false to suggest that all or indeed most of these
writers uncritically suppose that what they have found to be true
for their exceptional samples actually holds true for all scientists
and technologists. What the Mertonian sociology of science does
is much more important, and this is the second implication of
looking for the norms of science in only one research setting. The
Mertonian norms of science are not merely procedural rules,
they are also prescriptive. They not only indicate what scientists
do, they also indicate what scientists ought to do. I hesitate to
use the expression *moral norms* but, as I argued in the last chapter in comparing these norms with those implied by the functionalist theory of stratification, this form of reasoning can often give
the impression of smuggling in moral imperatives in the guise of
functional imperatives. And this is the consequence of the
position of Merton and his followers on the norms of science.
Non-academic scientists are considered to be deviant scientists
in so far as they do not live up to the norms of science as

stipulated, and they are considered to be frustrated academic scientists when their employment circumstances do not permit them to act like academic scientists.

Fortunately, there is a growing body of material which shows as conclusively as is possible in sociology that the Mertonian framework for the sociology of science is misleading to the extent that it fails to describe the worlds of science, it fails to explain how they operate, and it entails a moral structure of the scientific activity that scientists in increasing numbers are rejecting. In short, however adequate this sociology of science might be for some little science, it is quite inadequate for much of big science. A sociology of big science will take into consideration not only the norms of Nobel prizewinners and those who give their names to scientific phenomena, but also the working norms of the great majority of scientists who do not win Nobel prizes and who do not conceive of the work they are doing in these heroic terms. This is not to say that we simply assume that the bench chemist in a paint research laboratory or the physics graduate working as an electronics technologist will have totally different scientific norms from an Ostwald or an Einstein, for this is – to some extent at least – an empirical question. As the research of West and Krohn suggested, from rather different angles, unproblematic assumptions about the norms and values of any scientists are liable to lead us into difficulties.

Beyond the University:
New Frontiers for the Sociology of Science

One of the first challenges to the accepted paradigm of the sociology of science put forward by Merton and those who continued his work came, not accidentally, from an American sociologist who had carried out some research on the problems of scientific administrators in research institutes. Norman Kaplan published two long articles in *Administrative Science Quarterly* in 1959 and 1961, comparing the role of the research administrator in the United States and the Soviet Union. Apart from the intrinsic interest of these papers for those involved in the theory and practice of complex organizations, there is an aspect of Kaplan's work which is particularly suggestive for my present task of sketching the shape of a sociology of big science and particularly its normative structure.

Kaplan demonstrates that whereas the research administrator in the US is liable to be an independently important and highly paid executive, in the USSR he is much more liable to be a 'chief clerk'. Two consequences were seen to flow from this with respect to the Russian case. Firstly, there appeared to be less administration in these research institutes than in their American counterparts. And secondly, the Russian scientists were more willing to perform administrative functions than the American scientists, while indicating that this did not diminish (and possibly even enhanced) their research effectiveness. The implication in Kaplan's argument on these points is that the much vaunted stresses and strains that scientists are supposed to experience in non-academic research laboratories may have more to do with research administrators than with administration itself. On this view, the Soviet scientists accept certain administrative reponsibilities as part of the circumstances of working in a large laboratory,[3] and, far from interfering with their work, these administrative responsibilities can be turned to their scientific advantage when they rest mainly in the hands of the scientists.

This state of affairs is only possible where the researchers have higher status and more autonomy than the research administrators, as was the case in the Russian medical research institutes that Kaplan studied. He says:

Such a step would be extremely difficult in many American research organizations because, among other things, it would necessitate the reduction in status, prestige, and monetary rewards of the chief administrator as he is now defined (Kaplan, in Barber and Hirsch, 1962, p. 386).

It may therefore be fruitful to consider the problems of scientists and technologists in large organizations in terms of the vested interests of research administrators, and this may be particularly true for industrial laboratories. To put the matter in the most conspiratorial terms, we may explore the supposed antagonism between the 'science orientation' and the 'administration orientation' of industrial scientists in relation to the needs of the research administrator. It is to the advantage of the research administrator to persuade his organizational superiors that scientists and technologists do not wish to be bothered by administrative detail, and, further, that there is some inherent incompatibility between science and administration which makes the job of the research administrator so very difficult. It is also to the advantage of administrators to invent or (more charitably) to seek out as much administrative work as possible, and this often entails that people are forced into doing tiresome tasks whose rationale is not always entirely clear.[4]

If we add to the general problems of administration in any large organization the special problem that is implied by the supposition that most if not all industrial scientists and technologists are frustrated university 'pure' researchers, then we clearly have the basis for the voluminous and ever-expanding literature on 'administering research and development' which adorns the shelves of sociologists of science and the more progressive laboratory executives alike. Some of this work I have dealt with in Chapter 3, and I need only recall the names of Marcson and Kornhauser, Strauss and Glaser, in order to remind the reader that there has been no lack of attention paid to the problems of the workers in big science.

It is fitting that Kaplan, in an extended review of the books of the first three of these men, should have taken the opportunity this occasion presented to raise some fundamental problems concerning the actual norms of big science, and to dispel some current myths about science and research in organizations.

The View from Industrial Science

The major thrust of the attack on Marcson, Kornhauser, and Strauss concerns the use they make of the category of *professionalization*. Kaplan sees a tendency for this to be used as a cover which obscures the real problems, and indeed he makes a good case that there are so many different role relationships which scientists and technologists may be involved in, that it is misleading to speak of a single profession of science. He sums this up well in his article: 'Organization: Will it choke or promote the growth of science?' This is an aspect of the sociology of science which I have only hinted at from time to time in previous chapters but which must continually be borne in mind. Referring to myths about science and scientists, he says:

The most widely held one is that science is all of a piece, that all the sciences are pretty much alike with, perhaps, the exception of the social sciences – if one is inclined to include them at all. Yet we know that some fields are considerably better developed than others, and that all science cannot be organized in the same way. Differences in the kinds of equipment used, in the kinds of problems dealt with, and in the duration of the research projects characteristic of the field should presumably exert some effect on the organization of research.

Perhaps it is sufficient to think of the sciences in terms of the usual categories of natural, physical, and social. The National Register of Scientific Technical Personnel lists eight major sciences (e.g., chemistry, biology, physics, etc.) subdivided into 545 categories. In addition, there are 22 interdisciplinary sciences (e.g., biochemistry, biophysics, etc.) subdivided into 215 categories, plus 25 categories of social sciences. Finally, there are 12 kinds of engineers subdivided into 125 categories. Altogether there are 910 subcategories in the National Register.[5] I do not wish to imply that there are 910 different kinds of scientists and engineers. However, I suspect that there are significant differences among a large number of these types (Kaplan, in Hill 1964, p. 105).

Further, he claims that the proto-typical professional role relationship – that between the professional and his client – which so characterizes the traditional professions of medicine and the law, is one in which the large majority of scientists and technologists are unlikely to find themselves. Indeed, it is in their rather more marginal roles of technical consultants or specialist salesmen that scientists are liable to experience this professional relationship. Tied in with this is the underlying assumption of most American sociologists of science that Robert Merton has correctly characterized the norms of science and, more important, that industrial scientists and technologists have internalized these norms to some extent. While few would claim outright that these norms constitute the institutional motivation to do science for those who work in industry in exactly the same way as they do for academic and research institute scientists, as I have emphasized many times, the current assumption does set up these norms as, at the very least, standards of orientation for all scientists. This Kaplan queries.

We must continually be careful to distinguish between two close although importantly distinct views. One is that industrial scientists do in fact violate the 'norms of pure science'. Very few people would deny this, and, as I argued in the last chapter, most scientists appear to violate them to some extent. The second, and analytically quite separate view, is that industrial scientists acknowledge these norms and experience strains of one kind or another in so doing. There are difficulties in this second view, highlighted in the empirical studies of Krohn and West, and in the more theoretical reflections of Kaplan. In addition, as I have shown in the previous chapter, there are other good reasons for doubting the necessity or universal validity of the Mertonian norms of science.

In a piece of research reported in 1964, John R. Hinrichs isolated three possible attitude sets, and tested them out on samples of academic chemists and industrial chemists. Two of these sets, or components as they are termed in this paper, are the usual ones about 'freedom and support in research and a belief that industry raises barriers to worthwhile scientific activity' and 'relatively expedient attitudes and acceptances of business values, possibly at the expense of science values'. The third component, however, is of particular interest in so far as it 'was interpreted as indicating acceptance of industrial research with the belief that there is little serious conflict between science and industrial values' (Hinrichs, 1964, p. 290). Hinrichs found that those chemists with the highest scores on satisfaction measures were much more likely to manifest this third component than either of the other two, although he does rather give the impression that these people had somehow internalized the norms of science *and* industry and had synthesized them into some happy compromise.

It is difficult to comment on what a compromise between the Mertonian norms of science and 'commercial' science might look like, and I consider that speculation along these lines is likely to be unrewarding. What is more rewarding is the notion that scientists might select, from the congerie of norms and values that they are exposed to in the institutions of higher education from which they obtain their qualifications, some norms and values that fit in with the circumstances of their likely employment. This notion has the advantage of realism in that it recognizes the high possibility of imperfect socialization in universities and other places that train scientists and technologists; it is sensitive to the real differences that clearly exist in this socialization from one institution to another; and lastly, it gives us a positive incentive to look out for those cases in which young men and women undergo scientific education in the expectation that they will end up in one type of employment rather than another. This latter consideration is very important because it serves to remind us that people (and especially those who are able to take advantage of the opportunities of higher education) do not always present themselves as blank sheets, the tabula rasa of the crudest behaviourists, to be mutely imprinted by the patterns and the hopes and the rules of the ongoing social structures in which they find themselves. Socialization, and especially socialization into a scientific or technological discipline, is very much a two-way process, and it is blatantly fanciful to presume that *all* the potential workers in big science internalize *all* the norms of science, even if we allow that they are all exposed to them in a similar fashion. There will undoubtedly be *some* and perhaps many schoolboy enthusiasts, such as those described by Hutchings (see Chapter 3), who appear to have been captured by the norms of 'pure' science at school and who spend their undergraduate years imbibing more and more of it – each experience reinforcing their original motives and prescribing more and more of their behaviour – until they become academic researchers in their own right and abrogate real science to their own kind. But just as surely will there be others who will see science as a career, notably as a comparatively painless avenue of upward social mobility, and who will accept and build upon those aspects of their scientific training that they deem important for their prospective occupational spheres, whether in universities or in industry, and who will reject those other aspects of their training that they deem inappropriate or, even worse, complete liabilities.

I am arguing, therefore, that the norms of science, like science itself, are not all of a piece. There is clearly a procedural core, though it is more convenient and less confusing to regard this as the logic of science, and (as I dealt with this at length in the previous chapter) I shall only pause to reiterate that this core is by no means settled, though the area of disagreement about it is somewhat less than several of the main protagonists admit. Outside this core of the logic of science there revolve sets of scientific norms, some of which are important to some groups of scientists and others of which are important to other groups of scientists. There is little doubt that Merton and those who followed him in constructing the main body of the sociology of science in America have described and explained the operation of one of these sets of norms for one group of scientists with a great deal of success. Nevertheless, enough work has been done to show that these norms and this group do not constitute the whole of science, and the assumption that they do has seriously hampered the development of the sociology of science, for the assumption precludes the asking of certain crucial questions about scientists and technologists who work in non-academic contexts.

What are these crucial questions? The first concerns the holy of holies of pure science – publication. It is one thing to ascertain publication rates of different groups of scientists and technologists, but it is quite another thing to look behind these rates and to inquire how important scientists consider publication to be and the reasons they give for their judgements on the matter. If one sort of scientist absolutely depends on the publication of his work for his continued employment and advancement in his job, and another has good reason to believe that publishing scientific articles is irrelevant to his job prospects, then – whatever other reasons there may be for the former to rank publication highly and for the latter to rank it not so highly in a list of those things that are important to him in his work – the obvious pragmatic point cannot be ignored. No one, not even the academic research scientist, works entirely in a vacuum; however unworldly a man may be he still lives more or less in the world.

The next question concerns the old chestnut of basic and applied research, the distinction which I have been at pains to dissect in the foregoing pages. The basic/applied research distinction plays a positive though largely implicit role in the orthodox account of the norms of science that I am here criticizing. Given a clear, unproblematic, and agreed distinction between basic, fundamental, or pure research on the one hand, and applied, or mission-oriented, research (not to speak of experimental development) on the other hand, it is easy to give the constant impression, without actually having to argue or provide evidence for the view, that the former is in some way *real* science and that the latter is less *real*, or deviant, science. As I have already argued (see Chapter 1, Appendix), the basic/applied distinction has a very real and important function in terms of hierarchies within science, though even this may be more limited than we think, in the allocation of status and prestige to different types of investigators and projects. Although the distinction has been criticized here and there it has very rarely been explicitly defended and, more important, no one to my knowledge has seen fit to ask working scientists and technologists if they use it, how they use it if they do, and whether they think that it makes scientific as opposed to administrative sense. In bio-medical research, at least, it appears to make very little scientific sense.

A most interesting comment on all of this, particularly revealing because it comes from industrial rather than academic research experience, appears in an article by the head of basic research at the Ford Motor Company in the United States. The writer, J. E. Goldman, is discussing the place of basic research in industry and he cites the example of the development of an economic fuel cell. He goes on:

If somebody, some place, is going to make an important discovery in fuel cells, where and how is this likely to happen? You are forced to recognize that this will probably come out of the catalyst, because the development which will spell the difference in fuel cells – both in economics and practicability – will probably happen in the catalyst: Find a cheap, simple catalyst and fuel cells may come into the picture.

So you decide on the following course: You mount a first-class program in understanding fundamentals of catalysis. This is meaningful basic work for an industrial laboratory. It may involve fundamental research in electrochemistry, in solid state physics, in radiation effects or diffusion. If you start out by getting top notch people you have bought two things: knowledge of what's going on in the world, and a weighting of the odds in your favor that innovation will take place within your own organization (Goldman, 1964, pp. 39–40).

This statement is useful in two respects, for what it says and for what it leaves unsaid. It says enough to reinforce the notion that the basic/applied distinction tends to break down at crucial points when we leave the administrative sphere and bring in technical considerations. It does not say, though it strongly implies, that calling an industrial laboratory a *basic* laboratory and framing the research it does in these fundamental terms might indeed attract top notch men. And this is the sociological and not the technical usage of the basic/applied distinction.

The third and final question to which I shall draw attention here concerns the satisfactions and dissatisfactions of working scientists and technologists. The orthodox model of the norms of science assumes that scientists who are prevented from behaving in accordance with the norms will become dissatisfied, and if they do not seem to be dissatisfied, then notions of resocialization into the organizational normative system are employed to explain away the discrepancy between theory and practice. The very assumptions on which this type of analysis proceeds will preclude an investigation which wishes to find out whether or not different groups of scientists acknowledged the norms of pure science in the first place.

I have already cited a few pieces of research from American investigators which have asked these questions in one form or another. There have also been studies in Britain, inspired largely by the development of the sociology of science in the United States. Two of these in particular deserve extended discussion in this inquiry into research on the actual norms of science, for they represent, in differing ways, more empirical evidence for many of the speculative criticisms that I have been making of the Mertonian sociology of science. The first of these studies, by Cotgrove and Box, may conveniently be seen as a half-way stage between the orthodox view and the one I am presenting here. Although, as will be clear, their findings knock great holes in the orthodox theory, they retain it at crucial points and seem unwilling to draw out the full implications of their work. The second study, a doctoral thesis by Ellis, betrays no such reticence and explicitly presents itself as a clear and reasoned rejection of the sociology of science of Merton.

The Fate of the Orthodoxy in Britain

Cotgrove and Box, on a sample of over five hundred science students and nearly four hundred industrial chemists, postulate three sorts of scientific identity (1970, Chapter 2). These identities accompany specific scientific roles, as follows: *public* scientists, whose role was an academic one concerned with the discovery of knowledge, *private* scientists, whose role was a professional one concerned with the application of knowledge, and the *organizational* scientists, who had a non-scientific role. (The authors previously used the term 'instrumental' scientists in place of organizational, and perhaps it would have been better to retain the original term as it does give an indication that these are the scientists who use science very much as a means to an end rather than as an end in itself.)

It is instructive to note that their results derive from an analysis of these two distinct samples – the traditional student group (in this case chemistry students at three English universities), and the traditional industrial group (scientists from nine laboratories where research and administrative personnel were surveyed). The problems that appeared to interest Cotgrove and Box were those that, as I have shown, have interested many other sociologists of science. But they conclude their first major paper (Box and Cotgrove, 1966, p. 26) with the contention that 'the thesis that there is a conflict between the needs of professionals and the organizations which employ them requires some modification', and they draw attention to 'the degree of commitment to those clusters of values which *have been assumed* to characterize members of professional occupations' (emphasis added).

Their three types of scientists, then, are the groups that exhibit differential attachment to these assumed values, which are taken to be (*a*) high commitment to publication of results, (*b*) autonomy based on personal expertise, the professional career aspect, and (*c*) commitment to science as an end in itself, which entails personal disinterestedness. These are derived in a deliberate attempt systematically to relate the Mertonian norms of science with the different types of scientists that obviously exist. Referring to Merton, Barber, and others for their derivation of these values, they note: 'that these values are not just abstract logical derivations, but are characteristics of highly esteemed scientists, has already been demonstrated in the literature' (ibid., p. 27).

The crucial variable here is, of course, 'highly esteemed', and the assumption that the values of science, as derived from a general theoretical position as well as from a selective portrayal of the words and deeds of some great scientists, will satisfactorily apply to all scientists, great or minor, in all settings, is not sustained by the work of Cotgrove and Box. The interpretation they put upon their findings, however, is not unambiguous. They argue that because not all scientists subscribe equally to the values of science, as defined in the literature of the sociology of science, then we must recognize that there are different kinds of scientists and that they are attached to science in varying ways. The public or dedicated scientists are the 'real' scientists, whereas the private and the organizational scientists are in some ways lesser scientists.

We might justifiably ask how they arrive at these three types in the first place. The main source for these values or norms of science is, of course, the previous literature in the sociology of science which, as the quotation above reveals, Cotgrove and Box consider to have 'demonstrated' their existence. That their reading of the literature has been less than close is further suggested by the fact that they cite the studies by Krohn and West that have been discussed at the beginning of this chapter, in *Science, Industry and Society* amidst other references, to exemplify a point about the rewarding of discovery in the scientific community. The impression is given, therefore, that the researches of Krohn and West simply augment the orthodox account of the norms of science (Cotgrove and Box, 1970, pp. 16; 37, note 7). They either ignore the fact that the results of Krohn and West make it clear that *something* is wrong with Merton's theory, or present these results in a way that implies that they make no real difference to the theory.[6]

When they present their own findings, however, Cotgrove and Box, in apparent innocence, add fuel to the very fire that Krohn, West, and Kaplan, had started on the other side of the Atlantic. They found that just under 70 per cent of their industrial chemists accorded low importance to the publication of their work; 44 per cent were not highly committed to a career in science; and 50 per cent were satisfied with little autonomy in their work (1970, p. 33). These results *could* be explained in terms of the fact that on entering industry these pure or real scientists had collided with the limitations of their new work situations and some – the proportions cited – had already succumbed to the vagaries of industrial science.

This interpretation is rather undermined by the findings from the chemistry student sample. It transpires that 51 per cent of the students attached low importance to publication, 28 per cent attached low commitment to a scientific career, and 36 per cent attached low importance to research autonomy (ibid.).

If we accept these figures at their face value, then we are left with the conclusion that less than half the chemistry students and less than a fifth of the industrial chemists were 'public scientists' ('public scientists' – those high in publication, commitment, and autonomy – accounted for 43 per cent of the students and 17 per cent of the industrial scientists). There has to come a time when results like these lead us to doubt the reality and utility of the norms of science as hitherto assumed. Cotgrove and Box all but draw this implication from their research but, perhaps misled by what they call their 'interaction approach' to the sociology of science, they fail to do so.

This is the gist of their contention that 'there is no necessary connection between being qualified and employed as a scientist, and a full identification with the norms of science' (ibid., p. 14). In fact they go on, using the terminology and insights of Goffman and others, to argue that the public or dedicated scientist is the only type which fully 'embraces' the scientist role. This is of course entirely circular, though still interesting, for the scientist role is defined precisely by those characteristics on which the public or dedicated scientist is differentiated from his fellow (lesser) scientists.

Thus, Cotgrove and Box establish empirically that there are three distinct types of scientists – only 16 per cent of the students and 24 per cent of the industrial chemists did not fall entirely into one of their hypothesized types – but they resolutely ignore the possibility that this finding could undermine some of the traditional ideas about science.

Much previous work in the sociology of science [they say] has failed to distinguish between the institutionalized values of science, and the internationalization and acceptance of such values by scientists. It is problematic, and by no means self-evident, that all those who possess a B.Sc. have fully internalized and accepted the values of science (ibid., p. 23).

On the basis of findings in many ways rather similar to those of Cotgrove and Box, Norman Ellis has taken a further – and, in my view, largely justified – step. Ellis argues that it no longer makes much sense to conceive of the values and norms of science as Merton has done and as many other sociologists have uncritically continued to do. The evidence forces a change in the theoretical base of the sociology of science (Ellis, 1969; and in Barnes, 1972).

Ellis proceeded in the conventional fashion. He sent questionnaires to fourteen departments in three universities and to fourteen non-academic laboratories, mainly industrial but including government and research association laboratories. His total sample was 390, made up of 51 scientists and 46 technologists from the universities, and 210 scientists and 83 technologists from non-academic workplaces. A particularly noteworthy feature is that each completed questionnaire was followed up by a personal interview in which the respondent's written answers to questions were clarified and discussed, and extra information was gleaned.

The main thrust of this research is to establish that the academic/non-academic context is the most significant criterion on which scientists and technologists differ, and that far from the non-academic scientist being simply a frustrated academic, he has quite different scientific norms and values. As Ellis says, the dilemmas of the industrial scientist 'appear to derive from the peculiarly fragmented and unstructured character of their employment situations rather than from an inherent incompatibility between "science" and "industry"' (Ellis, 1969, p. 8).

Ellis replicates the findings of Cotgrove and Box, and others I have mentioned, on the attitudes of industrial scientists to publication. Although there was a small group, about 9 per cent of the non-academic scientists, who considered publication and the policy of their firm regarding it to be extremely important to them, generally speaking the industrial scientists considered it to be somewhat unimportant for them. In terms of the amount of dissatisfaction that stemmed from problems about publication, it appeared not to play anything like a major part in their overall job satisfaction. A very interesting point emerges in this context – a point which, incidentally, illustrates the great value of the personal interview in social research.

Ellis says:

A considerable number of QSEs in *both* of these groupings [i.e. the scientists who considered publication important and those who considered it unimportant] did not distinguish between the conventional 'public' scientific paper or technical article, and the internal technical papers which are only seen by other QSEs within the organization. It was therefore necessary to clarify with every interviewee whether or not the publications he had listed in the questionnaire were genuine publications or private papers of limited circulation. The fact that many of these QSEs did not draw a distinction between public knowledge and private (commercial) knowledge, is a very significant finding in itself. When these individuals were asked to specify which of their 'publications' were actually public, and which were private memoranda, it seemed as though I was forcing upon them a viewpoint which they themselves did not share (ibid., p. 78).

This position recalls to mind the finding of Hinrichs, cited above, that the most satisfied scientists in his study were those who saw no insuperable contradictions between science and industry. It is also near the position of Cotgrove and Box's private scientist – the scientist whose role is bound up with the commercial application of science.

I have elsewhere quoted Lord Macaulay on Francis Bacon's attempt to bind science and utility – what 'some people may think . . . a low object' (Sklair, 1970, p. 12) – and even today the comment is still apposite. The practical application of science in most quarters has lower prestige than science in its 'pure' form, unsullied by considerations of human welfare as opposed to the nourishment of the imaginations of those élites whose lives are comparatively well-nourished already. The sociology of science as it has developed, particularly in America, has contributed to this unhealthy misallocation of prestige and, by implication, denigrated the efforts of those scientists not working in academic settings. This is a curious trait in a sociology of science which, as I argued in the previous chapter, sees the persistence and progress of science as inextricably joined to a liberal capitalist form of society.

If they have no particular problem of publication or, as Ellis goes on to demonstrate, of research autonomy or free time to pursue their own research or frustrated ambition to pursue basic research in their own fields, then what are the main sources of dissatisfaction that industrial scientists experience? In order to answer this question Ellis constructs a 'saliency of dissatisfaction' index, a measure which purports to combine the importance of an item with the amount of dissatisfaction it produces (Table 2, pp. 222–3). Of the seventeen items, those with the highest salience of dissatisfaction scores were, first and second, 'the extent to which my qualifications and experience are being fully utilized' and 'quality and quantity of assisting personnel'. Third and fourth were 'prospects for promotion up a scientific/ technical research career ladder', and 'salaries of R & D personnel'. These findings clearly show that the industrial scientist is much concerned and dissatisfied with those conditions in his work environment which prevent him from doing his *scientific* job properly. The impression one receives strongly from this and other research on scientists in industry is that a significant proportion of the time of these often highly qualified workers is spent on routine tasks which could be carried out by unqualified ancillary staff. This state of affairs obviously causes much frustration for industrial scientists and there is some evidence that university scientists also suffer in this way to some extent (see Hirsch, 1968, pp. 23–33).

In a chapter provocatively entitled 'The Real Problems of Non-Academic Research QSEs', Ellis traces much of the discontent experienced by these scientists back to the rather haphazard development of British industrial research laboratories since the Second World War. In many cases it seemed that the position of the research laboratory in the general framework of the enterprise as a whole was rather uncertain – almost as if large companies had to have research divisions but were not entirely sure of what to do with them. Thus, the research personnel feel isolated and out of the mainstream of the life of the company to which they may have dedicated many years of loyal service. On this interpretation, therefore, it is not surprising to find that the fifth most salient source of dissatisfaction from the list of seventeen that Ellis examines is 'the opportunities research personnel have to influence overall company policy'. Many of these latter points are further substantiated by a survey carried out by Elizabeth Paul for the Royal Institute of Chemistry (RIC).* This survey was based on more than 1,800 questionnaires from five categories of RIC members – chemistry undergraduates and postgraduate researchers, university staff, graduates with less than five years' industrial research experience, and senior industrialists. Particularly interesting is the fact that the recent graduate group working in industry were, on the whole, quite similar in terms of their work dissatisfactions to Ellis's industrial scientists, many of whom were in fact chemists. Underutilization of skills and lack of supporting staff were high on the list of grievances that these scientists expressed. Another important item which clearly worried many of them concerned uncertainty for the future, and one does not need to read between

* This is known as the Eaborn Report, after the chairman of the RIC committee which sponsored the study. I am here concerned only with Miss Paul's survey and the conclusions she draws from it.

the lines to divine the underlying fact that many younger graduate scientists in industry have little confidence in the ability of
company management to plan adequately for research needs in
industry in the age of big science. Indeed, the whole survey is
something of an indictment of both university chemistry education and the attempts of industry properly to transmit its needs
for scientific manpower to the educational sphere. A reading of
only the 'official report' which precedes the survey and its
conclusions would hardly betray this state of affairs.

The conclusion that Ellis reaches might hold for the larger
part of British industrial science, and perhaps it might also apply
outside of Britain. 'The major problem which was faced by
most of these QSEs,' he says, 'is the lack of any formalized
career or salary structure' (Ellis, 1969, p. 263). In most of Europe
and in America academic scientists, like other academics, have a
rather more formalized career and salary structure than industrial
scientists, though it cannot be denied that a measure of uncertainty does exist, especially for the younger academic. This is not
the only difference between academic and industrial scientists,
but it is one and there is no doubt that it is important.

The norms of some scientists, therefore, appear to differ quite
substantially from the norms of other scientists. The relevance of
the academic as opposed to the non-academic environment for
scientific research is clearly of prime importance. This operates
through the constraints of academic occupations contrasted with
industrial (or civil service) occupations, and thus through the
differences in *science* that pertain to the different work settings.
Whether these differences imply that one environment produces
real science and another something less than science, one scientific revolutions and another normal science, or even that one
produces science and another merely technology, is a problem
with both evaluative and practical dimensions. To repeat what I
have already said; it is not good enough simply to define away
categories of scientists because they do not fit into a preconceived
picture of science.

As I argued in Chapter 4, the work of Kuhn (and Polanyi) is
very suggestive in this context. At different times and in different
situations, different emphases are laid on the rules of science.
When these differences are such that we can no longer call the
activity *scientific* is not a matter of fact, or arbitrary decision, or

even to be resolved by some mystical appeal to Nature or Truth. It is variously a matter for the scientific community itself or some other community to decide. The sociology of science, to be realistic, must learn to appreciate that (as in other social institutions) some scientists are more powerful than others and that the ability to define reality to a greater or lesser extent rests with the more powerful.

Those who control academic science and those who control industrial science are not the same people nor do they necessarily have the same views. Different workplaces promote different science. Further than this one cannot go for the present. It is to be hoped that the sociology of science will develop in such a way that these hypotheses might be tested and improved. As a contribution to this end I shall try, in the conclusion to this part of my argument, to show how the model of the social institution of science with which I started may be modified to generate some researchable problems.

Conclusion

The version of the sociology of science I have been criticizing in the last three chapters, and the version I have been trying to insinuate into its place, have two main aspects in common. First, they both have something to say about most of the *elements* in the social institution model introduced in Chapter 2. Second, they both place the *norms* of science in a central position. The difference between the two versions, however, far outweighs their similarities.

The great difference is that the Mertonian theory of science is functionalist in doctrine as well as functionalist in method, whereas mine is functionalist in method only. By this I mean that not only does Merton explain how the social institution of science works by reference to the deleterious consequences of the non-observance of the norms but he also specifies one set of norms and the necessity for all engaged in the institution to abide by this set of norms. This is a special case of the general structural–functionalist doctrine that all social institutions must be normatively integrated to a high degree (though the degree is almost never identified except in the negative sense that you know when the level of integration has fallen below it by the fact that the system has broken down!).

My version, on the other hand, is functionalist to the extent that it pays attention to the structural arrangements that emerge to satisfy institutional needs, and that it recognizes that problem solution is the major need of all systems. (If this is considered to be a tautology, then so much the better. [For the more general form of the argument to follow, see Sklair, 1970.]) It is contrary to functionalist doctrine, however, because it postulates that (*a*) the definition of the problems and the needs to which they refer are generally determined by those with the most power in any social institution, and (*b*) although normative integration is possible, it is historically somewhat uncommon. Most people at most times and in most situations do what they do because they see no viable alternatives, or because they are literally forced, or because they are mistaken as to the true relationship between their actions and their interests, or a mixture of all three. Only rather rarely are societies and their institutions run on the basis of the willing, informed, and reasoned consent of their members.

I do not exclude the social institution of science from this general analysis of institutions. It is not an accident that academic science differs in important organizational and normative respects from industrial science – universities and industries have different though sometimes overlapping needs. This is clearly manifest in their respective charters for science, their staffs, and their material apparatus.

In the Mertonian account the norms – in the rather idealized form in which I have criticized them – are drawn from the very nature of the scientific enterprise. If they have a place in any model of the social institution of science, then it is uncertain where they fit. They appear to be both causes of the behaviour of scientists (in their role as 'institutional motivators') and consequences of the demands of science (the 'ethos' factor).

In my modification of Malinowski's model the norms of science act clearly as intervening variables which mediate between the more autonomous causal factors and the results of the operation of the social institution of science. Thus, this model now takes the charter, the staff and the material apparatus as the primary data for the explanation of how any institution works; the norms as a secondary, dependent factor, and the functions as its internal results as well as the impact of the institution on other social institutions.

The relationships between the material apparatus and staff of an institution on the one hand and the charter/ideology on the other, have been most thoroughly discussed by Marxists, in terms of base and superstructure. The French communist philosopher Louis Althusser, in particular, has made outstanding contributions to the theory of ideology and his treatment of the notion of 'determination in the last instance' is very fruitful in the present context. He argues (Althusser, 1969, Parts Three and Six) that although ideological factors can be shown to be extremely important in the origins and growth of social formations, the economic factor is determinant in the last resort. This is not an empiricist but an *a priori* judgement, in the sense that it is part and parcel of the system of scientific concepts which Marx developed to explain and to change the world. Thus, it seems to me to be fruitful to construct theory in the sociology of science from the conceptual judgement that although all three are causally influential, the material (economic) factors – apparatus and staff – are relatively autonomous with respect to the ideological factor – the charter.

The diagram on p. 180 illustrates this.[7]

It has often been argued that an important deficiency of functionalism is its inability to weight system parts, or rather always to weight the normative integration of systems most heavily. As I have suggested, it seems empirically plausible and theoretically useful to consider that either charter or staff or material apparatus could seem to be causally important in attempting to explain any particular concrete historical problem concerning any social institution. For science it may be hypothesized that at some periods the contemporary charter of science influences the staff it will attract and the material apparatus within which it operates. At another period, factors concerning the staff itself might play the most influential part; and at yet other times the material apparatus stimulates changes in the charter and the staff. Much of my analysis of big science in previous chapters suggests that since the Second World War the latter process has been working and that, in general, the material apparatus and the staff of science and technology are usefully seen as, indeed, determinant in the last instance.

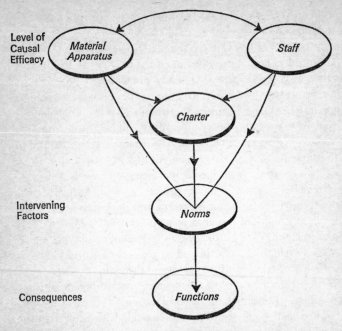

In all of this the norms that various groups of scientists actually hold are consequences of the operations and interrelations of the first three factors. The evidence that I have reviewed gives little support to the view that the norms of science are even relatively independent factors, and if the arguments against Merton have been successful, then the most important theoretical prop to any independent role for them collapses.

With this picture of the social institution of science in mind I close Part II, with the hope that some of the hints thrown out in my destructive criticisms may be of some use to those who will take up the tasks of constructing a new sociology of science.

In Part III, I shall take up the theme of the impact of science on society, the social functions of science.* This is the next step in the process that I have traced in this book whereby science has been progressively demythologized, set in its industrial environment, peopled with workers, and translated to the public. Science, after all, is not exclusively for the scientists – it affects us all.

* I have not said very much here about the impact of the other major social institutions on science. It should be clear from what has gone before that they are considerable.

1. Merton says that 'the pattern of institutionalized evasions develops when practical exigencies confronting the group or collectivity (or significantly large parts of them) require adaptive behaviour which is at odds with long-standing norms, sentiments, and practices, or correlatively, when newly-imposed requirements for behaviour are at odds with these deep-rooted norms, sentiments, and practices' (1963, p. 318). This is a very good partial analysis of the situation I have been tracing whereby big science and the Mertonian norms collide. What still remains to be established is that the Mertonian norms *ever* operated in science. It is ironic that Merton's general sociology thus contains the seeds of the destruction of his sociology of science.

2. It is very difficult to comprehend the meaning of Hagstrom's criticism of West when he says: 'Since he [West] did not specify alternatives, he found, as was to be expected, that most scientists possessed some values they prized more highly than conformity to certain norms of the scientific community' (Hagstrom, 1965, p. 154, note 3). This statement seems to imply a marked reluctance to consider the possibility that the belief of some sociologists in the existence of these 'certain norms' could be the results of mistakes about the scientific community. It is even more surprising when we note, for example, that Hagstrom himself makes essentially the same point as West about the reputation of a scientist influencing the reception of his work (ibid., p. 24).

3. As a Soviet science policy-maker has said, 'a good organizer of the scientific activity must unfailingly be a first-class specialist in his branch of science' (Kurakov, 1966, p. 25).

4. Kaplan in another paper cites the example of the Marks and Spencer's executive 'who happened to ask a clerk *why*

he was checking through certain invoices. Within two years this single question led to the elimination of between 22 to 26 *million* pieces of paper . . . In that same period the central administrative staff was cut from 2,000 to 1,500' (in Hill, 1964, pp. 117–18).

5. It is worth noting here that Berelson, in his study of graduate education in the United States, points out that although in 1960 there were over 550 fields in which the doctorate is awarded, for nearly 400 of these fields there is only one institution which does so (as quoted in Hagstrom, 1965, p. 220). This is, of course, complementary to and in no way incompatible with Kaplan's remarks.

6. They are, however, not alone in this. See Storer (1966, p. 135); Hagstrom (1965, pp. 136, 154, 156, 161); and Hirsch (1968, pp. 65–6, 81).

7. I am very grateful to Mrs Wilson of the Geography Department at L.S.E. for making this diagram.

Part Three
Science and Social Change

6 The Social Functions of Science

The social functions of science are only very imperfectly known. Whereas there have been very many studies and surveys carried out on the work lives of people, their religious affiliations and their voting intentions, and so on, there have been very few studies of how people feel about the scientific and technological changes going on around them.[1] Among the innumerable volumes of research in the social sciences, there are practically no specific investigations into the social effects of science and technology.

As I have already pointed out, it is only comparatively recently that reliable facts and figures about science and technology – under the umbrella of R & D – have been systematically collected, and many (especially the poorer) countries have practically no information of this sort. This lack of any systematic hard data and the lack of detailed knowledge about the contemporary social consequences of science makes the task of this chapter particularly difficult.

A realistic account of our situation, in my view, must acknowledge that we are at present in the modern world in the *middle* of a scientific and technological revolution.[2] This has been variously referred to as the Second Industrial Revolution, the Age of Automation, the Computer Age, and, most simply and most powerfully by the French social philosopher Jacques Ellul, as the Technological Society. Whatever label we affix to the great transformations that are taking place, the full effects have yet to be felt, far less understood. And it is the proper understanding of this revolution which (in the view of an increasing number of people) is the most important social and political task of our age.

An investigation of the social functions of science, therefore, is an investigation into the sort of world that we shall leave to our children.

The Institutionalization of Science

Science becomes socially important to the extent that it is institutionalized in society. The process of institutionalization is a key notion in modern sociology, and much of the work of sociologists consists in tracing how social activities become institutionalized and how this process helps or hinders particular sorts of social change. There are two aspects which are commonly associated with institutionalization, and it is convenient to label them as the practical and the normative sides of the process.

The practical side refers to the changes which will occur in any social activity that is not very well established within a society in terms of the actual practices involved. For example, part of the institutionalization of science will inevitably be bound up with the development of scientific careers and their interrelationships with the economy, the occupational and educational structure, and the industrial organization of modern society. In our society all of these spheres of activity are related in important ways with the emergence and development of careers in science. There are well-worn routes along which various types of scientists can travel in pursuance of their scientific roles, and it will be recalled that I have laid particular stress in previous chapters on the two most important of these routes, industry and the university. As a social activity like science becomes institutionalized, it experiences very significant changes in scale and the kind of relationships it has internally and with other important spheres or institutions in society.

The Scientific Role
One fruitful way to look at this involves, as I have suggested, the historical examination of the growth of distinctively scientific careers. This is best done in terms of the development of the scientific role (see Ben-David, 1971), though as I have insisted in previous chapters of this book, it is more realistic to consider

scientific *roles*. Indeed, the historical controversy around the genesis of the notion of scientific progress, between those who give the most weight to the artisans of sixteenth-century Europe and those who stress the part played by Renaissance scholars, is an interesting reflection of my concern to interpret science and the scientific role as widely as is useful. Zilsel, a major proponent of the view that the impetus for scientific progress (as opposed to cultural progress) came from superior artisans of the fifteenth and sixteenth centuries, linked the growth of science to the more general development of an industrial and capitalist society and the effects that this development was having on the organization and practice of crafts (Zilsel, 1945). This is not to say that cognitive challenges and intellectual impulses for scientific growth were not present also, but only that these 'inner' dynamics took place within a social context (see also Ben-David 1971, and Jenkins and Velody, 1969).

Unless jobs in science are provided for those with scientific interests, there will be few scientists from any but the independently wealthy classes in society. And, of course, in many ways this is precisely what happened up till about a hundred years ago in the West. Even as late as 1851 T. H. Huxley, the champion of Charles Darwin, could write in a letter to a friend:

... my opportunities for seeing the scientific world in England force upon me every day a stronger and stronger conviction. It is that there is no chance of living by science. I have been loth to believe it, but it is so. There are not more than four or five offices in London which a Zoologist or Comparative Anatomist can hold and live by. Owen, who has a European reputation, second only to that of Cuvier, gets as Hunterian Professor £300 a year! which is less than the salary of a bank clerk. My friend Forbes, who is a highly distinguished and able man, gets the same from his office of Paleontologist to the Geological Survey of Great Britain (quoted in Haines, 1957, p. 47, note 146).

This state of affairs by no means entirely prevents the growth of science, as the achievements of Huxley and his contemporaries clearly show, but it will inevitably restrict the pool of available scientific talent very considerably. This is obviously directly connected with the development of educational arrangements, both in universities and in technical institutes.

In addition to this we must not ignore the consequences of the familiar adage that industrial societies *need* scientific and technological manpower. This need results in the creation of particular occupational categories and has the feedback effect of reinforcing the demand for those who are to train and/or educate those who will fill these categories. This is, in my view, yet another reason why the artificial separation of the university and the industrial scientist may blur our vision of big science in modern societies.

In a pioneering study, MacLeod (1965) has traced the emergence of those who enforced the provisions of the Alkali Acts in the second half of the nineteenth century. Chief among these was Dr Robert Smith, the first Chief Inspector, and perhaps the first major civil scientist in Britain. Smith's job was to ensure that the chemical industry controlled its effluents, and the story of his scientific and political successes in this endeavour provides an excellent example of the complexity of the public scientific role in contrast to the comparative privacy enjoyed by the university or independent researcher.

Established occupations like this stimulated and were stimulated by the establishment of many other scientific and technological positions in industry, in government service, and elsewhere. Thus salary and service arrangements had to be made for these employees – usually neither managers nor shop-floor workers – and niches were or were not satisfactorily carved. Sons followed in their fathers' footsteps and became, say, industrial chemists or mechanical engineers. There arose qualifying associations which certified that those who passed their examinations and tests of experience were competent to carry out technically specialized tasks. Specialists grouped themselves together loosely or firmly, started publications in which they could communicate in their often somewhat private languages, and arranged meetings to discuss their common problems. Scientific careers, therefore, became normalized.

The scientific role, when it is restricted exclusively to the university context, becomes confused with the more general academic roles. Only if we regard it in the light of the institutionalization of science as such can we properly see a variety of scientific roles (see Ellis, 1969). But these practical aspects are only one side of the total picture.

Normative Institutionalization

Social activities and social relationships and their consequences make sense only within the normative framework that provides the context for them. This normative framework may be more or less binding, more or less shared in common, and more or less long-lasting and stable. In a very real sense the norms and values that operate in any social situation help us to make the actions of those involved meaningful in so far as they constitute the socially defined rules and expectations around which *patterns* of social action are built. Institutionalization thus refers also to the process whereby legitimizations are seen to be available for social activities, on whatever basis and where more or less acceptable to different groups or people in a society.

It is not difficult to take this view to extremes, as some American sociologists have done, and to argue that because there seems to be a need for institutionalization in any society, then this means that most people in society must agree on the basic values and norms which hold at a particular time or the society will disintegrate. This is the basis of the equilibrium–consensus theory put forward for many years by Talcott Parsons and his collaborators. Put simply, the initial insight which has run through much of social thought is, as here expressed in a recent sociological treatise by Etzioni, 'Human beings cannot reweave anew the normative fabric of society each morning; institutionalization is both inevitable and necessary' (1968, p. 15).

Of particular interest for our concern with the relations between science and society is the way in which many sociologists have seen the dangers of assuming too much to follow from this basically acceptable view. This doubt is cogently put by Walter Buckley in his attempt to make a case for the 'systems theory' approach to sociology. Buckley says:

> Institutionalization is not to be confused with legitimation in the sociological and social-psychological senses of these terms. It is an empirical question whether the institutional structure of a given society, or aspects of it, has a firm social and psychological foundation in an informed, cognitively and affectively undistorted, consensus on important norms, means, ends, and values (1967, p. 205).

We must pay particular attention, therefore, when we speak of the institutionalization of science in our or in any society, that we do not assume complete knowledge, let alone consensus, about the activities of the scientists and their reasons and justifications for doing what they are doing. The most difficult point with which we must grapple in this connection is how and why the social activity of science has achieved the scale and importance that it clearly has in the advanced societies while, as must also be fairly clear, the level of knowledge about and appreciation of science and its social functions remains low.

This lack of knowledge and appreciation exists at least on two levels, the élite and the mass, and I shall discuss these in turn. The élite level of the phenomenon is best summed up as the debate around the 'Two Cultures', brought to its contemporary head in the famous lecture by C. P. Snow in which this ex-scientist, politician, and literary intellectual bemoaned the fact that other literary intellectuals neither knew nor (worse) cared about the Second Law of Thermodynamics. This immense ignorance of those in the humanities means that 'the great edifice of modern physics goes up, and the majority of the cleverest people in the western world have about as much insight into it as their neolithic ancestors would have had' (Snow, 1964, p. 21).

The consequences of this cultural bifurcation are complex and various. Among the most important are the comparative difficulty that scientists have in entering not only the intellectual élites about which Snow is mainly speaking, but also the political and economic élites which, to speak roughly but not entirely in an unrealistic fashion, govern industrial societies. Although this picture is certainly changing, and more and more people with scientific training are reaching influential positions, it is still common to hear complaints that there are too few scientists in positions of power, that those in positions of real power often fail to consult the scientists on scientific matters, and that when they do consult scientists those with the real power rarely take much notice of the advice offered (see, for example, Jacobson and Stein, 1966). It is true that most pressure groups make these complaints – the military, businessmen, lower-ranking politicians themselves, for example – but it is also true that the educational and occupational pasts of top élites makes this particularly true for the scientists, especially those of the 'purer' varieties.

A second consequence of the ignorance of the greater part of the élite groups in society concerning science is much less concrete than the difficulty experienced by scientists in certain types of upward social mobility, though firmly related to it. This involves attitudes about science in general, the intellectual atmosphere that those in strategic positions in the universities, on the editorial boards of journals of opinion, in government and in the civil service, generate about scientific activities and pass on to those who are liable to be inordinately influenced by their views. Part of this is the impression that science, and especially applied science – not to speak of the often indistinguishable technology – is somehow vulgar, not the sort of thing that an educated gentleman would be doing. This particularly senseless and uninformed snobbery, some forms of which still exist, reinforced and (probably more importantly) was reinforced by a much more widespread and cognitively acceptable disquiet about those things on which intellectuals spend so much of their time reflecting. In short, many powerful thinkers begin to relate the catastrophes of the twentieth century to the progress and application of science.

The full story of this revolt against the machine, the opposition to science and technology, has yet to be written, and here I can only mention a few of the most important themes that bear upon the institutionalization of science and its social functions. The key term in this often extremely unsystematic protest against some or all of the features of the modern world is *progress*, and those who were suspicious of science and technology were very likely to identify progress as such with the consequences of science and technology. Thus we find rejections of progress, denials of progress, and accusations that people were better off before the so-called progress had taken place. We find intellectuals arguing that progress should be slowed down, or stopped altogether in some cases, and even that we should destroy the progress we have already made and return to some rather more simple, usually rustic form of society. These, of course, are all implicit or explicit attacks on science and technology and the actual or supposed effects that they have on men and their collective lives.

On the level of the response of the intelligentsia to science and technology in the twentieth century, it may be useful to consider the protest and the opposition as a manifestation on the normative rather than the practical side of the institutionalization process. On the practical side there was little that the traditional intellectual élites could do to prevent science and technology from eventually establishing themselves educationally, industrially and politically, although in England especially but not exclusively, the progress of scientific education and technological instruction were considerably held back by entrenched academic groups (for example, as discussed in Cardwell, 1957). Even today, as Hutchings and others have shown, some of these old attitudes hang on, to the detriment of science and technology (see Chapter 3, above). However, as was suggested, given the increasing industrial and commercial and military demand for scientists and technologists, and the increasing willingness of the state and private enterprise to pay for their education and their research, there was little that the intelligentsia, who did not like science and technology, could do on the practical problem of stopping them. The possibilities on the normative front were rather more promising. The intelligentsia could discredit science from a moral point of view, and they could and many did indict science and technology for the evils and ills of modern industrial society. The technological civilization in which they were perhaps unwilling but certainly not uncomfortable guests became a target for all of those who had very little to lose from turning back the clock.

This critique of science – charmingly, though not entirely convincingly, dismissed by Snow under the heading of 'Intellectuals as Natural Luddites' – has, in my view, permeated the fabric of modern societies to the extent that it and its obvious counterpart, that science is our salvation and that technology provides the solution to our most pressing problems, interact in most interesting fashions. We do not have far to look for the reasons why science is considered to be both the root of all evil and the source of all good. The point is that science is both of these, and that most attempts to unravel this ambiguity and to release men from the ambivalence to science that this entails have appeared to be merely verbal tricks.

Thus, when we are told, very sensibly, that science and technology are neutral, mere tools for man to use as he pleases, we are asked to forget that they have a serious tendency to create their own unforeseen and sometimes unforeseeable problems. Research into high-polymers creates masses of virtually indestructible objects. Work in high-energy physics, the investigation of the nature of matter, requires processes that may have dire consequences for those carrying out experiments, and perhaps many others who come into contact with them. The 'new biology' throws up conventional perils that will increasingly concern us all. As most people are not technically qualified to appreciate the explanations of why each of these is a spurious example, and thus that science is in fact neutral, the argument that science *is* neutral carries no more and probably a great deal less weight than the argument that it *is not*. Add to this some particularly stubborn examples, prime among which is the ubiquitous pollution of land, sea, and air, and it is not difficult to see that as time passes the critique of science and technology will not run out of ammunition.

Thus, in so far as certain élite groups in modern industrial societies are concerned, the theoretical point made by Buckley and others is borne out in practice. Science is obviously institutionalized in a practical sense, though this does not imply wholesale legitimation. Important social groups do not participate in the 'consensus' about science and its social role, for practical and normative institutionalization can and do vary from each other in a variety of ways. We may hypothesize that certain groups will always find the perils in any scientific advance, and that other groups will always find the potential benefits. We may further hypothesize that, for some groups, the practical varies indirectly with the normative institutionalization of science and technology. That is, the more practically institutionalized science and technology become – in terms of taking up more resources, manpower, gaining entry into more and more social arenas – the more these 'intellectual natural Luddites' will challenge their legitimacy. A recent confirmation of this occurred in a series of exchanges between F. R. Leavis (a particularly virulent scourge of the two cultures thesis of C. P. Snow) and Noel Annan, the man who had the temerity to compare the university with an industrial plant. It is significant that this debate and the ungentle correspondence which followed it took place in the columns of *The Times Literary Supplement*, was precipitated by a long review in that paper on computers, and that one of the most horrific images raised by Leavis was of computer-written poetry and its not unfavourable reception by a cultivated lady philosopher (TLS, 23 April 1970, et seq.).

G

The case of the masses is more difficult and it raises altogether different problems. The main difference is that whereas intellectuals tell us about their hopes and fears in their writings and through the mass media, the mass of the population remain silent. We have almost no reliable information whatsoever about what the general population knows or thinks about science and technology and their social consequences. The 'mass' in the mass media refers of course to the receivers and not the producers of the communication, as was forcibly pointed out by C. Wright Mills (1956, Ch. 13).

Of the fact that the great majority of the general public is very largely ignorant of modern science and technology there can be no doubt. As I argued at length in a previous chapter, it is also true that most *scientists* are largely ignorant of the content of specialisms other than their own and so, on one level, it would be utterly unrealistic to expect that the public at large might ever be in a position to evaluate technically the products of modern science. This, however, is not the point, for there is a great difference between technical evaluation of pieces of science and technology on the one hand, and a general idea of what is going on in particular areas of research, on the other.

A few comments will serve to hammer home this last point, for in many ways it is a crux of the whole argument. If we were to be convinced that science and technology were entirely inaccessible to the layman, with the obvious corollary that he had better leave them to the experts, then questions about the control of science, questions about public discussion of the social consequences of science and technology, and problems of communicating science, would all be rendered redundant. We would then have entered the great technocracy, dreamed of for centuries by men of goodwill and men of evil alike, and undoubtedly we would find that the practical and the normative institutionalization of science and technology were firmly in step (see Elsner, 1967). Can science be popularized? may be one of the questions on whose answer hangs the fate of democratic society as such.

It is still too soon to answer this question properly. There are two interlinked facets of the problem of the popularization of science on which evidence can be brought to bear. One is the public demand for education about scientific matters, and the other is the willingness of scientists and other qualified persons to expend time and energy in supplying such material. In this, as will be noted, I am simply assuming ability on both sides: I am assuming that the general public is capable of assimilating enough rudimentary knowledge about science to understand what is going on and that scientists are able to translate the gist of what they are doing into language and concepts that the untrained mind can accommodate. I assume that the barriers to the successful accomplishment of both of these tasks are not predominantly intellectual for most laymen and most scientists.

The Communication of Science

In a very real sense the ideal of 'secondary education for all', proudly proclaimed in the 1944 Education Act in this country, and in similar legislation in most advanced countries in recent decades, should have resolved the first of these problems. Provision of an adequate and stimulating science education, even to non-specialists at fairly low levels, should have ensured that most people who had passed through such a system would have at least a basic minimum competence and interest in what is surely the most persistent influence of our time. As science and technology change our lives in a variety of ways we might all be expected to be curious about what makes them tick.

Here is not the place to go into the present state of science education in this or any other country. Let it suffice to say that there has always been an undercurrent of criticism from both inside and outside the teaching profession. Shortages of science teachers are the rule rather than the exception and many recent reports in Britain have indicated that there are dramatic improvements needed if supplies of scientific and technological manpower are to meet demands. The one thing that is clear is that weaknesses and inadequacies in science education are liable to mean that the general population will have little incentive to follow up the science that they learn in school and that their enthusiasm for science will be strictly limited.

It is worth quoting, to illustrate these points, a composite stereotype based on recordings made in 1968 in schools in England, in which twelve- and thirteen-year-old pupils talked about their attitudes to science and scientists.

Scientists spend their time inventing things or messing about with chemicals (8 per cent). They may invent good things like new drugs and . . . well, other things I can't name but also things that are not very good (18 per cent) like H-bombs and other weapons, giving diseases to animals; and the thousands of scientists breeding germs. They are usually men . . . well, there's more scope for them and anyway ladies aren't wanted (8 per cent). They have to be very brainy or clever (7 per cent) but I think they're mad or eccentric because of it or because they don't care what they do (7 per cent) . . . in fact they have to devote their whole life to it (7 per cent) and do nothing else . . . it must be grim to be disconnected from the world. No, I don't read magazines about science . . . they're too complex and difficult to understand (8 per cent). We aren't given enough information or programmes about scientists but I've enjoyed the TV programmes I've seen out of school (10 per cent). I suppose we never see scientists doing normal kind of work but I think they do too much as they like (7 per cent) and there ought to be more control over them by a non-scientific body, or they could be limited to specific problems, e.g. curing of cancer. No, I'm not thinking of becoming a scientist (9 per cent) (Selmes, 1969, p. 11).

The essential ambiguity of this account, a more anecdotal rendering of the point I made above about the curious inextricability of the positive and negative aspects of science, is further reinforced by two previous American studies on the images of the scientist held by high school and college students respectively (in Barber and Hirsch, 1962). Mead and Métraux, in an analysis of the essays of several thousand American high school students, found that there was an outstanding discrepancy between an 'official' and a 'personal' view of science. Generally speaking, when the students were asked to write about scientists as such they produced favourable responses. Science, they wrote, was a good thing; it is essential to security, better health, and comfort. When asked to consider it in more personal terms, specifically (for boys and girls) the sort of scientist they would and would not like to be and (for girls) the sort of scientist they would or would not like to marry, the responses were over-whelmingly negative. So alarming and widespread were some of the images conjured up that the writers felt impelled to recommend that the mass media take firm action to rectify the situation, in the following decisive terms:

What is needed in the mass media is more emphasis on the real, human rewards of science – on the way in which scientists today work in groups, share common problems, and are neither 'cogs in a machine' nor 'lonely' and 'isolated'. Pictures of scientific activities of groups, working together, drawing in people of different nations, of both sexes and all ages, people who take delight in their work, could do a great deal of good* (Mead and Métraux, 1962, p. 244).

The results of a study of college students' images of scientists by Beardslee and O'Dowd (1962) are not dissimilar to the results from the studies on schoolchildren. The strengths – high intelligence and drive, and valuable work – and the weaknesses of the scientist – lack of interest in and success with people, impulsive, liable to be nonconformist and radical at times when loyalty is at a premium (sic) – are once again mixed up in a veritable bundle of contradictions. This is yet another example of the justifiably confusing and ambivalent picture that contemporary science presents. That these comments apply equally to United States Congressmen as to schoolchildren and college students is nicely demonstrated by a piece by Harry S. Hall on the reactions of American politicians in the 79th Congress, 1945, in a special committee on atomic energy (Hall, in Barber and Hirsch, 1962).

On the purely informational level there is evidence that scientific occupations are becoming better known to and more highly esteemed by the general public. A study carried out in March 1947 on how Americans evaluated jobs showed that more people considered themselves unable to judge scientific occupations than other types of occupations. The most outstanding case was that of the *nuclear physicist*. Over half of the respondents admitted that they did not know enough about the job to evaluate its standing. On further probing it was found that of those who claimed to know something about what the nuclear physicist did, more than half had only the vaguest notion or were actually wrong. The prestige ratings of various scientific occupations (reported by Hodge, Siegel, and Rossi) resulted in 'scientist' being ranked eighth out of ninety jobs, 'government scientist' equal tenth, and 'nuclear physicist' eighteenth (in Bendix and Lipset, 1966, pp. 324–5).

A second study carried out in June 1963 found that although the overall pattern was very similar to that of the previous study, in the words of the investigators, 'perhaps the most dramatic

* We shall see later on in this chapter how the mass media have risen to this challenge.

change is among the scientific occupations' (ibid., p. 333). In fact, 'government scientist' had improved its prestige position to equal fifth and 'scientist' and 'nuclear physicist' shared third position. Thus in sixteen years nuclear physicists and scientists in the United States had soared up the prestige scale till only US Supreme Court justices and physicians (medical doctors) exceeded them in the public esteem. In addition the proportion of 'don't knows' with respect to nuclear physicists declined from 51 per cent in 1947 to 10 per cent in 1963. It is gratuitous to remind the reader that nuclear physicists have been particularly busy during these years.

This is not to say, however, that public interest in and public awareness of science and technology have increased in the same way, though many indicators do point to the fact that more and more people are interested in and aware of scientific and technological matters now than in the past, and that this is increasingly the case. Unfortunately, most of these indicators are indirect and the evidence for these claims is somewhat circumstantial.

The most obvious example of this increased interest and awareness is in the area of space research, and especially manned space exploration. The purists would probably maintain, against this and many if not all other examples in this book, that the amount of science involved is minimal – and they would often be correct. My point here is that science only has social consequences when it is expressed through phenomena like space vehicles and events like moon landings. As I have often emphasized in previous pages, in my view the sociology of science is credible only when it develops into a sociology of science and technology. Space research, thus, though largely a matter of engineering and technologies, represents to most people an important component of the impact of science on society.

From the launching in November 1957 of the first man-made satellite around the earth, the Russian Sputnik, activities in space have commanded extraordinarily high, and worldwide, audiences. A survey carried out in 1957 showed that in Norway, France, Austria, Belgium, and Germany over 90 per cent of those polled had heard about the launching and knew that the Russians had accomplished this feat. In Italy, Canada, Japan, and Britain between 70 and 90 per cent had this information. Polls in Mexico City and Rio de Janeiro gave figures of 71 and 57 per cent for knowledge of the launching, and 67 and 51 per cent for knowledge that the Russians were responsible. As the writer from whom I quote these figures exclaimed: 'The only other event in recent history that can match Sputnik in general public awareness was the explosion of the atomic bomb in 1945' (Almond, 1963, p. 74).

The highpoint of this interest and awareness came, undoubtedly, when the astronauts from Apollo 11 stepped on to the surface of the moon in July 1969. It has been estimated that in America 53·5 million households watched an average of fifteen and a half hours TV coverage; that fifty foreign national networks exceeded all previous records for satellite time, giving the largest world television audiences ever; that 4,000 reporters covered the launching and that fifty-five countries were represented (Diamond, 1969, p. 10). It is interesting to speculate why all this interest and awareness was stimulated by the moon landing, and if the answer is in the form that it is perfectly obvious why people should react in this way to this type of happening, then the question remains unanswered and the answers become even more difficult to achieve.

In part, interest and awareness are interrelated with the build-up to an event and the coverage of it by the mass media, so that the procedure whereby we measure interest and awareness by what the mass media do is bound to be somewhat artificial. This, however, cannot be the whole story, for in an enterprise on this scale – the television networks are reputed to have spent around $13 million on coverage for Apollo 11 – we are forced to accept that, for whatever reasons, the public were interested and aware of what was going on, and that the media followed public opinion as much as they constructed it.

As I have already pointed out, the space race was as much about the cold war and American–Soviet rivalry, and internal American politicking and money-making, as it was about science and technology. All of these factors combined to ensure that the world would be left in no doubt that this was an American triumph, and that Americans would be left in no doubt that the vast expenditures of time and energy and manpower were seen to have culminated in the achievement of the stated objective. Nevertheless, it remains true that (and not satisfactorily explained why) competition between the great powers in this and other scientific and technological fields has had such high priority. Those who answer criticisms within the United States about the expenditures of billions of dollars on space projects while the cities degenerate and the poor remain poor, argue that the billions of dollars thus spent would not have been available for social and welfare purposes. Be this as it may (and there are many who do not accept this line of reasoning of the NASA apologists), it still does not explain why there is more national and international political capital to be gained from sending up satellites than eradicating slums, from landing men on the moon than providing the expensive opportunities for the children of the poor to have better and more satisfying lives than their parents.

We may rephrase the question and ask why some scientific achievements are so newsworthy, and we may go on to ask if successes and challenges in other scientific and technological fields are similarly newsworthy. There have been several interesting studies on the presentation and extent of science and technology coverage in the mass media, and particularly in the newspapers and this does provide us with some albeit impressionistic evidence as to how and to what extent science and technology are being reported and popularized. It also provides us with information on what those in control of the mass media consider the public to be interested in and the limits to which they go in putting across a picture of science and technology in contemporary society.

Science and the Mass Media

Crude measures of column inches leave us in no doubt that the amount of coverage of science and science-related news in the mass media has increased considerably over the last few decades, as is clear from the results of a study carried out by Ruth Davies, Julia Morris, and myself. The following table summarizes this.

The total amount of science news in American and British newspapers, although on the increase, still accounts for a very small proportion of the total content of these newspapers. Medical news and matters pertaining to health constitute a very substantial part of the total. Once more, we shall be in trouble with the purists, who might with some justification deny that the television programmes such as *Dr Kildare* or *Emergency*

Ward Ten have any science content at all, or that stories about astronauts on foreign tours are even remotely related to science and technology.

Table 6.1. Science and Technology Coverage in column inches, and as percentage of total column inches in newspapers (from Davies and Sklair, 1972)

	Feb. 1949		Feb. 1959		Feb. 1969	
Express	262	(1·24%)	550	(0·95%)	783	(1·21%)
Mirror	237	(0·65%)	469	(0·86%)	913	(1·46%)
Standard	197	(0·91%)	330	(0·85%)	615	(0·81%)
Times	314	(0·83%)	1089	(1·49%)	3327	(2·95%)

Again, the answer is clear. As far as the general public is concerned the mere exposure to mission control or to the operating theatre is exposure to a world that is, however specifically marginal to science, remote enough from the everyday world to count as the esoteric realm of science. It is no accident that one of the current stereotypes of the scientist is the man in the white coat with the test-tube or the hypodermic needle. In the same way, the routine exploits of the astronaut make news precisely because he is an astronaut, and as such has a part in the great scientific–technological events of our time. Thus, in February 1963, the Field Enterprises Educational Corporation offered the sixteen American astronauts operational at that time over $3 million for their personal stories. The fact that, in partnership with *Life* magazine, the offer was later reduced to just over $1 million and accepted at that figure, does not materially affect my point. The astronauts are valuable property, the essential human angle to one of the greatest science stories possibly of all time.

Many interesting points emerge from this array of researches on the presentation of science in the mass media. For example, a study of doctors and medical researchers in Wisconsin showed that about 60 per cent of the 144 respondents sometimes picked up information about new research developments within their own special fields and from the mass media, and particularly from newspapers and magazines (Shaw and Nevel, 1967). This is, of course, extremely suggestive in view of the great difficulties of communication in modern science that have been expressed at least from the time of Bernal onwards. It also gives a curious support to the imaginative idea, put forward by Price in 1966, for a 'Science Daily Newspaper' which 'might carry the daily world total non-archival production over all sciences, technology and medicine and have room over for a bonus page of social and political news of science too' (in Reuck and Knight, 1967, p. 208). It is, after all, not a little wry that we have daily papers for the horse-racing fraternity and none for the community of science![3]

There have also been several studies on the notoriously difficult subject of the impact of science reporting, of how much of the material is understood, and of the possibilities that science news and discussion might change attitudes and beliefs about particular topics. Another extremely important topic on which there has been very little systematic research concerns the ways in which the mass media present science and technology, and the nature of the relationships between the interests of those who control the mass media and the material they disseminate (see, in general, Krieghbaum, 1968).

As anyone who works in newspapers will testify, the contact between the communicator and the public is indirect. In newspapers, and to a greater or lesser extent in all of the mass media, the editorial function operates as a sort of 'gatekeeper' between the production and the distribution of the material to be broadcast. Tannenbaum (1963), a prominent American communications researcher, has argued that this is particularly the case with science news, and that whereas editors had doubts about what the public could and would understand about science and technology, science writers and scientists themselves felt that the public was able and even eager to assimilate more unadulterated science.

This tendency of editors, especially on the more popular mass-circulation newspapers, to dilute science and technology with liberal doses of personality material and sensational projections into some horrific or Utopian future, perhaps does help to sell papers – the whole point of reporting science at all, as one is constantly reminded – but the long-term effects of trivial-izing this type of material on the credibility and status of science are not at all clear. Edwin Diamond, a persistent critic of the excesses of the space race, puts the point well in his indictment of the Apollo 11 story, 'The dark side of the moonshot coverage', from which I have already quoted some staggering figures. He says:

What will save the media from their own inadequacies during the next 'story of the century'? Will anyone be prepared to do basic digging and clear interpretation? Who will even care? Certainly not shortsighted editors who offer official histories, or ratings-minded producers who perform as ringmasters for a Big Top on the tube, or reporters bereft of imagination who ask astronauts' wives 'how do you feel now?' or journalists who see themselves as participants and allies of the Government. As veteran journalist James Cameron recently pointed out in the English weekly *New Statesman*, the media used to be criticized for 'sensationalism' – blowing up petty matters into big stories. Now, he says after watching the Apollo coverage, the charge is exactly the reverse – the media have succeeded in trivializing momentous stories. 'The papers and the telly, confronted with genuinely significant and even vital events, reduce them intuitively to a sort of basic piffle . . . a level of numbing banality' (Diamond, 1969, p. 16).

It remains to be seen what the mass media make of the other great science story of our age – the New Biology, stretching all the way from organ transplants to the ubiquitous creation of life in the laboratory. It is the case that, generally speaking, bio-medical subjects are the most popular of all science and tech-nology material in the mass media, and the level of interest of the public in bio-medical and especially health-related matters never seems to wane. Thus, we may speculate that in this area there is more information of a scientific nature put across than in space or physics or ecological science stories. Man, or rather Western man, apparently never tires of hearing about his body, and (a somewhat more recent phenomenon) his mind. The sexual aspects of the bio-medical sciences, often in the forefront of material in this area, do nothing to diminish the general interest of one and all in this connection.

Part and parcel of the what and how of the presentation of science and technology in the mass media is the question of knowledge about the subjects discussed and the effects of the information that people receive from the media on their beliefs and attitudes. Two interesting studies on this, one on environmental issues and the other on fluoridation, illustrate some of the possibilities and difficulties of research in this area.

First of all let us hypothesize on the basis of common sense on what we should expect to find. Generally we should expect that those exposed to information through the mass media would be better informed in terms of having more and more accurate knowledge about the issues in question. This expectation is borne out by the findings of two American investigators, Brinton and McKown (1961), on the effects of local newspaper coverage of a fluoridation controversy on knowledge and attitudes. The study was carried out in the Californian city of Menlo Park at the time when the neighbouring city of Palo Alto was going through a public debate on whether or not to fluoridate its water supply, and the researchers attempted to find out what effect regular reading of the Palo Alto *Times* (which carried extensive coverage of the controversy) had on the residents of Menlo Park, who were not, of course, directly involved.

Responses from about 200 subscribers/regular readers of the paper and about 100 non-subscribers/not regular readers were obtained, and not surprisingly the former group indicated that they had received information about fluoridation from newspapers far more frequently than the latter group. On a ten-item test of knowledge about the issue the subscriber group scored on average 4·20 against 2·66 items for the non-subscribers. Though both of these averages are low, the difference is quite significant. It is interesting to note that the writers specifically point out that the level of education of respondents might be thought to have independent importance here, but that this is not the case to any great degree as the subscribers with only high school education had a better knowledge score than non-subscribers who were college graduates. Reading the newspapers, then, does seem to lead to more knowledge about fluoridation.

The findings on the formation of attitudes are rather less clear-cut than those on knowledge. The fact that does emerge is that more of the subscribers appeared to have a firm opinion about fluoridation, a good majority in favour, than the non-subscribers. Asked how they would vote on the issue, over half of the non-subscribers and only a third of the subscribers said that they did not know or that they would not vote. Further, the spread of attitudes among the subscribers and the fact that they had discussed fluoridation with relatives and friends much more than the non-subscribers, suggest that the newspaper coverage did have an effect, even when – as in the case of these respondents – there was no direct involvement in the controversy.

Studies on the effects of the mass media on environmental issues supplement these findings. Three researchers at the University of Minnesota (Donohue et al, n.d.) set out to test the hypothesis that people with extreme attitudes on certain issues would be less likely to possess understanding and accurate knowledge about these issues. This corresponds to the almost orthodox views of social psychologists that people tend to see what they want to see concerning the facts of controversial issues in which they have a stake. For example Levine and Murphy showed that of two groups of people, one pro-Communist and the other anti-Communist, the former remembered much more of a selection of pro-Soviet material while the latter group remembered much more of the anti-Soviet material used in the experiment (in Maccoby et al, 1958, 94–101).

Another well-known study by Berelson and his colleagues on 'political perception' (ibid., pp. 74–85) similarly showed how voters in the 1948 American presidential election tended to misperceive the views of the candidates in the direction of their own ideas. The more involved the voter was, the greater the tendency to 'push' and 'pull' the views of the candidates.[4] Exposure to the mass media, however, was found to be the most important single factor in *correct* perceptions of the positions of the candidates on the important issues of the election. The findings of the Minnesota study cast an oblique light on all of this.

The researchers interviewed 435 people in three areas in which two environmental issues, the siting of a nuclear power plant and the use of DDT, had been widely and publicly discussed for several months preceding the study and during it. The method used in this experiment consisted in each respondent being asked to read an article on each issue from one of the four metropolitan daily newspapers in the area. After having read the articles the respondents were then asked to recall information about each issue. Attitudes towards the siting of the nuclear power plant and the use of DDT were then recorded for each person interviewed and these were matched with the recall and accuracy of information and understanding on the issues.

It was found that accuracy of recall did not appear to be related to the views put forward in the newspaper articles themselves – fifteen different articles on each issue were used and the results on those expressing favourable attitudes to one or other issue were not significantly different from those expressing unfavourable attitudes, holding other things constant. Further, and this seems to me rather revealing, people tended either to recall content accurately or not to volunteer information at all. Thus, people seemed to be somewhat reluctant to express themselves on matters of fact about these environmental controversies when they were not fairly certain of the facts.

Donohue, Tichener, and Olien also looked at the ways in which understanding of the material was related to the concern that the respondents felt personally about the issues. It is clear that these factors, plus level of education and attitude, were interrelated, the limitations of the sample size make it difficult to come to any very clear conclusions. Nevertheless, the following suggestions are supported by the data in varying degrees. In the first place, the authors strongly claim that, contrary to the orthodox expectations to which I have drawn attention, persons with extreme attitudes towards the issues tend to understand more not less about these issues than those with more neutral attitudes. And although understanding increases with higher levels of education, as we should expect, the relationship between understanding and extreme attitude remains when we control for education. Second, in general, understanding and concern appeared to be related.

Some Continuing Problems

This interesting study, of course, is no more than a drop in an ever-expanding ocean. Science and technology are remaking our world and will continue to do so for the conceivable future, and yet there is but a handful of studies on public reactions to and perceptions of crucial issues like pollution and the state of the environment as a whole. It is surely curious that probably the most researched single scientific or technological issue – fluoridation – although important enough in its own right, should be so marginal and insignificant compared with, for example, the destruction of the eco-system which threatens to make human life on earth impossible in the not-too-distant future. On one level it is perhaps surprising that fluoridation always causes great excitement and that the hint of projects to introduce fluorides into public water supplies invariably stimulates the creation and growth of Pure Water Associations and similar bodies (see Crain et al, 1969), and yet general environmental pollution from a variety of agents, until very recently, was quite dead as a public issue.

The severity of the pollution problem – it is not over-dramatic to call it a crisis – cannot be doubted, if we accept the word of those scientists and technologists who have expressed themselves on it. Indeed, environmental pollution is one of the key areas in which the social functions, unintended and often unrecognized, of science and technology do manifest themselves in the most extended and extensive fashion. This is extremely clearly and dramatically set out in a recent essay by a prominent American ecologist, LaMont C. Cole, provocatively entitled 'Playing Russian Roulette with Biogeochemical Cycles'. Cole says:

Never before has man been able to spread a particular pollutant over the entire surface of the earth. DDT is a case in point. It has been recovered from the fat of Antarctic seals and penguins, from fish all over the high seas, and from the ice of Alaskan glaciers. We have been incredibly lucky that DDT has not turned out to be a more noxious pollutant than it is. If it had possessed certain properties that no one had known about until it was too late, it could have brought an end to life on earth. If you are comforted by the thought that DDT is apparently not so bad as it might have been, reflect on this fact: the US Food and Drug Administration estimates that we are now exposing ourselves and our environment to over half a million different chemicals, all of which must eventually be imposed on the earth environment. And this number is estimated to be increasing by 400 to 500 new chemicals per year.
Can our run of luck continue? . . . (in Helfrich, 1970, p. 4).

But this is a comparatively new problem, whereas the phenomenon of air pollution has been recognized for at least 700 years in England. Royal ordinances of 1273 and 1306 tried to control the effects of the burning of bituminous coal which was then replacing wood and charcoal in the industrial fires of the day. There is ironic justice in the fact that John Evelyn's tract of

1661, *Fumifugium or the Smoake of London Dissipated* was reprinted in 1961 by the National Society for Clean Air, in London. Water pollution, too, in many and various ways, represents similar threats to man's continued use of the world. One of the worst bodies of water – the great Lake Erie – has reached such a state of decay that the authorities of many cities on its banks require mandatory typhoid inoculations for those who wish to sail on it.

However important the subject of environmental pollution is, and it should be clear that I consider it to be very important indeed, my purpose here is not to document the real threats that it poses to our international survival but to use it as an example of the social function of science and technology. Thus it is not part of the charter or the purpose of science to pollute the environment, though one of the functions, an unintended though often well recognized consequence of science, is to pollute the environment.

As I have indicated at many points in this chapter, there is very little hard information on the impact of science and technology on social life, but it would be interesting to hypothesize that for most people, science and technology mean pollution as much as moon landings, terrifying weapons as well as the advances of medicine, nerve gases as well as new sources of protein. It would be valuable, for example, to know whether the mass media stressed the positive or the negative effects of science and technology or whether they tried to maintain some balance. It would also be valuable to know whether the positive aspects of some areas were stressed and the negative aspects of others.[5] It needs very little imagination to speculate that one of the reasons why newspapers and magazines appear to give such muted attention to pollution may be the powerful constraints of their advertisers in the background. It would be similarly very fruitful to investigate the positions for and against the Apollo project of the mass media and the politicians in those states that benefited economically from the space contracts, and the positions of those from the states which had only a minimal share in the vast amounts of virtually risk-free profits generated by the *moondoggle*. (A *boondoggle* is a project which promises generous and unproblematic rewards for its supporters. The term *moondoggle* was first introduced, to my knowledge, by Etzioni, in his 1964 study of the space race, entitled The *Moon-Doggle*.)

But we have very little systematic information on these and other questions stimulated by reflecting on how science and technology are portrayed in the mass media, and I cannot emphasize too strongly the view that research into these matters is long overdue and that without this type of research as a basis it is difficult to go on and ask further sociologically meaningful questions about the functions of science and technology in modern society.

As it is, we read in newspapers and magazines, we hear on the radio, and we see on television and in the cinema, the sort of world in which we live and the benefits and disasters that science and technology bring to it. However unwilling we are or want to be, sooner or later we are all compelled to locate ourselves in the technological society. It is perhaps too soon to speak, as some have done, of a new mode of being to which modern man has to adjust himself – if there is a new mode of being then it is selectively present, it appears in patches somehow superimposed upon the old modes of being which stubbornly persist. Thus the Soviet science city of Academigorodok stands in what was a decade ago a Siberian forest; Route 128, the road that carries the academics and ex-academics of the Massachusetts Institute of Technology to their sophisticated science-based factories, is not too far from the sleepy New England townships of the other world; and, in what is probably the single most pervasive symbol of the ambivalent meeting place of the old world and the new, the nuclear power station rises out of the quiet and unspoiled countryside to remind us all of where our governments consider our priorities must lie. This is nicely summed up in an account of the public reaction to the siting of the Winfreth Heath nuclear power station in Dorset in the late 1950s. British law requires that planning permission be given for such activities and, as one commentator notes, other difficulties can arise:

In addition to the natural local antipathy to the planning permission granted the authority, which threatened to mar wild heathland of exceptional beauty, there were legal complications arising from certain 'commoners' rights' dating from the eighteenth century: part of the land had been set aside 'for the preserving of furze, turf, and other fuells' and a special act of Parliament was necessary to override these claims (Hodgetts, 1964, p. 131).

The old world, therefore, is stubborn, and there are sufficient numbers of people who survive and ensure, for the present at least, that the march of science and technology does not proceed unchecked by considerations of human welfare. This does not always need to be mindless reactionary conservatism, although the proponents of eternal scientific and technological progress have often seen that it is in their interests to brand all opposition to their views in this way.

These matters are rarely simple for, as I have more than once argued in previous pages, there seems to be a built-in ambivalence around many of the applications of scientific progress. The case of automation illustrates this well.

Automation, a word coined independently by Mr D. S. Harder, the manufacturing Vice-President of the Ford Motor Company in the late 1940s, and by John Diebold, chief of a technology consulting firm, refers to many things (see Diebold, 1952, p. ix). Indeed, one definitional dispute around the term, in hearings before a US Senate sub-committee on manpower problems, resulted in two experts disagreeing about the number of jobs eliminated by automation. The man from the Department of Labor estimated, on his definition, that 187,000 jobs per year were eliminated in this way; the automated devices manufacturer, on his definition, estimated job elimination at 2,080,000! (Mangum, 1966, p. 236). The truth no doubt lies somewhere between these figures, and if we remember that government spokesmen will always be at pains to minimize fears of general unemployment and that manufacturers will always wish to sell their products, then the discrepancy becomes a little more understandable.

Definitions, therefore, may have important social and political consequences, and this is not least likely to occur where technology is concerned. It is particularly useful to consider in this respect what have been called the 'myths of automation'. If we define automation as mechanization, as many have done, then it follows that present trends are simply more of the same things that have been happening previously. The machine, after all, is hardly a novelty. On the other hand, if we define automation as something entirely unprecedented, then we shall be more prone to see its development in terms of great new opportunities or dangers or both.

In a series of articles in the American magazine *Fortune* (now collected in a short book), Charles Silberman (1967) has stripped away much of the mystique surrounding automation itself and its supposed impact on society, and especially employment. Silberman convincingly demonstrates that American industry and commerce are far less automated than is commonly supposed and that even where automation has taken place its impact on employees is not always catastrophic. A key notion here is that of 'structural unemployment', roughly the oft-quoted fears that automation, both on the factory floor and in the office, would throw large numbers of people out of work and deny them re-employment because their old skills and training were no longer needed. This rests partly on the ill-founded assumptions that automation itself does not provide many low level jobs, that large numbers of people cannot be trained for skilled occupations, and that very few new jobs are in fact created by the greater efficiency implied by these new developments.

Silberman documents many of these points with clear examples which show that even professors, politicians, and business technologues are not entirely free from error in this complicated field, and that, for the moment, the automation revolution is not upon us.

Particularly impressive are Silberman's analyses of the 'automated petroleum refinery' in Texas which in fact produces only 0·6 per cent of the refinery's total production; the 'automatic lathe' which has nothing to do either with automation or computers; the 'automated bakery' in Chicago which still employs 450 people per shift; and, finally, the fascinating story of the TransfeRobot – the automaton of the late 1950s which captured the imaginations of the *New York Times*, Congressional Committees, *Life*, and Donald Michael, author of *Cybernation: The Silent Conquest*. Unfortunately, few people wanted to buy the TransfeRobot and the *one* satisfied customer who was traced had paid about $10,000 for the saving of a single employee (ibid., pp. 5, 6, 7, 25). Further studies on the New York printing unions (Kelber and Schlesinger, 1967) and on the use of electronic data processing in offices (Rhee, 1968) confirm this view. In the former the authors leave us in no doubt that strong unions can force employers to arrange the introduction of considerable technological changes into a major industry with the minimum of social and economic upheaval to the workforce and, more positively, if the changeover is properly organized then the full benefits of the change can accrue to the advantage of all concerned.

It would, however, be somewhat misleading to minimize the very real strains of ambivalence that run through all of these studies. There is no question that new processes are being increasingly introduced and that the excesses of the enthusiasts and the denigrators alike can obscure what is really happening in the industrial, commercial, and administrative centres of advanced societies. There is no denying, for example, that the computer has firmly arrived on the scene. Estimates for 1966 suggest that about 30,000 computers were in use in North America, about 7,000 in Europe, and about 2,000 in Japan. This represents almost forty times the number of computers in use in 1957, and the number continues to grow very fast (ibid., p. 11).

Though little might be generally understood about it, the rise of the computer has not gone unnoticed by the public. The famous placard which originated at the University of California, Berkeley, in 1964 as a symbol of opposition to the conveyor belt of the multiversity parodied the ubiquitous IBM punchcard. It said: 'I am a human being; please do not fold, spindle, or mutilate.' People, then, require to be treated at least as well as the data cards of the technological society – automated or not.

This is summed up in a most revealing fashion by the results of a survey on automation carried out in 1959. Of those who were familiar with the term, about a third thought that automation was a good thing, and 55 per cent considered that it was *both good and bad*. (Similar results from an American Harris poll in 1965 confirm this finding.) Only 4 per cent thought it a bad thing, and the rest had no opinion. The writer, Robert S. Lee, detected two major sets of beliefs about automation, which he labelled the *progress* image and the *dangers* image. He comments on these as follows:

The progress image consists of favorable beliefs about the implications of automation, primarily in terms of the richer and easier life that automation will bring about . . . On the other hand, the dangers image is predominantly concerned with the ill effects of automation on people, particularly in the work setting . . . What is the connection between these two images or belief systems? The answer to this question is probably the most important finding of the study – there is only a slight relationship between the two images. *A relatively strong belief in the image of automation as progress does not preclude belief that automation also is a threat* . . . The content of these belief systems implies that the positive side of automation is not simply the reverse of the negative. In this case positive and negative are qualitatively different in a psychological sense. They do not necessarily contradict each other . . . The double image of automation therefore explains the widespread ambivalence tapped by the general attitude question. A considerable number of people see *both* the positive and negative implications of this advance in technology . . . about half of those who believe that automation will raise the American standard of living also believe that it will create much unemployment (Lee, in Riley, 1963, pp. 89, 92).

To generalize from automation to a wider perspective and to put these sentiments in a nutshell – people want the benefits of science and technology without the disadvantages. People want some of the products of industry without its effluents; people want a reduction in tedious routine work without unemployment; people want comfort without loss of human dignity.

The social functions of big science *should* be to provide the former of each of these dichotomies and to prevent the latter. But the actual consequences of science and technology all too often appear to aggravate the latter while providing the former. As Lee concludes:

It is doubtful that public fears about the consequences of automation can be allayed by the clever use of public relations. That the two images are relatively independent implies, for example, that such fears could not be countered by playing up the beneficial and glamorous aspects of modern technology. Such communications could be easily believed and accepted without dislodging concern about the dangers of automation (ibid., p. 106).

This chapter has presented a somewhat gloomy picture of pollution, mass ignorance, and apathy about science, the trivialization of genuinely great scientific and technological achievements, and the disturbing view that even if big science is institutionalized in a practical sense in modern industrial societies it cannot be said to be normatively institutionalized. I have tried to steer between the twin horrors of hysterical catastrophism and blinkered adulation. Big science, like the computer, is probably here to stay and we may as well make the best of it. Even now in the last third of the twentieth century it is difficult to assess the real possibilities for human society implied by the unique rise and development of science and technology that we, in the first and second worlds, have experienced. The difficulties are multiplied when we reflect on the role of science and technology in the 'modernization' of poor countries – the Third World – for, if we can with some justification assume that the populations of the technologically advanced countries are in some ways sympathetic to science and technology, we are clearly far less justified in assuming that the populations of the poor countries will welcome science and technology as providing solutions to their problems. In the final chapters, under the heading of 'Alternative Futures', I shall examine some of the possibilities of progress and the varying roles that science and technology might play in solving people's problems.

NOTES

1. See Stehr (1971) for an interesting report of a German study along these lines.

2. This 'revolution' may, however, be responsible for, or at least compatible, with the 'social freezing' noted by Marcuse in *One-Dimensional Man*, as I discuss in my (1971) paper on 'The Opposition to Science and Technology'.

3. *Nature*, in 1971, began to publish three times per week.

4. It is a revealing comment on the social sciences in the United States in the early 1950s to note that the authors of this study conclude on the positive functions of these political misperceptions. These, they say, add to political rationality by widening the gap between the parties and reduce tension in the individual by structuring tensions in the community. The parallelisms between this and the approach popularized by Coser's *The Functions of Social Conflict* are clear.

5. See Davies and Sklair (1972) for the results of a small study.

7 Alternative Futures (I)

Science and technology are supposed to liberate man, not enslave him. Science and technology are supposed to give man the power to control his environment, not the tools to fight against the deleterious effects of science and technology. Science and technology are supposed to hold great promise for a happy future, not great dread of impending catastrophe. The interest that the non-scientist and the non-technologist has in science and technology centres, very reasonably, on these issues. Of what use is a man on the moon when people on earth are hungry? Of what use is supersonic transportation when people live in slums? Clearly, then, questions about how science and technology may help to create the future are political as well as technical, and in these concluding chapters I want to deal with some of the problems that are raised when we blithely assume that science, technology, and the never-ending progress of industrialization will satisfy all our needs.

Three sorts of problems are involved here. One concerns what men want in the present and in the future, their aspirations. Another concerns the specific possibilities opened up by the rational and controlled application of science and technology. The third concerns the ways in which aspirations and technical possibilities interact. Where the latter typically condition the former we have the technocratic state in which men have to adjust to the demands of their science and technology. Where aspirations guide technical possibilities then we have the situation of *alternative futures*, in which men can truly be said to choose with the minimum of constraint the structure of the world in which they live.

Aspirations and Control

The aim and ideal of technocracy is to arrange social life in terms of technically solvable problems. Metaphysics, questions about the meaning of life for example, are simply ruled out, and in their place are put questions of quantity which are assumed to operate qualitatively. 'More' and 'bigger' and 'faster' rather than 'better' and 'worthier' and 'happier' become the criteria on which progress is judged, and indeed the former are seen to be the necessary conditions for the attainment of the latter. This implies that men must be trained to want things that can be easily measured, identified, and produced, rather than things which defy definition, are difficult to measure with our available tools, and cannot easily be produced on the assembly lines of advanced industrial nations. A bigger GNP is a sensible goal in a technocratic society. Happiness as such is not. The problem is not solved by assuming that happiness is an inevitable consequence of a bigger GNP, for it clearly is not.

There are many actual examples of how the possibilities opened up by science and technology have had adverse effects on the aspirations of people in various social groups. A direct case is that of technological unemployment, where workers lose their jobs because of the development or invention of new processes. In this context, technological change is often quite clearly opposed to the interests of those involved, at least in the short term. True enough, in some cases these changes do redound eventually to the advantage of those displaced, but there is no doubt that in most societies in which these events take place the aspirations of the majority of those involved are taken into account in only the most cursory fashion.

A somewhat more indirect example concerns the conduct of pharmacological research. The international drug companies, enjoying the benefits of an oligopolistic market, have less interest in satisfying human needs than in creating them. In spite of the energetic attempts of the American Food and Drugs Administration and perhaps partly due to the toothlessness of the actions of successive British governments, the pharmaceutical industries of these and other rich countries have poured out medical and cosmetic preparations in vast numbers over the past decades. As has been pointed out, the profits and advertising expenditure of this industry are very high compared to others,[1] and one may be forgiven for the cynical reflection that people usually need less persuasion to purchase the necessities of life and survival than the luxuries attendant on the false needs with which the rich and poor are so liberally endowed. The balance of research carried out by the drug companies between work directed towards the relief of human suffering as against work directed towards the beautification of the already privileged in most countries provides a striking example of the way in which technical possibility influences human aspirations.

When we consider this relationship between possibilities and aspirations from the opposite direction, namely the situation in which the satisfaction of human needs and the fulfilment of men's aspirations are the *point* of science and technology and not an occasional and unintended consequence, then we are beginning to explore the much vaunted promise of modern times. Here it is immediately necessary to distinguish the reality from the illusion (or perhaps more to the point, from the hypocrisy). That most writers on the subject claim that science and technology should and in fact do serve human welfare and human values does not by itself prove the point. The fact that many of these writers are 'retired' scientists or scientists *manqué* will further increase our scepticism, and it is at this point that the *problem* of the control of science and technology forces itself into the debate. This is notoriously difficult because even the most democratically minded in the most democratically organized societies appear to believe that science and technology cannot properly operate or develop under conditions of democratic control. That is, the ideal of a participatory democracy seems not to apply to the case of science and technology.

Democracy and Science

The reason for this, at first sight, is simple enough. Scientists and technologists are usually highly trained people whose knowledge and skills have been earned after years of study and practice. They are, in a word, experts, and like many experts in our society they have not only specialized information but they have also specialized languages in which to communicate with each other. Almost every new development brings with it a new vocabulary of terms or symbols. All of this conspires to isolate scientists from other men and to insulate science from the societies in which it is carried out. The case is different but not, I would maintain, totally dissimilar, for technologists and technology. In terms of the distinctions I made in the previous chapter, technology is the expression of the practical institutionalization of science and it is through technology that most people experience the institutionalization of cognitive science. For example, we are all familiar with electric lighting and cooking appliances, and many of us have a fair knowledge of the principles of electricity as they apply to these appliances. The same holds true for the operation of, and principles behind, the internal combustion engines and the mechanical systems which contribute to the near paralysis of our cities most days. At this level, in fact, we are a remarkably sophisticated society, and the least educated members of advanced industrial societies have a vast fund of technical expertise and knowledge without which, of course, it would hardly be possible to survive. We rarely consider our talents in this respect precisely because these things are the bread and butter of modern life. It appears, then, to be perfectly possible to translate the content of science and particularly technology in order for the instructions for millions of devices, processes, and machines to be understood and operated by the public at large. This is clearly because at the stage when a product is ready to be marketed and sold to the general population the scientists and technologists responsible for its development (or some other relevant technically competent persons) are forced to do this translation. The ordinary consumer, therefore, is deemed to be competent to buy wisely and to use properly the fruits of science and technology. But at this point, in most cases and in most societies, the process stops. Beyond consumption the ordinary consumer is not generally deemed to be able to appreciate what goes on in science and technology; the private language remains untranslated and the esoteric knowledge remains uninterpreted.

As I have already said, this raises political as well as technical questions. The problems of control of science and technology in modern society are a special case of the general problem of democracy, I shall argue, and not, as others have argued, simply irrelevant to the general problem of democracy because the masses do not and could not be expected to understand sufficient science and technology to make intelligent decisions about them. This latter argument rests on the same fallacy as the argument used by many élitist theorists and those who consider all but the most superficial forms of democracy to be hopelessly inefficient. That the masses could understand enough about science and technology in order to participate in decision-making in this area is not an *assumption* of my argument; it is a proposition that I shall support with evidence. This is necessary if my original concern, that technical possibilities should respond to the aspirations of men, is not to rely on the benevolence and enlightened despotism of scientific and technological élites; instead aspirations ought to guide technique because men can freely choose the structures of the societies they want.

The first part of the argument concerns the issue of how much and what kinds of science and technology people must know in order to make intelligent decisions. There are probably genetic limitations on the numbers of people in any population that are capable of becoming, even in the very best environment, theoretical physicists or molecular biologists, but even this much is by no means certain. In any case, very few people would agree that one actually has to be a working physicist or biologist to make sensible decisions of policy in these fields and in their applications. The reason for this is that it is probably impossible to be a working scientist or technologist, with all that this entails, and at the same time to devote more than a small fraction of the available time and energy to policy-making bodies. It is one thing for a working scientist to be a sometime member of a Science Advisory Board, it is quite another thing for him to be a full-time science or technology policy-maker as such. As with the laboratory administrator (as we have seen in Chapter 3), the opportunities that such jobs allow for scientific research may well be rather limited. Further, the generalist, who has a greater knowledge of a variety of fields than the specialized researcher, is often seen to be the most suitable candidate for the important policy posts throughout the world. Clearly, then, one does not have to be a working scientist to be a policy-maker in science and technology, if we are to judge by present experience, and perhaps it might even be a disadvantage to be one.

The generalist proposal, that policy-making in science and technology should be in the hands of those with a broad outlook

covering many fields, looks at first to be altogether more plausible. This brings to the fore the debate around the criteria for
scientific choice which has occupied many writers for many
years. If the criteria for scientific choice are exclusively technical
(scientific and/or technological), then the view that only scientists and technologists should be permitted to make these
decisions gains great credence. If, on the other hand, the criteria
for scientific choice are both technical and non-technical (social,
political, economic, or any mixture of these or others), then it is
very difficult if not impossible to maintain that scientists and
technologists alone should be empowered with these decisions.
The generalist, thus, is the man who not only has a broad knowledge of the whole of science and technology but also has some
understanding of what is often termed 'the social relations of
science and technology'. And it follows that, in many instances, the people who know most about the impact of particular pieces of science and technology are the people who
actually experience it in their day-to-day lives, and it is totally
unlikely that these people will happen to be scientists or technologists, whether specialists or generalists, in more than a small
fraction of these cases. Therefore, if we accept that non-technical
people have a part to play in science and technology policy-
making, and that at least some of the criteria for choice in these
matters are external rather than internal (i.e. technical), then the
question of who should make decisions about science and technology surely depends on the exact nature of the criteria for
choice.

The Criteria for Scientific Choice

The major exponent of the need for such criteria is perhaps
Alvin Weinberg, an influential American science policy-maker,
who published an article on the subject in two parts in the
journal *Minerva* in 1963-4. Weinberg's argument may be considered to be the current orthodoxy in the field though, as I shall
show, all that it has done is to confuse the basic issues and to
distract attention from the real problems of science policy-
making, which are, in my view, only special cases of the general
problems of advanced industrial societies and their pretensions
to democracy. I shall further put forward the view that present
trends in the whole area of science policy continue the theory

and practice of the political sociology of science that I identified in Part Two, and that whether in its Soviet or Euro-American varieties, its implications are both sociologically problematic and profoundly undemocratic.[2]

Weinberg's starting point, which is the essential starting point for any writer in the field, is to state categorically that nowadays science and technology are too expensive in money and manpower to be left entirely unplanned. (Indeed, this is the reason why the first part of this book is devoted to the scale and costs of science: these matters are insufficiently appreciated in most sections of society.) It is big science to which the argument about criteria for choices refers, rather than little science, which in common with the arts may be supported in most countries as a small cultural expense. In the United States the proportion of total Federal expenditure devoted to R & D increased from under 1 per cent in 1940 to nearly 16 per cent by 1965. Big science is big business. Present political noises in most industrial societies about problems of the environment and the quality of life reflect obliquely a realization that something is wrong with science and technology as it impinges on the lives of ordinary men. Science and technology, therefore, must be seen to be responsive to a minimum of democratic social control.

To substantiate this position Weinberg distinguishes between internal and external criteria for scientific choice. The internal criteria are concerned with the scientific worth and potential of the field in question; the external criteria are, curiously, techno-logical, scientific, and social merit. Leaving social merit to one side it is not immediately obvious what the real difference is between the internal and the external criteria. The former are supposed to answer the question 'How well is the science done?' and the latter the question 'Why pursue this particular science?' (Weinberg, 1967, p. 71). What makes Weinberg's discussion (and the discussion of practically all those who write about these topics) so unsatisfactory is the failure to see the spurious nature of the distinction between internal and external factors when it is made in these terms. For science and technology, too often the reply to the question 'Why do such and such?' is precisely that it is able to be done so well; and the answer to the question 'Is it well done?', restricted as it must be to the scientific and/or technological community, closes this particular circle even more tightly. Weinberg examines the relationship between the internal and the external criteria of choice in the most cursory fashion, but this is inevitable given that he initially distinguishes between different scientific fields and holds that criticism of and evaluation by practitioners in one field of those in another counts as the operation of external criteria of scientific merit. This – if I may coin a phrase – is rampant technicocentrism. To the high-energy physicist the complaint of the molecular biologist that too much money is being spent on the immensely expensive accelerators (playthings) of modern physics is certainly external comment, but to the non-scientist it very much looks like schoolboys squabbling over the distribution of their seasonal cake.

This lack of social perspective is revealing. The dust-jacket of every science and society book proclaims the relevance of the subject for our daily lives. The authors rarely descend from the deliberations of the technically accredited committees: 'Beyond the Ivory Tower' (to quote the title of a recent work) there seems to be only more ivory tower. The token mention of social needs and values, imported like a Negro into the white liberal dinner party, only reinforces the impression that everything is all right as long as no one asks any questions about what happens when the book is done, when the party is over. Weinberg's discussion of social merit, his only genuine external criterion in my view, illustrates this perfectly.

It is perhaps unfair to expect a sophisticated analysis of social values and the requirements of human welfare here, though Weinberg does explicitly state the opinion that 'the most valid criteria for assessing scientific fields come from without rather than from within the scientific discipline that is being rated' (ibid., p. 82). What, then, are the external, social considerations that must be taken into account when making science policy? Weinberg identifies two difficulties in this 'most controversial criterion of all', namely 'Who is to define the values of man, or even the values of our society?'; and how can we be sure that 'a given scientific or technical enterprise indeed furthers our pursuit of social ends' (ibid., p. 76). Unfortunately, there is no discussion at all of the first of these important questions, and the treatment of the second is quite inadequate. It is easy to bemoan the failure of one of the leading writers in this field to get to grips with the urgent problems he has set himself. It is more difficult to try to start the job oneself. To do this, as I have already indicated, it is necessary to approach the matter of criteria for choice in science and technology as a special case of choice in democratic society, and to pay special attention to the possibilities of knowledge and understanding of technical issues in this respect.

The idea of informed public debate is at the very heart of the notion of democracy I wish to propound. This implies neither that everyone should know everything about everything – a patently ridiculous requirement – nor that everyone should be equally interested in everything – a patently unrealistic requirement. What it does imply, at the least, is that everyone should be given an opportunity to find out about those things that most affect his life, and that society be organized in such a way that people are positively encouraged to have an interest in these things. *Interest* may be used in a significantly ambiguous manner in this discussion: it is in our interest (to our advantage) to be interested in (unapathetic about) many things. Just as people may be interested in things which are not necessarily in their interests, it is even more true that people are very often not interested in things which are most certainly in their interests. For example, it is often said that certain types of young people nowadays are interested in 'the drug scene' and that this is not in their (best) interests; on the other hand it is often said that the very low turnouts in local government elections show that the majority of voters are uninterested in matters which will affect their vital interests. We may label these interpretations of interest in both senses as the 'official' or the observers' view.

The participants' view might look very different. The young man or woman using certain forms of what many reliable medical authorities consider to be relatively harmless drugs for amusement or paths to creative experience, might well regard those who assert their right to legislate what is and is not in his 'best' interests with some suspicion. Why, it may be asked, are alcohol and tobacco tolerated and their use in moderation deemed not contrary to the best interests of most of the population, whereas certain other drugs are banned? The answer to this question is complex and clearly includes such factors as the tax revenue that alcohol and tobacco bring in, the probability that most of those responsible for the bans either smoke tobacco or drink alcohol or do both and few if any of them have ever experienced the drugs they ban, and the general opposition to the various drug cultures stimulated by the mass media (and misleadingly undifferentiated so as to prevent any legal distinction between hard and soft drugs from being easily acceptable). In both senses, then, the interests of the lawmakers and those whose actions are being affected by the laws can differ considerably.

The case of apathy in local elections may be similarly understood. The manifest point of having elections at all is to give people the choice between a variety of alternative candidates and policies. In the Free World democrats often sneer at the so-called elections in totalitarian countries such as the Soviet Union and Egypt where unopposed candidates are returned to the most important state offices with majorities of between 99 and 100 per cent. Apathy at election time in their own countries, therefore, is seen by these democrats as a shameful waste of rights and opportunities. The citizen who does not vote, however, may see the matter quite differently. He may see himself as a member of a tiny minority against a monolithic majority, with no chance of a change, and so the election is a foregone conclusion and it is not worth the effort to cast his vote. More likely the apathetic voter will fail to distinguish the *real* difference between the candidates, for he may feel that none of the alternatives will represent his interests. Perhaps he has voted in the past for different parties in response to the promises of one and then another, and nothing very much has happened to improve his situation. His apathy, then, is a rational act (or nonact), for if he believes that none of the candidates will do much for him then it is simply not worth voting. His best interests will not be served by a time- and energy-consuming interest in local politics as it stands, and he might either attempt to change the system, or failing that he might, as perhaps a majority of people do, withdraw from any meaningful participation in local political processes.

This latter issue illustrates one of the crucial problems of democracy and one that has its parallels with the questions of science and technology policy with which I am primarily concerned. It is not enough to ensure that there are no formal prohibitions on participation in political affairs for the creation of a healthy democracy. It is likewise not enough to ensure that there are no formal prohibitions on learning for the creation of an informed public. For the creation of a healthy democracy and an informed public which is an essential part of it, as opposed to a naïvely *laissez-faire* liberalism – the invisible hand in the velvet glove – there needs to be a positive encouragement to citizens. Let us take the case of big science policy and look at what does happen and what could happen.

Effectively, the man in the street, the ordinary elector, has no direct say in big science policy-making and very little indirect say. As I related in Chapter 1, most research and development is paid for either by governments, from taxes, or by private industrial firms, often in terms of a percentage of profits or turnover. In America, which accounts for about two thirds of non-Communist R & D expenditure, most of the funds spent in the 1960s by the Federal government went for space and military purposes. I have already discussed the contract system and it is clear that the application of the 'public interest' in circumstances such as these raises serious doubts as to the operation of truly democratic principles. But at least the Apollo project did achieve its major objective, unlike many expensive military projects. In 1969 it was reported that Senate investigators were examining the failure of projects on which over $9,000 million had been spent. The eventually cancelled B-70 bomber had lost $1,500 million; $512 million were lost on a nuclear-powered aircraft; the Dyna-Soar space plane lost $405 million; and the Navajo and Skybolt missiles had consumed more than $1,100 million between them. 'All of these projects were totally abandoned. But [said the correspondent] in no case were they abandoned before the companies involved were paid in full for their efforts' (Harlow Unger, *Sunday Times*, 19 October 1969).

This appears to be only the tip of the iceberg. Underestimation of costs of major defence contracts is the rule rather than the exception, and it is tempting fate to have a system which encourages privately owned specialist companies, a large proportion of whose business comes from government and especially military contracts. This may not be totally unrelated to the fact that among the top executives of these firms are to be found unusually high numbers of retired military personnel. However one looks at it, public control over the choice of big science projects and expenditure leaves something to be desired. I have given these rather shocking figures not simply to insinuate abuse, although I must confess to a natural suspicion whenever public funds are privately disposed of, but also to show that either those responsible for making big science policy in these extremely expensive fields are criminally negligent and/or incompetent in a not inconsiderable number of cases. Criminality will be punished by the law where it is detected and guilt sustained, (it may be noted that this type of fraud is somewhat less risky than, say, robbing banks) though the incompetent may be more difficult to dislodge. In any case, the gist of my argument is that with a little training most of us, adequately motivated, could hardly do worse than many science and technology planners apparently do. What lesson can we derive from this?

Keeping People out of Science

In the first place, there would seem to be an excellent reason for those at present in control of big science and its funding to let it be widely understood that the issues involved were so technical and the knowledge required was so esoteric that only a select few could be considered competent to carry out this work and make the crucial decisions. In mock democratic spirit they might claim that 'society' or 'the people' or 'public opinion' decides what should be done, in general terms, and they, the experts, go ahead and make sure that it is done. The role of the public, therefore, is restricted to the provision of a general mandate for action. But, as we have seen, and as few citizens in the advanced industrial societies would wish to deny, there is rarely if ever any real debate about big science or its consequences, precisely because the issues are deemed to be too technical for the layman and sometimes even for the politicians themselves. The only choice that is given is in terms of the typically false dichotomy between growth and stagnation or between defence and destruction. The methods of the parties in the major democracies may differ, sometimes very considerably, but in the contemporary world the alternatives to more science and technology are conceived in such a way that reasonable and intelligent people, if they accept the premises, could not fail to agree to the technocratic or quasi-technocratic conclusions. And the very possibility of a critical scrutiny of the premises is rendered most unlikely, not by any formal prohibition (for that is not the way of enlightened democracy) but by a discouragement from all sides and an official climate of support for the professional, the expert, and the neutrality of technical information and decision-making. Therefore, whether it is to protect a lucrative racket or to protect a position of privilege, or whether it is simply to prevent the uninitiated from interfering with his work, the science policy-maker has every reason to dissuade members of the public from the view that the processes of making the decisions of big science are of legitimate concern to the unqualified.

There is another, rather more general reason why it is to the advantage of certain groups in advanced industrial societies that there should be little if any public discussion about science and technology or public participation in the decisions that are made about big science. I shall restrict myself to only a few preliminary comments on this theme, for it will be the main issue in the last chapter. I refer of course to the assumption that we want a society in which large proportions of our national product go towards research and development in order to increase our national product even more, presumably in order to be able to invest yet more in R & D, and so on . . . I shall only say at this stage that countries where most people are well fed and well housed and somewhat educated are in a different position with respect to this matter than poor countries. E. J. Mishan, in a recent book which elaborates many of these points, has aptly labelled this assumption 'growthmania' and, like every mania, if most people suffer from it then those that do not are apt to be considered if not maniacs themselves, then at least a little odd.

We have isolated some potential motives that those responsible for big science policy might have for excluding the rest of the population from their deliberations. As I have said, there is no intention on my part to suggest any sort of conspiracy theory that might argue that these policy-makers deliberately mislead the public, obstruct the efforts of anyone trying to discover what they are doing, or that they systematically attempt to abuse the considerable powers that they possess. Obviously, all of these things do happen here as in most other similar institutions; the point is that the exclusion of the public from decision-making in this and other areas does serve a set of interests which can be traced to a particular group of people, which is not to say that their interests necessarily conflict dramatically with those of the public.

When we add up these factors, the social image of the expert whose knowledge and talents are asserted to be inaccessible to ordinary men and women, plus the sheer immensity of big science and its curious detachment from day-to-day existence, plus the vested interests that those in a position to help the public to come to terms with the problems have in maintaining the system as it is, it is hardly surprising that the population at large is not only as good as disenfranchised in matters of science and technology but also that it seems not to mind very much. Even on the infrequent occasions on which public opinion is aroused by a technical issue, e.g. the Anglo-French Concorde project or the Torrey Canyon oil tanker disaster in Britain, the antiballistic missile system (all $20,000 million of it) or the great Nevada radiation cloud leak in the United States, it is either too late for the outcry to make much difference, or decisions are taken in any case which pay only the scantest attention to what the people might want.

Bringing People into Science

Situations such as these force political decisions on us, and these are decisions which indicate how serious we are about democracy. I have already suggested that there are good reasons for not leaving all the decisions about big science in the hands of the big scientists, whether specialists or generalists, though of course it would be foolish to exclude them from participation in such decisions simply because they are big scientists or administrators. Indeed, it is clear that those who are technically trained and competent have the essential role to play that all specialists in all societies might play, namely to tell us what is possible and impossible, likely and unlikely. The crude objection to science policy-making (often distinguished from technology policy-making) – that new knowledge is unpredictable and so we cannot plan science – is so philosophically weak as to be laughable, except for the fact that many liberal–conservative philosophers and scientists appear to accept it as an impeccably logical argument. For their benefit one may briefly suggest that science policy, like any other type of policy, does not pretend to certainty, neither does it pretend to magical powers of prophecy. Nevertheless, if vast sums of money are devoted to a particular branch of science, then the likelihood of advances there are greater than if it is neglected; if large numbers of mathematically trained researchers are attracted to biology rather than physics, then we can expect certain types of developments in the bio-medical sciences; and finally, if we build a 300 GeV intracontinental accelerator, then we can be sure that certain types of new particles will be identified. It is in a rather occasional and special sense that new knowledge is utterly unpredictable. Therefore, scientists and technologists will be able to make intelligent predictions about the consequences of their work, and though it would be unreasonable to expect them to be totally accurate all the time, it is reasonable to expect them to be very accurate some of the time and fairly accurate most of the time.

In the only case study known to me of a serious experiment involving lay advisory committees on research – in the US Department of Agriculture – it was said that 'the advisory committees did not destroy the freedom of the scientist' (Mainzer, 1958, p. 322). It is, however, impossible to generalize from this experience for my purposes here because the lay advisors turned out to be mainly the large-scale producers and their representatives; neither the small men nor the consumers appeared to be able to achieve membership. Current experiments with methods of technology assessment in the USA, USSR, and China might well, in the next few years, provide further relevant information.

Before any of the philosophers or scientists or other defenders of Western civilization go into paroxysms of rage at the notion of science by public committee, let me at once note both that this is in no way implied by what I say and that if indeed anyone thinks that it is, then it only proves how deeply ingrained are some attitudes in the minds of some of our most educated citizens. And let me also reiterate the distinction I have made between little science for purely cultural reasons and big science as a public responsibility. (Not that culture cannot have unintended consequences – who would have thought that the Beatles would become significant earners of foreign currency for a hard-pressed economy, and be rewarded in traditional British fashion for their efforts.) Where small sums of money are granted to scientists in order that they might have the leisure and a little equipment or research assistance to follow their hunches, it would be as ridiculous to expect them to spend a lot of time and effort at first justifying and then explaining the success or failure of their work to interested members of the public as it would be to expect recipients of small grants for poetry or painting to do the same. However, where very large sums of public money are concerned and where significant manpower consequences will arise from the carrying out of the project, it is as reasonable to expect the scientists and technologists to justify what they intend to do publicly as it would be to expect the architects and designers involved in the rebuilding of a city centre to do the same. The analogy is altogether too near the bone as many people who have visited some of our towns and cities might agree. All too often private profit – usually largely risk free – rather than civic need provides the motivation for urban redevelopment as it does for big science.

Once we have established (or at least planted the seed of) the notion that big science can in some meaningful fashion be planned, and that the planners need not always and at every stage be scientists or technologists themselves, and that public involvement is desirable, we are left with the apparently insurmountable problem of making science and technology intelligible to a willing public. I am assuming, no doubt thus betraying a naïvely Utopian prejudice, that in the unlikely event that both big scientists and the authorities were to make great efforts to demythologize big science, and were to succeed in showing the public that decisions in this area could be democratically reached if certain cognitive conditions were satisfied, the public would be willing to receive instruction in technical matters. It might be worth considering some sort of test for the citizen which he had to pass in order to win a place on one of the Councils of Public Discussions on Decisions in Big Science, in much the same way as people nowadays have to pass driving tests before they can be allowed to drive cars on the public highway.

This is not a study in the sociology and politics of education, and so I can only point out some general reasons why this problem of instructing the public in technical matters appears to be insurmountable, and the recommendations that I shall make will seem rather piecemeal. Apart from the vested interests of those at present in control, which results in the tendency to withhold from all but a very few popularizers of science a modicum of professional respectability, let alone high esteem, the phenomenon of 'the opposition to science and technology' must not be ignored. Indeed, the low prestige that the science community accords to its popularizers is often related to the ambivalent feelings that many people in advanced industrial societies appear to have about big science. The link, of course, is the Frankenstein or the ecological catastrophe syndrome. It is not difficult, with a little knowledge of current developments in a few selected fields, to present a convincing enough case for the probability that the new biology will create monsters or that big science in general will poison our atmosphere or melt our ice-caps. What makes this so easy to do is the fact that the alarmist position, especially on pollution, is in many cases more than justified by the available technical evidence. Popularizers who point this out, and who help to stimulate anti-scientific attitudes, are thus regarded by those whose work is thereby brought into the public eye in a critical fashion as interferers and trouble-makers. It is usually easier to rebuff such attacks by impugning the scientific credentials of the popularizer than by meeting his arguments.

All of this will tend to put obstacles in the way of an improved public comprehension of scientific matters, and to see why this is so it is necessary to reflect for a moment on the nature of the mass media. In general it is true to say that whenever controversy is generated in large-circulation newspapers or magazines or on television rational argument and a careful weighing of the evidence are less often decisive in the resolution of the debate than are the personalities of the protagonists and their respective public relations skills. (These latter factors are also important even in some purely academic disputes.) When these tendencies lead to sensationalism and large undocumented claims and to blanket *ad hominem* refutations the cause of popularizing science is ill served. Exposure to science and its disputes does not always necessarily lead to an informed public for the simple reason that if the exposure leaves behind a mess of false ideas and misleading impressions then perhaps those exposed are worse off than they were before. Studies of the presentation of science and technology in the mass media, from Britain and America, give little indication that the picture I have drawn is unduly pessimistic, though there are, of course, honourable exceptions.

Education, whether or not it starts in the home, is supposed to continue in the school, and undoubtedly it is in the school that the future citizen will be most influenced with respect to an interest in and a willingness to learn about science and technology. I have already, in Chapter 3, discussed some of the work that has been done on the attitudes to science of school-children and university students, but most of these respondents constitute a somewhat self-selected élite. As far as the majority of children are concerned – those who leave school around fifteen years of age and have no further formal education, and who make up the majority of the electorate – the situation is often irreparable although, as I mentioned at the beginning of this chapter, at some levels all who can operate satisfactorily in an advanced industrial society will have an historically unique collection of technical skills and knowledge. But these are mostly, as it were, 'after the event' skills and knowledge, and what is necessary for real public participation in big science decision-making is that the mass of the population should have the confidence and the desire to come in to the process *before* it is too late to do anything about what is happening.

Most very expensive projects, especially civil and military aviation ones, provide examples of this. The defence of the Anglo-French Concorde is increasingly of the variety: well we've spent so many millions of pounds on it already, we may as well finish it. Perhaps the first law of R & D economics (Real-politik) might be expressed as: where there are risk-free profits to be made free enterprise will encourage governments to throw good money after bad! As the US military examples I have already quoted suggest, projects tend to be cancelled after vast sums of public money have been spent on them and not before. It is little wonder then that people who are interested enough in these problems and who take the trouble to instruct themselves on the issues involved become discouraged and disappointed in the potentialities of the democracies in which they live. And it is no wonder at all that most of the population appear to assume that there is very little point in bothering about these problems, for their chances of influencing decisions in these areas are practically nonexistent.

Broadly, education has its positive and negative dimensions. It is only realistic to speak about the education of young people and adults in the various aspects of science and technology which clearly do affect their lives if certain political possibilities are opened up to them. It is perhaps the case that there are some people who have a desire to learn on a wide front as part of their genetic apparatus, but it is certainly the case that environmental variables strongly influence the individual's desire to learn in general and that the social organization of the school, the neighbourhood, and the wider political community in which the individual is located, can make a very great difference to his basic educability. If the experiences of those nations with widespread educational systems teach us anything, they teach us that given favourable conditions a large proportion of the population of every nation is capable of assimilating the knowledge and skills necessary for modern living, and a lot more besides. There is no reason *a priori* why well-planned education could not be very effective in any context to a level where people could at least have an intelligent opinion on problems raised. I am *not* suggesting for a moment that the people collectively do the science or technology; I *am* suggesting that they could have an appreciation of what is being done.

Already, in circumstances of great public disquiet, like the furore that greeted the decision over the siting of a third airport for London, and the fairly regular uproars over contaminated food, relevant groups do organize and try to act collectively. Where the level of public alarm is high, then we may assume that the potential for education is present although, as I have suggested, this need not always have totally desirable consequences.

The ideal state of affairs, accordingly, would be as follows. A proposal is made and, after some not altogether random though informal public and private discussions, it is deemed to be worthy of serious consideration. If it is a very expensive proposal and one that would need support on a variety of levels, financial, educational, political, and so on, then it might enter some formal process whereby information about it could be made readily available and displayed in places where people are liable to see it rather than where they are not. There would seem to be no reason why people who lived in the same street or in the same block might not meet informally though purposively to discuss the proposal and perhaps to call on local 'experts' who could be relied upon to answer questions about it and to explain it. These local groups might be loosely organized, say through local schools or police stations or pubs, into larger units where further discussions might take place and people might benefit from the views of people very different from themselves.

To the protests of the 'realists' who would reject such a scheme out of hand with the objection that the vast majority of people would not take the trouble to attend these meetings or that under conditions of perpetual consultations nothing would ever get done, there are simple answers. First, if people were given the opportunity that a nationally sponsored and supported scheme such as I describe could offer, and they chose not to take advantage of it on several occasions and permitted important decisions to be taken without their participation, then they would have less cause for complaint than they have now. In this case, a valuable experiment in practical democracy would, in my view unfortunately, have failed. But to find out we must try it.

Second, the thesis that it is massively inefficient and time-wasting is unconvincing because, as things stand at present, major proposals do in fact take many years of committee work, expert consultation, and often political debate in parliaments and in other high places before decisions are reached. While all this top-level activity is going on it would be quite possible for the public to become involved in the processes of deliberation, debate, mutual education, and finally representation in the actual decision. It must be borne in mind that in complex situations simple yes–no decisions are rather unlikely to be the most important. It is far more likely that many choices will have to be made between a variety of alternatives and that with a wider body of decision-makers we can expect even more alternatives. Again, all or nothing decisions, though sometimes called for, probably occur less frequently than decisions which imply branching paths. For example, a major proposal like the channel tunnel scheme contains a large number of related problems, each of which might have a set of alternative solutions, and each of these solutions might create new sets of problems and so on.

At every point the path has branches and each branch in its turn becomes a new path with its branches. So it is not a matter of 50 million British citizens or 200 million Americans having a big meeting and saying yes or no to one specific proposal, but a fairly long-term multi-faceted process whereby ordinary people might become involved in those parts of the decision-making which they felt to be most closely related to their interests.

In the channel tunnel example everyone in Britain and France would have at least a minimal financial interest if the money were to come from their taxes. The communities at each end of the proposed tunnel, both actual and potential, would have an interest in terms of the changes in their patterns of living that such a scheme would inevitably bring. The engineering problems involved in such a venture and the alternative methods put forward are clearly technically complicated to a high degree, but it is difficult to believe that they are so complicated that the general principles behind the choices of those putting forward the plans could not be explained and illustrated to the untrained public. If, for example, the adoption of one method meant that a massive investment in one type of engineering would be necessary and that this would in all probability constrain the development of other types of engineering, and perhaps make it probable that other projects in the future would use this method, then – apart from the engineering and technological merits of the method, which are obviously matters of great importance – the possible consequences of all this for, say, the ordinary consumer of domestic appliances in ten years' time might also be taken into account.

These considerations are especially relevant in the development of new materials. Plastics provide a good illustration of the problems in this area. At first, hard-wearing, almost indestructible, and now possibly entirely indestructible plastics seemed a great boon to all and sundry. They quickly found a multitude of uses both as improvements on existing materials and, in response to the insatiable desire of manufacturers to enlarge their markets, in entirely new ways. Now, of course, we are faced with the phenomenon of literally millions of unwanted, useless, or obsolete objects which we cannot get rid of precisely because of the quality which originally had made them so wanted and useful – their indestructibility. Thus we see the essentially ambivalent nature of scientific and technological progress.

The moral of this story for the channel tunnel proposal is that the more ordinary people who have no particular reason for favouring one or other of a variety of proposals and sub-proposals the more likely it is that these little flaws might be spotted. If a massive investment were required to develop, say, a material capable of withstanding enormous water pressures and also transparent so that travellers could watch the fish, and if it were likely that to recoup some of the R & D costs all sorts of other uses were to be suggested for it so that our civilization would be likely to utilize it in every possible case, then it would be only sensible to put it before as wide a panel as possible in order that the benefit of the total national experience might be directed to consider possible snags.[3]

To repeat my earlier claim: if we are serious about the ideal of a participatory democracy, then all of these suggestions would not seem as ridiculous as they undoubtedly will do to many responsible people in advanced industrial societies. It is, nevertheless, legitimate to ask whether or not public participation in the formation and evaluation of big science policy would result in different decisions in fact being taken. Even if my notions of participatory democracy find sympathy here and there could it not be argued that the end result would not be so unlike what we now have? Science and technology, perhaps, would continue very much as before. This view is often expressed with the implicit and sometimes explicit belief that science and technology have an intrinsic dynamic, an internal mechanism which ensures to a greater or lesser extent that they will continue to develop once a certain take-off stage has been reached. Thus, the argument goes, other than a certain educational and/or therapeutic effect, public participation in the decisions of big science would not significantly change its progress one way or another. Leaving aside the very real importance of the education and/or therapy involved – and these may be absolutely crucial and sufficient reason for the whole thing in any case – the argument about the intrinsic dynamic of science and technology seems to me to be the next line of defence of those who find the idea of the democratization of science and technology unpalatable, but who might admit some of the points I have made. For the intrinsic dynamic view has a most important bearing on what I have termed 'alternative futures'. And this is where big science and our theories of social change collide, for though science and technology were always supposed to provide us with a future full of so many exciting alternatives, it often appears to be the case that big science, while providing some alternatives, cuts out many more.

Therefore, I shall conclude this book by speculating on some of these futures and to do this I shall look at both the possibilities of those of us who live in societies where science and technology already dominate and at those societies where this is not yet the case.

NOTES

1. *Advertising Age* (26 August, 1963) reported that of the top 100 US industries, drugs and cosmetics had the highest advertising-to-sales ratio (15·4 per cent).

2. I do not intend to obscure the fact that the values from which my work stems suggest strongly that the profoundly undemocratic will tend to be sociologically problematic over time. The reasons for this position, which is an hypothesis rather than an article of faith, are given in Sklair (1970, Part II).

3. In his otherwise very enlightened book, *Scientific Knowledge and Its Social Problems*, Raverty (1971) finds no place for the public in these matters.

8 Alternative Futures (II)

It is beyond doubt, and a fact generally to be welcomed, that science and technology have penetrated into most parts of the world. Transistor radios, it is reported, are to be heard practically everywhere, and aeroplanes land in the most obscure places. The fruits of modern medicine, particularly, are being spread around the globe relatively quickly and in significant amounts. However, if my arguments in the previous chapter about the role of the public in big science policy-making in the developed countries carry any weight at all, then it is quite clear that citizens of the underdeveloped countries have practically no choice whatsoever in the sorts and quantity of science and technology their societies will have. They are therefore both in a better and a worse position in this context than people in the richer countries.

They are in a better position because their societies are not yet *made up*, which is another way of saying that, whether successful or not, their societies are being put through a series of more or less conscious social changes. Crucial decisions might not yet have been taken (or more relevant, put into practice), and so a whole range of options is still open. The populations of underdeveloped countries, on the other hand, are in a worse position than those in richer countries because, without the very science and technology and its socio-economic concomitants that are still only possibilities, they are in a weak position to ensure that their wishes are met or even taken into account. This operates at two levels. Technologically backward countries, especially those who rely on the sale of single commodities in the world market for their foreign earnings, tend to be at the mercy of their richer neighbours. The governments of poor countries often do not have a free hand to follow policies which might interfere with the interests of those of rich countries. The growth of the giant multi-national companies, in particular, weakens the poor with respect to the rich. It can also, as I shall show later, have a very debilitating effect on the growth of scientific research in underdeveloped countries.

This international hierarchy is often mirrored by an intra-national hierarchy in poor countries. By this I mean that the ruling groups in these countries more often than not consist of small and very unrepresentative élites who have attained positions of power through hereditary privileges and who use these positions of power to safeguard their privileges. Typically, these men and women are educated in the West and have very little understanding of the problems of the peasants or workers in their own countries. It is hard to escape the conclusion that many of the leaders in this Third World do not really care whether or not their countrymen are well-fed and adequately housed and educated (see Dumont, 1969). This is not a simple issue and it would be naïve to assume that these élites hold back economic and techno-logical development only or consciously in order to resist the erosion of their privileges. I cannot go into the wider implications of this crucially important question, but I must expose the ways in which the situation bears on the role of science and technology in modernization and the satisfaction of men's basic needs. And this will lead us back into the relations between the international and the intra-national hierarchies I have described. We shall see that this is a most powerful double-bind for the underdeveloped countries and one whose resolution will neces-sarily have major consequences for human history.

Techno-economism
In spite of the very real differences that exist between the Western and the Soviet models of development (and perhaps we might add the Chinese case as a separate category rather than a sub-category of the latter, for it may well come to present a real alternative), it is true to say that one model of development or modernization has dominated this field. I shall label this model, for convenience, techno-economism. Techno-economism holds that all of the most important problems that face mankind can only be solved by the rational application of science and technology for economic development. Thus, indicators such as the Gross National Product of a country, the industrial produc-

tivity per man-hour of its workers, and the balance of payments between imports and exports, are taken to measure the economic performance of the country as a whole and, indeed, its general standing in the world. Those things that tend to improve economic performance are by and large deemed to be good, and those things that interfere with it, and tend to lower the rate of economic growth, are deemed to be bad. Therefore, as can be seen from this brief characterization, techno-economism is not only a theory of socio-economic change but also a political and a moral philosophy.

If we imagine industrialization as the vehicle of techno-economistic progress, then we can fruitfully picture science and technology as the engine that drives the vehicle ever onwards, ever more smoothly, and ever faster. We might say that Soviet and Western modernization have almost identical engines, rather different vehicles, and run on parallel tracks. The theory accordingly invites all countries who have not yet done so to get on to one or other of the tracks. To conclude, let us picture the Western train (the United States, followed closely by Western Europe, and at irregular intervals by a host of smaller and slower wagons); the Soviet train (Russia, similarly followed); several others who appear to change back and forward from one track to another; a few who appear to be able to have a wheel on each track at the same time and keep going; and a large group of nations who do not seem to be able to get on to any track at all.

The point is that countries are either going in the direction decreed by techno-economism or they are going in no direction at all – quite literally, they are said to be standing still. Even some very rich countries, and this has been said particularly of Britain in the last few years, are accused of standing still relative to their rich competitors. This is not to say that Britain has stopped growing from a techno-economistic point of view but only that its *rate* of growth has fallen behind other, often poorer countries. Such is the logic of techno-economism.

In most of the writing on the subject the implication is clearly that every country would prefer to be on the track, one way or another. Those on the track wish to improve their performance at almost any cost and so almost any price is thought to be worth paying to get started in the first place. This type of cost–benefit analysis (used here not quite in its technical sense) is consistent with a basic tenet of techno-economism, namely that all worthwhile things are measurable and all important problems can be solved by its methods. Unquantifiables are of necessity left out of the analysis, and even when the defenders of the doctrine attempt to quantify them their natural enemies, those opposed to techno-economism, complain that the fallacy of 'quantifying the unquantifiable' is being committed. Either way techno-economism triumphs, and factors such as amenity value, social disruption, historical interest, and natural beauty tend to be ruled out of account.

The costs of industrialization or modernization have always been obvious enough to those who would but stay a moment and observe. Both Marx and Engels wrote passionately about the plight of the working man (and woman, and child) in nineteenth-century England and America. Engels in *The Condition of the Working Class in England* (1845) and Marx in Volume I of *Capital* (1867), particularly in the chapter entitled 'The Working-Day', documented in scathing terms the exploitation of the working masses specifically occasioned by the capitalist mode of production.

Capital cares nothing for the length of life of labour-power [says Marx]. All that concerns it is simply and solely the maximum of labour-power, that can be rendered fluent in a working-day. It attains this end by shortening the extent of the labourer's life, as a greedy farmer snatches increased produce from the soil by robbing it of its fertility (Marx, 1961, p. 265).

The rationale of large-scale enterprise, Marx explains, eventually forced manufacturers to accept limitations on these cruder forms of exploitation, and so we may understand the limited success of the Factory Acts in nineteenth-century England. But this is the factory system and the industrialization that follows from it, albeit in its more or less capitalist form, to which Marx refers. Whether or not the worst horrors of the traditional type of industrial revolution constitute part of a necessary stage in human history, it cannot be denied that Marx and most other writers, bourgeois or not, considered the early stages of industrialization to be very unpleasant for those who worked on the factory floor, however exciting and rewarding they might be for the entrepreneurs and their allies.

One imaginative suggestion came from a contemporary of Marx. In *The Crown of Wild Olive*, first published in 1866, Ruskin, as a recent commentator puts it, 'advised England to establish colonies where the goods it needed would be manufactured, at a great enough distance to prevent industrialism from contaminating the mother country' (Grampp, 1970, p. 456).[1]

Again, this is not to minimize the benefits that industrialization has undeniably brought to the rich countries and, to a lesser degree, to the poor countries. But what techno-economism asks us to believe is that the methods and indeed the whole ideology of past industrial revolutions, on the basis of the rational and widespread application of science and technology, will: (1) work again in approximately the same way for contemporary poor societies as they did for contemporary rich societies at various times in the past; (2) involve a similar and similarly *acceptable* balance of benefits to costs to the participants; and (3) in fact represent the wishes of the populations whose lives are to be changed, especially in terms of the wider sociological implications of the changes. Let us examine each of these three assumptions in the context of science and technology as a tool for modernization.

(1) Perhaps the only point on which everyone agrees is that science and technology change over time. Therefore, the technical basis of the chemical industry in nineteenth-century Germany will differ widely from the potential for a chemical industry which might be created in Nigeria in the last quarter of the twentieth century. Nowhere is this so dramatically illustrated as in power. The industrial revolution that most conspicuously took place in England between about 1780 and 1830 was due as much to the large-scale industrial use of steam power as to any other single factor. By 1900, with the growth of the industrial and domestic applications of electricity, a new energy source transformed the scene as had steam before it. The Soviet Union, for example, whose major industrialization began after 1917, did not pass through the steam phase in the way that England had done. Likewise, countries which are beginning to industrialize in the next few decades may well miss the conventional hydro-electric phase, in some senses, and start off with nuclear energy as a source of power (see Woodruff, 1966, esp. pp. 214–17).

This is well argued in a paper by Mohammed Yusuf, an officer with the Pakistan Atomic Energy Commission, entitled 'Why Pakistan Should Have a Nuclear Power Programme', read to an international conference in 1962. 'Economic studies indicate that nuclear power would already be cheaper than other fuel in East Pakistan ... atomic revolution can give a second chance to countries which missed the industrial revolution' (in Smith, 1964, p. 92).

Given these massive changes, then, it is unlikely that the methods and ideology of techno-economism, based as they are on an industrial revolution that has long since passed (and in some ways passed into disrepute), will operate for contemporary poor societies in their attempts to industrialize as they did for their rich neighbours many years ago. Most people know this, of course, but there appears to be an almost irresistible tendency to forget it or to treat the fact as a mere irritant on the thrusting body of techno-economism.

(2) Arguably the most important difference between the contemporary poor countries and their rich neighbours when *they* were beginning to industrialize is that the latter were working in more of an isolated context than it is possible for the former to do nowadays. This itself is due largely to scientific and technological developments, particularly in the field of communications and the growth of the mass media on an international scale. Again, the Soviet Union in the decades immediately after the revolution provides a useful comparative half-way house. The planners were familiar with the modes of economic and technical development in America and in the rest of Europe. Indeed, as Maurice Dobb points out, there was a good deal of discussion about the relative merits of the English method of high quality expensive production as against the American method of standardization for mass consumption: the Russians chose the latter (Dobb, 1966, pp. 16–17). It is, however, doubtful whether the average urban or rural worker knew anything at all about technical, economic, and social conditions outside Russia.

This situation is now quite different. With the spread of the transistor radio, the possibilities of cheap television transmission, the distribution of mass circulation newspapers allied to determined campaigns to wipe out illiteracy, and the physical facts of increased internal migration within poor countries back and forth from the village to the towns and cities, more and more people, who might in previous generations have been outside the mainstream of industrial civilization, are now swept into it whether they like it or not. True as this may be on some levels, it is tragically false on others. Foreign technology gives poor peasants information about the possibilities of a better life in rich countries, but it rarely gives them the opportunities to achieve these possibilities for themselves. The cruellest dilemma is that of medical science and technology which has succeeded in cutting the infant mortality rate in many of the poorest countries but is unable to ensure that the children saved at this early stage are properly fed and cared for thereafter. Childhood in an Indian or African subsistence village is an experience totally different from childhood in an American or European suburb, and those in each situation are becoming increasingly aware of the fact.

The costs and benefits of the use of science and technology for modernization, therefore, present for people in contemporary poor societies a social reality which differs significantly from the reality of the situation faced by contemporary rich societies when they were beginning to industrialize, because they are that much more visible to the former than they were to the latter. Not that the costs and benefits experienced by the present rich countries would be simply replicated if the poor countries were to follow their lead for (as I argued above) the changes that have taken place in science and technology in the past century, not to mention political and other changes, make this unlikely in the extreme. However, and this much we may grant to techno-economism, certain general trends may be traced with confidence for the future of potentially industrializing poor countries from the past experience of the rich countries. The costs and benefits of the private motor car, for example, are clear enough for all to see, as are those of high-density urbanization.

It may be noted that I have stressed this factor of visibility as a *difference* rather than as an *advantage* for the citizens of the poor countries. It would be an advantage if there were signs that the benefits were being maximized and their costs minimized, but for both the reverse seems to be the case. As I said at the beginning of this discussion, those in underdeveloped countries are in the position of pioneers, in a sense, at a time when many of the major institutions of their society have not yet been firmly established. There is an element of choice, and this leads me to the third assumption: that today's poor will choose (as it is argued that today's rich once did) on the basis of a techno-economistic view of the world.

(3) I have maintained, counter to techno-economism, that science and technology for modernization are unlikely to operate in the same way today as they have in the past, and that the perceptions of those in poor countries at the present with respect to the costs and benefits of industrialization are somewhat unique in historical terms. Techno-economism is perhaps weakened if my criticisms are correct, but its third assumption – the article of faith on which all else rests and by which all else is ultimately justified – may stand on its own. If it can be shown that the poor of the world want techno-economic progress then, it is often claimed, there is little more to be said. Even those who apparently feel that this progress may not be an unadulterated good often cannot refrain from predicating their views on this assumption. Loren Eiseley, an American anthropologist, in an essay promisingly entitled 'Alternatives to Technology' states the position thus:

When all the world is part of the great society, from East to West; when these uncounted millions of human beings each demand their two cars or their three cars and the many other things which our society enjoys; when all nations have factories, and all are turning out these goods – how many resources on this increasingly impoverished planet earth will it take to satisfy this material demand? (Eiseley, 1969, p. 176).

It is obvious from this that Eiseley cannot conceive of a world in which everyone does *not* demand all the things that rich countries enjoy. In spite of his title the writer can only be pessimistic about the techno-economistic future – it is precisely the *alternatives* to technology that cannot be seriously explored within this frame of reference.

It is essential to clear up one point before going any further, and that concerns the satisfaction of fundamental individual and societal needs. As I have dealt with this in detail elsewhere (Sklair, 1970, Chs 10 and 11), I shall mention only a few main points. No society will survive unless the biological needs of nutrition, sleep, and shelter for enough of its members are satisfied, to ensure that the basic institutions will be staffed. On the societal level, a sufficient number of children must be reproduced and socialized, mainly (but not necessarily) through the kinship system, to ensure the continuity of the society. This, of course, is not the whole story, but it will suffice for my present purposes. Techno-economism holds, in its milder form, that it provides the best way of fulfilling such needs; and in its stronger form, that in the contemporary world it provides the only way of fulfilling them.

The latter assertion is self-evidently false, but it is interesting to speculate about the reasons that people might have for arguing in this way. It represents a curious late twentieth-century determinism and is particularly manifest in the strivings of technologically advanced countries to keep up with and to outstrip the achievements of countries even more advanced in some respects than themselves. More and more sophisticated weapons systems, bigger and faster aeroplanes, a higher and higher level of industrial efficiency, are not merely held to be desirable – they are deemed to be necessary for national survival.

The assertion that techno-economism is the best way of fulfilling fundamental individual and societal needs is altogether more convincing, and so well has this case been argued and reinforced from all directions that those who deny it are made to feel at best lacking in compassion, and at worst criminally negligent of the obvious facts. I fear that I shall have to run this risk, for I intend to conclude this chapter, and thereby to sum up the main polemical intent of the book, by arguing, in the strongest possible terms, that although science and technology do have a part to play in satisfying people's needs, techno-economism as such is profoundly inappropriate as a framework within which this task might successfully be achieved.

Needs and False Needs

Techno-economism is the best way of fulfilling those very needs which it creates. These I shall term false needs, following the usage so persuasively argued by Herbert Marcuse in his books *Eros and Civilization* and *One Dimensional Man*. The point is not so much that these needs (typified by the 'need' of the housewife for a large variety of washing powders whose only significant difference lies in the packaging) are intrinsically false, but that they become so in concrete historical terms in societies that pay more attention to these needs than to the needs of minorities at home and majorities abroad for proper standards of nutrition and housing. Therefore, though it is probably true that techno-economism is the best way of satisfying false needs for some, it is not necessarily the best way of satisfying the fundamental needs of *all*. And this, it seems to me, is the real test for any theory of development; not whether it can provide neat suburbs and third cars for the affluent minorities of the world, but whether it can show the way to feeding, housing, and educating the under-privileged masses.

Science and technology unquestionably have a role to play in the satisfaction of the real needs of the poor, but not quite as they once did in contemporary rich societies, or indeed as they now do in these societies. As is becoming recognized by more and more of those involved in this area – though at the professional and institutional margins rather than at the centre – modern science and technology cannot be grafted on to underdeveloped countries other than in exceptional circumstances. The logic of techno-economism requires that each society has its scientific and technological base, and it is precisely the appropriateness of this recommendation that is being contested. If we reject the view that every society should design itself in terms of the richest societies, then it is natural that we should study the possibility that poor societies might borrow or adapt or develop those parts of modern science and technology that they consider to be par-ticularly applicable to their situations. The immediate attraction of this view is that poor countries will thereby get the science and technology they want rather than the science and technology they do not want. Is this realistic? Is it possible, in other words, to have the best of both worlds?

Briefly, the answer to this question is that those who already have the worst of both worlds, as is the case in most under-developed societies, and who have failed to reach the stage of 'take-off into self-sustaining growth' promised by techno-economism, might be quite well advised to attempt the best of both worlds. This is illustrated by drawing out the difficulties implied in this goal, which are mainly of two types – technical and political.

The technical difficulties stem from the natural suspicion that appropriate science and technology will mean makeshift or bits and pieces and inevitably inferior science and technology. It is practically impossible to discuss this issue realistically in terms of the principles involved, for it is only through the examination of a sufficient number and variety of cases that the borrowing of science and technology as and when required can be seen to be a viable course of action for poor countries. It is doubtful whether enough time has elapsed and enough serious attention has been given to this possibility for us to be able to form any firm conclusions. At the very least it is an open question, and at best some borrowing and adapting of the science and technology of the rich countries can clearly be beneficial to the poor countries. A few examples will suffice to show what can be done.

In discussing sugar production in Africa, René Dumont illustrates not only the social and practical benefits of a compromise between archaic and the most modern methods of sugar refining but also the economic advantages. The village sugar industry, as he calls it, can tie up twelve to fifteen times *less* capital, operating through a hundred small factories, than one large refinery will (Dumont, 1969, p. 90). Guy Hunter, in a book optimistically written and entitled *The Best of Both Worlds?*, reports that the Metal Box Company found that their most modern machine would fill the East African market in one month of production per year. Instead, they installed an out-of-date machine which had work for ten months and tied up very little capital compared to the other. 'This was an exceptional decision;' says Hunter, 'the developing countries are littered with examples of the best, latest, and most expensive equipment running far below capacity for lack of demand, or out of action for lack of maintenance' (Hunter, 1967, p. 37).

In agriculture, especially in methods of crop cultivation and animal husbandry, the role of selected appropriate science and technology provides further examples, although we must not forget that, as has been demonstrated for the Zande system of agriculture in the Sudan, traditional methods are sometimes not lightly to be dismissed (see Schlippe, 1956). Of all the areas in which modern technology has been made available to the underdeveloped countries this is the one that has attracted most research attention. The work of the American rural sociologist Everett M. Rogers is particularly noteworthy here. Rogers began by studying patterns of technical innovation among American farmers, and his recent major research project, *Modernization among Peasants* (1969), continues this work by comparing groups of peasants in Colombia, India, and Kenya. One of his more interesting findings, which has considerable relevance to the matter at hand, is that fatalism – long the explanant of development social science – is *not* in fact a very important variable in explaining why peasants resist modernization.*

A very important new development – which will undoubtedly continue to grow in importance – is that represented by the notion of *intermediate technology*. In its general sense this is what I have been talking about in these last few pages, but it has been set out somewhat more technically and specifically by E. F. Schumacher, Director of the London-based Intermediate Technology Development Group. Schumacher's views are clear and direct and I shall summarize them as they appeared in a recent paper.

He starts by acknowledging that most developing countries have a modern sector, usually in and around the capital and other large cities. Hopes that the modern sector would spread outward into the rest of these societies, however, have not been borne out in recent years. It is, accordingly, the people in the non-modern sector and their plight to which intermediate technology is particularly directed. Given that rural unemployment and the lack of opportunities in agriculture tend to drive very large numbers of people into the cities, thus further aggravating the problems in the modern sector, the need, Schumacher maintains, is to create 'agro-industrial structures'

---

* Compare the favourable review of this book by Daniel Lerner in *Public Opinion Quarterly* (1970), in which he speaks of the necessity 'to teach many millions of simple folk around the world to associate personal reward with personal effort, to acquire a work ethic appropriate both to what they want and what they get' (p. 311). Intemperate as is the whole review, Lerner's comments on 'Kusum Nair's stress on village India's passivity and quietism' entirely miss the point. As Nair explains in *The Lonely Furrow* (1969), white American farmers are just as capable of a 'quiet' life as Indian peasants. Lerner's mistake, a critical one, is to ignore completely the opportunity cost of activism and innovation – the fact that in reactionary systems of land tenure it is often simply not worthwhile for a peasant to increase his productivity with all the risk and extra labour this might involve.

in the non-metropolitan areas. The priority in these structures is not maximum productivity but the provision of the maximum number of *workplaces* compatible with the survival of the enterprise. Output per man, therefore, is not irrelevant, but it is less important than the provision of job opportunities. (The very act of drawing attention to the socio-cultural dimensions of the problem, in terms of my argument above, strikes a blow to the very heart of techno-economism.)

These workplaces, to be possible in sufficient numbers, must be provided very cheaply. In a very illuminating comparison, Schumacher argues that – on the basis of equipment cost per workplace – the indigenous technology of developing countries could be symbolized as £1-technology, and that of developed countries £1,000-technology. Intermediate technology is the rational quest for and development of (symbolically speaking) the £100-technology. This means that the methods of production and organization involved must be fairly simple, and that local materials and local markets should be utilized as far as possible. Thus, the idea is that in societies where labour, without a high level of industrial experience, is abundant intensive structures should be encouraged, and, in societies where large amounts of capital are not often available for the purchase of expensive foreign machinery, small-scale and less advanced productive methods should normally be encouraged. It is emphasized that intermediate technology is not universally applicable in poor countries, but that its applicability is very extensive and has a whole host of beneficial consequences when applied. One paragraph of Schumacher's paper is so important and answers so eloquently the doubts that spring readily to mind about the scheme, that I shall quote it in full:

The idea of Intermediate Technology does not imply simply a 'going back' in history to methods now outdated, although a systematic study of methods employed in the developed countries, say, a hundred years ago could indeed yield highly suggestive results. It is too often assumed that the achievement of Western science, pure and applied, lies mainly in the apparatus and machinery that have been developed from it, and that a rejection of the apparatus and machinery would be tantamount to a rejection of science. This is an excessively superficial view. The real achievement lies in the accumulation of precise knowledge, and this knowledge can be applied in a great variety of ways, of which the current application in modern industry is only one. The development of an Intermediate Technology, therefore, means a genuine forward movement into new territory, where the enormous cost and complication of production methods for the sake of labour saving and job elimination is avoided and technology is made appropriate for labour-surplus societies (Schumacher, p. 11).

It cannot be too often or too strongly emphasized that intermediate technology does not exclude the most modern techniques in some contexts. It is also the case that Schumacher sees it as a feasible way of introducing industrialization to the Third World rather than as an alternative to industrialization in the long run, though, as I have suggested, as a challenge to techno-economism it does open up such possibilities.

Intermediate technology, then, is one important part of an overall development strategy which rejects techno-economism but encourages growth. Contemporary debates in the sociology of development which distinguish modernization on the one hand and balanced growth (or proper, progressive development) on the other, catch the spirit of the view I am suggesting. I cannot here devote the attention it deserves to the concept of *balanced growth* and, indeed, some of its proponents may well feel that an approach which rejects techno-economism as does mine can too easily turn into an anti-science and technology posture which would destroy all progressive development. This is a risk and not an aim of my position.

All of this discussion, it could justly be argued, is taking place in a political vacuum. These technical issues of whether or not it is possible for a poor country to select the processes and machines and ideas from the scientifically advanced countries that it wants and needs and to reject the rest are, as I have said, technical issues. It is one thing to be technically competent to do something; it is quite another thing actually to do it. And the struggles involved in this occur within an ideological framework.

I began by drawing attention to techno-economism as a ubiquitous model of modernization, and I have been mainly concerned to sketch in some of its characteristics and consequences for poor countries. It is necessary to look a little more closely at the function of techno-economism as an ideology because, if my critique can be maintained, it is clear that techno-economism could only operate as an ideology and not as a scientific theory of modernization.

If we take ideology to mean a more or less coherent set of beliefs which expresses and thereby acts to further the interests of a concrete social group, then we may ask: which groups have interests which are effectively expressed and furthered by techno-economism? Now, if certain of the claims of techno-economism were in fact true, we could stop here and permit it to bask in the warmth of the honourable title: progressive ideology. It would be an ideology which furthered the interests of everyone, of all groups. But this, unsurprisingly, is not the case. Techno-economism is particularly consonant with the interests of those who are in a position to exploit science and technology in its commercial/industrial application. Increasingly, the best-placed groups for this purpose are those who own and control the large multi-national corporations. This is particularly true of those companies who are involved in what might be unkindly (though not unjustifiably) called the 'technology transfer racket'.*

Other groups which clearly benefit from the operation of techno-economism are those politicians and civil servants in poor countries whose careers are boosted through their connections with expensive, prestige-conferring projects. Further, sections of the indigenous bourgeoisie in such countries may grow very prosperous very quickly and very painlessly in a similar fashion.

I have no need to dwell on the position of those who suffer from the material consequences of the ideology of a techno-economism that fails to produce the goods – at best – and actually makes things worse – at worst. As I have already suggested, the costs of techno-economism when it works are bad enough; when it doesn't work, they are quite insupportable for all but a tiny over-privileged minority.

We are left, therefore, with a difficult set of problems. Techno-economism is the ideology of our times, and it is being challenged from all sides. The environment and resources lobby (to simplify an amazing variety of positions) attacks it on the basis that it will inevitably lead to physical disaster sooner or later. This lobby is generally reformist in so far as it considers that we can adjust our

* See below, pp. 259 ff.

rate of growth, our use of natural resources, and monitor pollution satisfactorily, *without* any radical change in the modes of production in East and West. This, indeed, is what has been happening in many industrial countries over the past few years and, though it will probably provide a breathing space for decades, and perhaps centuries, it does not appear to be a permanent solution.

The second main attack on techno-economism as an ideology is the cluster of views which embraces the conservationists and those who are genuinely anti-science. The primitivists have a long history behind them and, doubtless, in front of them too. However, their very position makes it unlikely in the extreme that they will ever command the necessary power to effect their policies, such as they are.

The third, and most potent attack on techno-economism *should* come from Marxism. The whole point of Marx's key distinction between use value and exchange value, after all, is to draw attention to the fact that in capitalist society production is for profit rather than use. Now if it so happens that some of the most profitable lines of production turn out to be those which cause great environmental damage and which squander scarce resources, then it follows that the capitalist mode of production is bound for destruction.* But what I have termed *techno-economism* is both wider and narrower than capitalism. It is wider because non-capitalist societies, like the Soviet Union, are just as likely to be organized to fulfil the demands of techno-economism as are capitalist societies. On the other hand, it is narrower because, whereas techno-economism is firmly bound up with the *raison d'être* of capitalism, it is only contingently connected with non-capitalist, and particularly Communist societies. In fact, it can be convincingly argued that Communism represents that stage of development reached when an industrial society has successfully overcome techno-economism within the framework of a democratic mode of production.

Marxists, for reasons which are obvious enough, have not devoted much attention to these problems. It was thought until fairly recently that the miserable and underprivileged peoples of

---

* I regard this as an eminently researchable hypothesis. Richard England and Barry Bluestone in their Union for Radical Political Economies paper 'Ecology and Class Conflict' (1971) supply a very potent analysis.

the world would be only too glad to deal with the costs of economic growth when they had achieved the standard of living that this appeared to imply. The evidence that is flooding in from a multitude of sources leaves little doubt that this was an overly simplistic view. The reactions of Marxists to this new crisis (however epiphenomenal the environmental crisis is, it is clearly critical) have tended to mirror the first and second types of rejections of techno-economism I have just outlined. Bureaucratic communists have become quite reformist in their concern that nothing should be allowed to interfere with industrial growth; whereas libertarian radicals have become increasingly primitivist and anti-science and technology.

The 'correct' Marxist position, deviating neither to the right nor to the left, would reject techno-economism totally, not half-heartedly as do the bureaucrats, and replace it with a progressive alternative, not a regressive one as do the libertarians. What this total, progressive alternative for a truly developing society might be is another and a more difficult problem. Here I have only been concerned to expose techno-economism for what it is – a dangerous ideology whose fate is inextricably bound up with the interests of those who control the production of commodities for profit. Until the political problems inherent in this situation are solved it seems rather unlikely that we can progress very far towards the solution of the 'development' problem. The most pernicious aspect of techno-economism, therefore, is its success in convincing so many people that the 'development problem' is technical, and not political, in nature.

Exploitation through Science

The global cup is overflowing – European and American farmers are regularly given sizeable subsidies *not* to produce certain food-stuffs; there is no lack of industrial productive capacity in some countries – but, of course, half the world is undernourished and lacking in the material essentials for even the most minimally bearable existence. We may gain a little insight into this dreadful paradox by examining the political and social circumstances that surround the uses, non-uses, and abuses of science and technology in the development of poor countries.

It is as well to distinguish the general socio-political factors which affect almost everything from those which have a direct influence on the application of science and technology. I shall begin with the latter.

The first massive fact is that, on practically any measure of science and technology, whether manpower or funds or publications or laboratories or educational facilities, about 95 per cent is carried on outside the underdeveloped countries. As Singer, from whom I have borrowed this estimate which he attributes to Cooper, says, 'This unequal distribution would not matter if the direction of advance, the scientific and technological priorities, and the methods of solving scientific and technological problems, were independent of where the work is carried on. This, however, is patently not the case' (Singer, 1969, p. 3).[2] The poor countries are doubly disadvantaged, internationally and intra-nationally. Internationally, the rich countries determine which problems they choose to solve by virtue of the research funds made available to their scientists and technologists. These, by and large, will be the problems of the rich countries themselves rather than those of the poor countries. False needs, such as space exploration and transplant surgery, occupy those in research and development in rich countries, not the real needs of poor countries. It is not the case that many of the problems of the poor countries are unamenable to scientific solution but that rich countries generally choose not to do the sorts of science that would solve these problems. As N. W. Pirie points out in his admirable book *Food Resources: Conventional and Novel* (1969), there is an enormous amount of scientific potential in the problems surrounding food supplies but, with some notable exceptions, this field has a low priority in the countries which spend most money on science.

This is also all too often the case in the underdeveloped countries themselves. In so far as it does exist, the international community of science ensures that its standards – inevitably those of its most powerful members – will greatly influence the problems and methods of the few scientists and technologists in the poor countries, so they too will tend to devote their resources to the problems set by rich countries.

The structure of scientific and technological work in the underdeveloped countries, therefore, is a special and particularly important instance of the phenomenon to which I have already drawn attention, and which is variously referred to as 'dualism' (see Singer, 1969), and in a rather wider societal and historical perspective, the problem of the metropole and the satellite (or centre and periphery) as developed by Andrew Gunder Frank (1969).

Professional issues are raised in this connection which tend often to be neglected. Scientists and technologists, as I pointed out in Chapter 3, must have career structures which will incorporate education relevant to the sorts of jobs that are likely to be available to them. If, as is generally the case, science and technology are geared to the needs of the rich countries, then even those scientists and technologists who would like to work in areas of direct benefit to poor countries might well be taking something of a professional risk by doing so. Educational and training facilities for these types of problems are not widely available, and the organization of science and technology – in academic and industrial locations – is weighted against the man who chooses to step out of the mainstream of rich science for any length of time.[3]

One further aspect of the relationship between rich science and poor countries should be elaborated, and this involves the implications of *commercial* science and technology. From a (fairly naïve) realist point of view anyone who can afford the subscription or has access to a technical library may learn something about what science is being done in the world today, with two major exceptions. In the first place, there is restricted science and technology which individual or groups of governments keep secret for reasons of national 'security'; secondly, there is that part of industrial R & D which private companies patent and sell or otherwise restrict its availability.

It is important to note the role of the huge trans-national companies here, those companies like IBM, General Motors, ICI, etc., whose value, and sometimes whose annual turnovers, exceed the GNP of many countries. As might be expected, the largest firms carry out most of the industrial R & D in the major scientific countries – in the United States, Britain and France about a third of the total industrial R & D is carried out by the eight firms with the largest research and development programmes (ISY, I, p. 46) – and it is instructive to discover that, although a sizeable proportion of the business of such large companies takes place in the underdeveloped countries, very little of their research does. However many reasons may be adduced for this state of affairs, unavailability of indigenous skilled personnel, the difficulties of maintaining expensive equipment in backward societies, and some of those professional matters to which I have just been referring, the international companies could plough back much more of what they have taken out by helping to build up those sorts of science and technology in the host countries which might be of mutual benefit.

The typical form of the relationship between rich and poor countries in this context is the technology transfer, and this usually occurs when a firm in one country has something scientific or technological or both that the other country wants. Often, of course, the owner of the technology has to persuade the other that it is really needed or wanted, and this is a key ideological task of the formal or informal techno-economistic advertising machine whose job has been much simplified by the rapid spread of communications in the last decade. Whatever the exact impact the common or garden film portraying American or European middle-class life has on the urban and rural poor of the Third World, it is certain to be considerable. We can therefore assume a demand, whether natural or artificial, for some of the fruits of foreign technology in poor countries. And this is where the technology transfer racket often enters the picture.

Commercial technology transfer is the process whereby the *owner* of a piece of science or technology (which can be an idea, a process, a machine, or simply technical information) agrees to its use by another party under certain conditions. It would be a comparatively unproblematic situation if the producer of the technology sold his product, like a shopkeeper selling his goods over the counter, to a buyer to do with as he liked. But this is frequently not the case, for two reasons. First, the vendors of the technology are often not those who have originally developed it. In one study of the petrochemicals industry it was found that 99 per cent of the licences issued for products and processes in this field were held by 'followers' of the producers and engineering firms, and only 1 per cent by the original producers (Stobaugh, quoted in Vaitsos, 1970, p. 17). Therefore, as in so many other cases, the middle-man must have his profit, and the price to the developing country of technology must rise accordingly.

But, it may be argued, the middle-man is providing a service to those who want the technology as well as to those who produce it. Be this as it may, the second reason is somewhat more complex and, in my view, a great deal more pernicious. It provides an excellent example of the way in which free enterprise works for poor countries in the international context.

Patents and licences involve not only material objects and processes but also 'know-how'. This latter notion is almost impossible to define, and, as tends to happen when commercial interests conflict over meanings and definitions of key terms, the legal profession develops a speciality to meet the difficulty and to reap the benefits of the confusion sown in the first place mainly by colleagues originally responsible for framing the laws. Indeed, patent lawyers are a growing body in most countries – they have work to do in poor as well as rich societies – and even the most cursory glance at *The Encyclopedia of Patent Practice and Invention Management* (Calvert, 1964) suffices to confirm one in the view that the whole matter is fraught with difficulty and ambiguity.

When a patent is granted it normally takes the form of a contract between the inventor or someone acting for him and the government of the country involved. The contract requires the inventor to 'describe and illustrate his invention and the best way known to him of using it' and it grants him 'the right to prevent others, except with his consent, from manufacturing, using or selling the invention for a limited period of time' (ibid., p. 617). The licensing of domestic patents abroad, however, raises further issues. *The Encyclopedia* explains that, in the case of the United States, that which violates anti-trust legislation domestically need not necessarily do so in the international context. The main criterion involved is the effect of the practice on the health of US trade and commerce. So, what might constitute an unacceptable monopoly in the home market 'might have a reasonable business justification in the radically different economic circumstances of foreign trade' (ibid., p. 300). The fact that American earnings on foreign licensing rose from $650 million in 1960 to $1858 million in 1969 speaks for itself.[5]

There is a growing amount of research available on the forms and contents of licences for technology transfers between rich and poor countries,[4] and a recent article by Vaitsos which addresses itself to these matters puts the issues particularly clearly. The theme of his argument is that the market price mechanism which is the usual basis of these types of technology transfer maximizes the interests of the privileged seller and minimizes those of the weak buyer. The price system is partly the consequence of the creation of artificial scarcity due to the original restriction of patenting. As what is patented is more often than not something over and above a material object, namely 'know-how', etc., there are many points at which the freedom of action of the purchaser of the technology may be restrained, and his costs and financial obligations increased.

Vaitsos draws attention to three general aspects of this situation in which developing countries especially find themselves disadvantaged.

First, there is the mechanism of 'tie-in' – prohibited incidentally in Britain and some Commonwealth countries – 'requiring a patent licensee to use, in conjunction with the licensed process or combination or product, only devices or materials supplied by the patentee' (Calvert, 1964, p. 307). Vaitsos reports on a study in Colombia which showed that *all* technology transfer contracts with information of intermediate products explicitly required their purchase from the seller of the technology (Vaitsos, 1970, p. 19). For example, the chemical company Pfizer is the sole supplier of the important drug tetracycline to its licensees, and the licensee of the Japanese Toyota company must import only Toyota components for the assembly of the cars. Extrapolating from a sample of pharmaceutical firms, the Colombian study estimated that Colombia as a whole 'paid for intermediate products in 1968 close to US$20,000,000 solely due to *price differentials* above those available in the "international" market for the same products'. This is even more vividly illustrated in a calculation of effective returns to the parent corporation with respect to the pharmaceutical sample: 'overpricing' accounted for 82·6 per cent, the remainder was reported profit and royalties! (ibid., p. 20).

Colombia, a poor country, stays poor.

The second aspect of this unequal struggle concerns the mechanics of the bargaining situation from the perspective of the different information levels of buyer and seller; and the third aspect concerns the legal framework, to which I have already referred. Such tricks as foreign wholly-owned subsidiaries paying 'charges' to the parent company, thus evading taxes; the fact that the seller of the technology invariably defines the situation, which definition the buyer is forced to accept due to inferior knowledge; export prohibition clauses preventing users of the technology purchased at so high a price from interfering in the markets of those who have sold it; all of these add significantly to the burdens of the poor countries which are trying to industrialize through the application of science and technology.

The sheer hypocrisy of the rhetoric of 'free enterprise' and the 'provision of optimum conditions for fair competition', when confronted by the effectively monopolistic conditions of much technology transfer from rich to poor countries, is quite breathtaking. In the Colombian study referred to above, a sample of chemical, textile, and pharmaceutical contracts revealed that 85 per cent had export prohibition clauses (ibid., p. 22). Further research in this area is in process and it remains to be demonstrated that the Colombian case is by no means a unique example of the abuse of economic power. For an increasing number of social scientists such demonstration will come as no great surprise.

I began this section by speaking of the 'technology transfer racket' and I was using this appellation not only in its morally pejorative sense but also in its sociologically descriptive sense. Sketching in these outlines of international technology transfer reminds one of nothing so much as the account of 'The Racket-Ridden Longshoremen' given by the American sociologist Daniel Bell. The analogy between the 'quasi-legitimate' economic function of the racketeer in the New York docks, and the role of the technology transfer agents in 'modernization' – both acting as a 'social cement' holding the social structures within which they operate together – is deep and illuminating. I shall leave it to someone with more taste for socio-political satire than myself to fill in the details and extract the final ounce of irony, but one would not have far to look for the technology transfer analogues of the 'distinctive economic matrix of the port', 'the hiring boss', 'payroll padding', and that which made it all possible in the last resort, 'the pattern of political accommodation' (Bell, 1962, Ch. 9).

A Belated Overview

The one factor in the technological relationships between the rich countries and the poor countries which has, as it were, lurked beneath the surface of all that I have so far said is the general socio-economic structure of the societies whose fates the introduction and successful establishment of science and technology is supposed to determine to a happy conclusion. The technology transfer racket would not be practically possible without the connivance and even, on occasion, the active participation of the governments of rich and poor countries; neither would the more blatant and wasteful instances of dualism take place if some people somewhere were not making profits at the cost of the lives of other people who are powerless to defend themselves.

As has often been pointed out, it may be quite useless to devote resources to agricultural research if the systems of land tenure in the countries to which the research is directed remain unchanged. It is, after all, not 'technically rational' for a peasant farmer to risk anything at all on a new method of cultivation if failure would mean disaster and success, at best, prohibitively high payments to his landlord or his money-lender or both. The problems of the brain drain discussed in Chapter 1 throw light on a whole variety of these issues. In whose interests is it that expensive educational systems are created to prepare people in poor societies for emigration to rich countries. A recent radical symposium on scientific research and politics has reported that about 85,000 engineers, scientists, and physicians are estimated to have immigrated to America between 1949 and 1964; this would represent about $4,000 million worth of education; and this latter figure is about the total of American foreign aid in this period (in Dencik, 1969, p. 149). Not all of this, of course, concerns the underdeveloped countries, but enough of it does to make the point.

The structure of industry in poor countries and the control of natural resources, often linked through the drive to rationalization carried forward by the international companies, provide the essential injection of reality principle into the argument around the necessity for each poor country to build up its indigenous science and technology. As I have indicated, I am personally not utterly convinced that this is either desirable or necessary for the satisfaction of the fundamental needs of the populations of the Third World. Perhaps I may be forgiven for thinking that the medium-term goal for, say, India, might better be seen as sufficient food, shelter, and primary education than as a second car for every family. Be this as it may, and it is an historical question for our successors to answer if the opportunity arises, there must be serious doubt whether in each poor country it is realistic to contemplate the creation of science and technology as a social institution similar to that found in the rich countries.

It is extremely difficult to generalize about large sections of the world. One permissible generalization though, the one which much of the argument in this chapter is intended to support, is that the techno-economistic panacea – do science and technology and all of your important problems will be solved – is not generally acceptable for all poor countries, and that evidence that it is clearly valid for any poor country is suspiciously lacking. The view that I have suggested, a view which itself will require many more cases over longer periods of time before it can be entirely vindicated, rests on a modified intermediate technology model. This model rests as much on socio-political as on technical grounds, for it depends for its practical success on the participation of local *populations* rather than local and international *élites* alone. And this raises issues about the possible roles that science and technology might play in helping men to achieve the futures that they most desire. It is in this way that the discussion about the lack of involvement in decisions of science policy that we find among populations in rich societies becomes most relevant to the part that science and technology have to play in propagating and improving human welfare. Here, as in all contexts, the Third World is seen to be the abstraction that it is, useful for certain purposes of analysis but also an obstacle that can seriously impair our visions of the one world in which we live.

Conclusion

It may at first sight appear that the problems of participatory democracy in science policy for citizens of rich countries, and the problems of how best to utilize science and technology for the benefit of people in poor countries, are related only in the most indirect fashion. And indeed, if we accept most current thinking on these matters – technicocentrism on the first, and techno-economism on the second – the connections between the two seem remote. However, if we care to consider the view that, in some respects, the very poverty of the poor is a consequence of the very prosperity of the rich, it may lead us to wonder if the scientific and technological underdevelopment of some countries is not, in some ways, a consequence of the scientific and technological progress of rich countries. And I have presented evidence in the previous pages that these speculations are not clearly false in some cases, and that they might provide fruitful starting points for research in a whole variety of areas.

I have tried to argue through three main themes in this book, themes which may be analytically distinguished but whose empirical interrelationship makes it often unrealistic to hold them apart for very long. The first theme involves the model of a social institution which has been used to organize much of the discussion, and which I have modified to meet the demands of the view of science that I have been developing. The second theme concerns the implications of this view of science, as a social activity like others in some respects and unlike them in others, for our interpretation of science and its social role. The third theme is that of science and civilization. For all of these, I have argued, it is important to investigate science as a social institution, internally and apart from other institutions, as well as externally, as an institution whose elements are linked in many ways to those of other key institutions in society.

Malinowski's model of the social institution as applied to science and technology contains all the elements necessary for the analysis that has been carried out. The particular construction of the model, the relations between the parts, however, are not so satisfactory. As I have suggested in earlier chapters, it is inadequate to conceive of social institutions in terms of charters or values simply feeding into personnel, and norms, which feed into material apparatus, and from which flow complex activities and functions. More realistic is the view that, for ongoing institutions, the charter, material apparatus, and staff act as independent factors relative to the functions or results of the activities of the institution and that these functions are mediated through the norms. This is not to say that any or all of these elements might not act as independent and dependent variables in particular problem-complexes, for this does happen. But, generally speaking, the position that has emerged from this examination of science and technology is that represented by the revised model which I presented at the end of Chapter 5. This is only a starting point for further research.*

The picture sketched there suggests that institutions have values, material apparatus, and staff, all of which interact in a variety of ways. Patterns of interaction and dominance clearly emerge. For example, in an institution where the material apparatus becomes very expensive, over time the value of knowledge for its own sake might be subject to significant tensions; changing recruitment patterns of personnel similarly might influence the values of an institution over time; these patterns, it has been argued, are mediated on the next level through the institutional norms and only via this mechanism can the functions of the institution be properly understood. Needless to say, the institutional norms in my scheme develop not only out of the internal needs of science but also from the external relations of science to other important social institutions. This simple model, therefore, is intended to provide a starting point for the analysis of science and technology from a sociological point of view, and is predicated on the assumption that other societal phenomena can be similarly treated.

A major difficulty implicit in the discussion of science and technology is the differences and continuities between them. As I have pointed out, the institutional model allows us to articulate these differences and, more importantly, ensures that we do not ignore their essential links and continuities. My second theme, encapsulated in the title of Chapter 3, 'Science as Work', and more broadly encountered in the notion of science as a social activity, emphasizes the continuities of science and technology, perhaps at the expense of blurring their real differences. This is a risk, a calculated risk, that one must take when attempting to advance a particular approach in the strongest possible terms. I have considered it more important to attempt to play down the

* Particularly important areas for research are: (1) the relations between different institutions, with special attention to the interaction of levels; and (2) the very processes of institutionalization and de-institutionalization. These are generally neglected problems in sociology.

often arbitrary differences that have been used to cut off science from technology than to concentrate on the discontinuities that do exist. My criticisms of some current thinking in the sociology of science, therefore, can be interpreted as part of a general strategy to undermine the view that the intrinsic nature of science is such as to require special explanations that set it apart from other social activities. Further, my criticisms of certain philosophies of science may be interpreted as part of the same strategy to undermine the view that science is *so* special an activity (or rather that scientific knowledge is so special) that no sociological factors are very useful in explaining how it works. Science is part of the everyday world, it can be illuminated in a sociological fashion, and it requires no very special sociological factors to explain how it operates. These are the positions supported in this book and they tend to minimize the differences between science and technology. I have been concerned less with knowledge *per se* and more with *organized* knowledge, and this emphasis ensures that science and technology are seen as social activities first and intellectual activities second.

The relationship between the practice embodied in this conclusion and the theoretical issues raised by the Kuhn–Popper debate is immediate. Theory is a form of practice, and the resolution of current controversies in the history and philosophy of science in favour of the Kuhnian as against the Popperian tendency exemplifies this. As I have interpreted these matters, the theoretical advantages of the Kuhnian approach (not necessarily, let it be said, each and every statement of Kuhn himself) reinforce and are reinforced by the practical advantages of a sociology of science such as I have been propounding here, which refuses to accept that science is exclusively a cognitive activity.

And this takes us to the third theme that has informed this book – the nature of the scientific civilization, the technological society. To attempt to designate science and technology as a key institution for advanced industrial societies, and as the key institution in some respects for these societies, has been one of my major purposes. That this is increasingly coming to be recognized on a wide front at this time cannot, I think, be denied.[5] In general terms, as I have argued elsewhere, it can be useful to examine science and technology in terms of the concepts of progress by which institutions and sometimes whole societies operate. Science and technology provide the paradigm case for one type of progress, innovational progress, and non-innovational progress in societal terms represents the alternatives to technological society (Sklair, 1970).

My arguments in the last chapter suggested that these non-innovational alternatives did not necessarily imply the complete rejection of science and technology as such. Rather, I put forward the view that it was the links between industry and the economy, and science and technology, what I termed techno-economism, which must be critically assessed, and my conclusion at this point is that techno-economism might be rejected and that science and technology might then be better able to serve the needs of mankind. This then is my sketch of one alternative future, and it rests on the hope that science and technology might be rendered more appropriate to human aspirations than is at present the case. And to repeat what I have said often in the previous pages, I am not unaware that these speculations must be predicated on the resolution of important political problems.

These political problems – the existence of the privileges of the few against the deprivation of the many, the consequences that flow from the ownership of property and possession of social power of some and the relative powerlessness of others, the availability of opportunities for the fortunate and the overwhelming restrictions of the unfortunate – will eventually be resolved. The success of their resolution will largely depend on the ways in which we organize our science and technology to give us all what we want. There is a great deal of work to be done.

NOTES

1. This idea is less fanciful than it at first appears if we remember, as was pointed out to me by Kit Carson, that England exported its convicts to Australia until 1854.

2. The relevance of this will not be lost on those who have paid critical attention to the issues raised by Merton, Kuhn, and Popper, as discussed in Chapter 4.

3. There are of course some exceptions to this generalization. In the University of London, for example, the School of Hygiene and Tropical Medicine has a unique role, and at Imperial College it is now becoming possible for some engineers to specialize in problems of the developing countries without serious professional disadvantage.

4. For the most comprehensive review of this subject to date, see Charles Cooper (1970).

5. These figures are from a paper by M. Okano in the journal of the Licensing Executives' Society, *Les Nouvelles* (June, 1972), p. 27.

6. As evidence of this, for Britain, one might mention the following indicators: the production of new journals and magazines in recent years on (roughly) the social relations of science, e.g. *Science Studies* (1971); the creation and activities of the British Society for Social Responsibility in Science; the apparent upsurge in interest and concern about problems of the 'environment'; and the increase in coverage by the mass media on matters of science and technology.

Bibliography

Almond, G. A., 'Public Opinion and the Development of Space Technology: 1957–60', in Joseph M. Goldsen (ed.), *Outer Space in World Politics*, London: Pall Mall Press (1963), pp. 71–96.

Althusser, L., *For Marx*, London: Allen Lane (1969).

American Society for Engineering Education, 'Final Report: Goals of Engineering Education', *Journal of Engineering Education*, 58 (1968), pp. 367–446.

Bachelard, G., *The Philosophy of No*, New York: Orion (1968).

Barber, B., *Science and the Social Order*, New York: Collier (1962).

Barber, B. and Hirsch, W. (eds), *The Sociology of Science*, New York: Free Press (1962).

Barnes, B. (ed.), *Modern Science*, Harmondsworth: Penguin (1972).

Bell, D., *The End of Ideology*, New York: Collier (1962).

Ben-David, J., *The Scientist's Role in Society*, Englewood Cliffs: Prentice-Hall (1971).

Bendix, R. and Lipset, S. M. (eds), *Class, Status and Power*, Glencoe: Free Press (1966) (2nd edn).

Bernal, J., *The Social Function of Science*, London: Routledge (1939).

Box, S. and Cotgrove, S., 'Scientific Identity, Occupational Selection and Role Strain', *British Journal of Sociology*, 17 (1966), pp. 20–8.

Brinton, J. E. and McKown, L. N., 'Effects of Newspaper Reading on Knowledge and Attitudes', *Journalism Quarterly*, 38 (1961), pp. 187–95.

Buckley, W., *Sociology and Modern Systems Theory*, Englewood Cliffs: Prentice-Hall (1967).

Bush, V., *Science, The Endless Frontier*, Washington: Government Printing Office (1945).

Calvert, R. (ed.), *The Encyclopedia of Patent Practice and Invention Management*, New York: Reinhold (1964).

Cardwell, D. S. L., *The Organisation of Science in England: A Retrospect*, London: Heinemann (1957).

Chambers, P., 'Education and Industry', *Nature*, 203 (1964), pp. 227–230.

Cipolla, C. M., *European Culture and Overseas Expansion*, Harmondsworth: Penguin (1970).

Clarke, R., *We All Fall Down*, Harmondsworth: Penguin (1969).

Cole, S., 'Professional Standing and the Reception of Scientific Discoveries', *American Journal of Sociology* (1970), pp. 286–306.

Cole, S. and J. R., 'Scientific Output and Recognition: A Study in the Operation of the Reward System in Science', *American Sociological Review*, 32 (1967), pp. 377–90.

Cole, S. and J. R., 'Visibility and the Structural Bases of Awareness of Scientific Research', *American Sociological Review*, 33 (1968), pp. 397–413.

Collins, H., 'The Sociology of the CO_2 Laser', M.A. Thesis, Essex University, 1971.

Committee on Science in the Promotion of Human Welfare (AAAS), 'Secrecy and Dissemination in Science and Technology', *Science* (1969), pp. 787–90.

Coombs, P. H., *The World Educational Crisis*, New York: OUP (1968).

Cooper, C., 'The Mechanisms for Transfer of Technology from Advanced to Developing Countries', SPRU, University of Sussex (mimeo, 1970).

Cotgrove, S. and Box, S., *Science, Industry, and Society*, London: Allen & Unwin (1970).

Crain, R. L., Katz, E., and Rosenthal, D., *The Politics of Community Conflict: The Fluoridation Decision*, Indianapolis: Bobbs-Merrill (1969).

Crosland, M., *The Society of Arcueil*, London: Heinemann (1967).

Danhof, C. H., *Government Contracting and Technological Change*, Washington: Brookings Institution (1968).

Davies, R. and Sklair, L., 'Science and Technology Coverage in Four British newspapers, 1949–1969' (mimeo, 1972).

Dencik, L. (ed.), *Scientific Research and Politics*, Lund: Student-litteratur, (1969).

Diamond, E., 'The dark side of the moonshot coverage', *Columbia Journalism Review*, 8 (1969), pp. 10–17.

Diebold, J., *Automation: The Advent of the Automatic Factory*, New York: Van Nostrand (1952).

Dobb, M., *Soviet Economic Development Since 1917* (rev. edn), New York: International Publishers (1966).

Donohue, G. A., Tichenor, P. J., and Olien, C. N., 'Attitudes and Mass Media Learning about Two Environmental Issues' (mimeo).

Dumont, R., *False Start in Africa*, London: Sphere (1969).

Dupré, J. S. and Lakoff, S. A., *Science and the Nation: Policy and Politics*, Englewood Cliffs: Spectrum (1962).

Eiduson, B. T., *Scientists: Their Psychological World*, New York: Basic Books (1962).

Eiseley, L. C., 'Alternatives to Technology', in Aaron W. Warner et al (eds), *The Environment of Change*, New York: Columbia UP (1969), pp. 165–80.

Ellis, N., 'The Scientific Worker', Ph.D. Thesis, University of Leeds (1969).

Elsner, H., Jr., *The Technocrats*, Syracuse: Syracuse UP (1967).

Etzioni, A., *The Active Society*, New York: Free Press (1968).

Fletcher, C., 'Cosmopolitisme et Professions Intellectuelles', *Sociologie du Travail*, 11 (1969), pp. 1–21.

Frank, A. G., *Capitalism and Underdevelopment in Latin America*, New York: Monthly Review Press (1969) (rev. edn).

Freeman, C., 'The measurement of scientific and technological activities', UNESCO (1969); 'Measurement of output of research and experimental development', UNESCO (1970).

Freeman, C. and Young, A., *The Research and Development Effort in Western Europe, North America and the Soviet Union*, Paris: OECD (1965).

Freeman, I. M., 'Populations: Particles and Physicists', *American Scientist*, 50 (1962), pp. 360A–2A.

Gerard, R. W., *Mirror to Physiology: A Self-Survey of Physiological Science*, Washington: American Physiological Society (1958).

Gerstl, J. E. and Hutton, S. P., *Engineers: The Anatomy of a Profession*, London: Tavistock Publications (1966).

Glaser, B. G., *Organizational Scientists: their Professional careers*, New York: Bobbs-Merrill (1964).

Goldberg, L. C., Baker, F., and Rubinstein, A. H., 'Local-Cosmopolitan: Unidimensional or Multidimensional?', *American Journal of Sociology*, 70 (1964/5), pp. 704–10.

Goldman, J. E., 'Basic Research in Industry', *International Science and Technology*, 36 (1964), pp. 38–46.

Goodman, N., *Fact, Fiction and Forecast*, London: OUP (1967) (2nd edn).

Gouldner, A. W., 'Cosmopolitans and Locals: Toward an Analysis of Latent Social Roles – I' (and II), *Administrative Science Quarterly*, 2 (1957/8), pp. 281–306 (444–80).

Grampp, W. D., 'On Manufacturing and Development', *Economic Development and Cultural Change*, 18 (1970), pp. 451–63.

de Grazia, A. (ed.), *The Velikovsky Affair*, New York: University Books (1966).

Greenberg, D., *The Politics of American Science*, Penguin (1969).

Grubel, H. G., 'The Reduction of the Brain Drain: Problems and Policies', *Minerva*, 6 (1968), pp. 541–58.

Hagstrom, W., *The Scientific Community*, New York: Basic Books (1965).

Haines, G., IV, *The German Influence upon English Education and Science, 1800–66*, Connecticut College Monographs (1957).

Halmos, P. (ed.), *The Sociology of Science* (Sociological Review Monograph) (1972).

Harbison, F. H. and Myers, C. A., *Education, Manpower and Economic Growth*, New York: McGraw-Hill (1964).

Hewlett, R. G. and Anderson, O. E., Jr., *The New World, 1939/1946*, University Park, Pennsylvania: Pennsylvania State University (1962).

Helfrich, H. (ed.), *The Environmental Crisis*, New Haven: Yale UP (1970).

Hill, K. (ed.), *The Management of Scientists*, Boston: Beacon Press (1964).

Hinrichs, J. R., 'The Attitudes of Research Chemists', *Journal of Applied Psychology*, 48 (1964), pp. 287–93.

Hirsch, W., *Scientists in American Society*, New York: Random House (1968).

Hodgetts, J. E., *Administering Atoms for Peace*, New York: Atherton Press (1964).

Hornig, D. F., 'A Look Ahead', in *Science, Government and the Universities*, Seattle and London: University of Washington Press (1966), pp. 8–25.

Hunter, G., *The Best of Both Worlds*, London: OUP (1967).

Hutchings, D., *The Science Undergraduate*, University of Oxford Department of Education (1967).

Hutchings, D., *Technology and the Sixth Form Boy*, Oxford University Department of Education (1963).

Jacobson, H. K. and Stein, E., *Diplomats, Scientists, and Politicians: The United States and the Nuclear Test Ban Negotiations*, Ann Arbor: University of Michigan Press (1966).

Jeffries, C., *Illiteracy: a World Problem*, London: Pall Mall (1967).

Jenkins, W. I. and Velody, I., 'Behavioural Science Models for the Growth of Interdisciplinary Fields: The Cases of Biophysics and Oceanography', OECD Background Paper (1969).

Kaplan, N., 'Professional Scientists in Industry: An Essay Review', *Social Problems*, 13 (1965–6), pp. 88–97.

Kelber, H. and Schlesinger, C., *Union Printers and Controlled Automation*, New York: Free Press (1967).

King, M. D., 'Reason, Tradition and the Progressiveness of Science', *History and Theory*, X (1971), pp. 3–32.

Kornhauser, W., and Hagstrom, W., *Scientists in Industry: Conflict and Accommodation*, Berkeley and Los Angeles: California UP (1962).

Kreilkamp, K., '*Hindsight* and the Real World of Science Policy', *Science Studies*, 1 (1971), pp. 43–66.

Krieghbaum, H., *Science and the Mass Media*, London: London University Press (1968).

Krohn, R. G., 'The Institutional Location of the Scientist and his Scientific Values', *IRE Transactions on Engineering Management*, 8 (1961a), pp. 133–9.

Krohn, R. G., 'Science and the Practical Institutions', *Proceedings of the Minnesota Academy of Science*, 28 (1961b), pp. 163–72.

Krulee, G. K. and Nadler, E. B., 'Studies of Education for Science and Engineering: Student Values and Curriculum Choice', *I.R.E.* (EM-7) (1960), pp. 146–58.

Kuhn, T. S., *The Structure of Scientific Revolutions*, Chicago: Chicago UP (1962) (2nd edn, 1970).

Kurakov, J. G., *Science, Technology and Communism: Some Questions of Development*, Oxford: Pergamon (1966).

Lakatos, I. and Musgrave, A. (eds), *Criticism and the Growth of Knowledge*, Cambridge: Cambridge UP (1970).

Lakoff, S. A. (ed.), *Knowledge and Power: Essays on Science and Government*, New York: Free Press (1966).

Lavine, T. Z., 'Sociological Analysis of Cognitive Norms', *Journal of Philosophy*, 39 (1942), pp. 342–56.

Lenin Academy of Agricultural Sciences of the USSR, *The Situation in Biological Science*, Moscow: Foreign Languages Publishing House (1949).

Les Nouvelles, 'Prospects and Problems – Licensing in Developing Countries', special issue (June, 1972).

Lévi-Strauss, C., *Structural Anthropology*, New York: Basic Books (1963).

Macleod, R. M., 'The Alkali Acts Administration, 1863–84: The Emergence of the Civil Scientist', *Victorian Studies*, 9 (1965), pp. 85–112.

Maccoby, E., Newcomb, T., and Hartley, E. (eds), *Readings in Social Psychology*, New York: Holt (1958).

Machlup, F., *The Production and Distribution of Knowledge*, Princeton: Princeton UP (1962).

Mainzer, L. C., 'Science Democratized: Advisory Committees on Research', *Public Administration Review*, 18 (1958), pp. 314–23.

Malinowski, B., *A Scientific Theory of Culture*, New York: OUP (1960).

Mangum, G. L. (ed.), *The Manpower Revolution*, Garden City: Doubleday (1966).

Marcson, S., *The Scientist in American Industry*, Princeton: Industrial Relations Section (1960).

Martins, H., 'The Kuhnian "Revolution" and its Implications for Sociology', in Nossiter, *Imagination and Precision in the Social Sciences*, London: Faber (1972).

Marx, K., *Capital*, Moscow, Foreign Languages Publishing House, (vol. I) (1961).

Medvedev, Z. A., *The Rise and Fall of T.D. Lysenko*, New York: Columbia UP (1969).

Mees, C. and Leermakers, J., *The Organization of Industrial Scientific Research*, New York: McGraw-Hill (1950).

Merton, R. K., 'The Unanticipated Consequences of Purposive Social Action', *American Sociological Review*, 1 (1936), pp. 894–904.

Merton, R. K., 'Science, Technology and Society in Seventeenth-Century England', *Osiris*, 4 (1938), pp. 360–632.

Merton, R. K., 'Singletons and Multiples in Scientific Discovery: A Chapter in the Sociology of Science', *Proceedings of the American Philosophical Society*, 105 (1961), pp. 470–86.

Merton, R. K., 'The Ambivalence of Scientists', *Bulletin of the Johns Hopkins Hospital*, 112 (1963a), pp. 77–97.

Merton, R. K., 'Resistance to the Systematic Study of Multiple Discoveries in Science', *European Journal of Sociology*, IV (1963b), pp. 237–82.

Merton, R. K., *Social Theory and Social Structure*, Glencoe: Free Press (1963c).

Merton, R. K., 'The Matthew Effect in Science', *Science*, 159 (1968), pp. 56–63.

Mikulak, M., 'Darwinism, Soviet Genetics, and Marxism-Leninism', *Journal of the History of Ideas*, 31 (1970), pp. 359–76.

Mills, C. W., *The Power Elite*, New York: OUP (1956).

Mishan, E. J., *Growth: The Price We Pay*, London: Staples Press (1969).

Musgrave, A., 'Review', in *British Journal for the Philosophy of Science*, 20 (1969), pp. 92–4.

National Manpower Council, *A Policy for Scientific and Professional Manpower*, New York: Columbia UP (1953).

Nef, J. U., *Western Civilization since the Renaissance: Peace, War, Industry and the Arts*, New York: Harper Torchbooks (1963).

Nieburg, H., *In the Name of Science*, Chicago: Quadrangle (1966).

OECD, *The Measurement of Scientific and Technical Activities* (Frascati Manual), Paris (1970).

Parsons, T., *The Social System*, Glencoe: Free Press (1951).

Paul, E. A., 'Survey' in *Report*, London: Royal Institute of Chemistry (1970), pp. 57–259.

Pelz, D. and Andrews, F., *Scientists in Organizations*, New York: Wiley (1966).

Pirie, N. W., *Food Resources: Conventional and Novel*, Middlesex: Penguin (1969).

Polanyi, M., *Science, Faith and Society*, Chicago: Chicago UP (1964).

Polanyi, M., 'The Growth of Science in Society', *Minerva*, 5 (1967), pp. 533–45.

Popper, K. R., *The Logic of Scientific Discovery*, New York: Science Editions (1961).

Price, D. J. de Solla, *Science since Babylon*, New Haven: Yale UP (1961).

Price, D. J. de Solla, *Little Science, Big Science*, New York: Columbia UP (1965).

Price, D. J. de Solla, 'Measuring the Size of Science' (mimeo, 1969).

Pym, D., 'A Manpower Study: The Chemist in Research and Development', *Occupational Psychology*, 38 (1964), pp. 1–35.

Ravetz, J., *Scientific Knowledge and its Social Problems*, London: OUP, 1971.

Reuck, A. and Knight, J. (eds), *Communication in Science*, London: Churchill (1967).

Rhee, H. A., *Office Automation in Social Perspective*, Oxford: Blackwell (1968).

Riley, J. (ed.), *The Corporation and its Publics*, New York: Wiley (1963).

Roe, A., *The Making of a Scientist*, New York: Dodd, Mead (1953).

Roe, A., 'Scientists Revisited', *Harvard Studies in Career Development*, No. 38 (1965).

Rose, H. and S., *Science and Society*, London: Allen Lane (1969).

Schlippe, P., *Shifting Cultivation in Africa*, London: Routledge (1956).

Schumacher, E. F., 'Social and Economic Problems Calling for the Development of Intermediate Technology' (mimeo).

Selmes, C., et al, 'Attitudes to Science and Scientists', *The School Science Review*, 51 (1969), pp. 7–22.

Shaw, D. L. and van Nevel, P., 'The Informative Value of Medical Science News', *Journalism Quarterly*, 44 (1967), p. 548.

Sherwin, C. W. and Isenson, R. S., 'Project Hindsight: A Defense Department Study of the Utility of Research', *Science* (1967), pp. 1571–77.

Silberman, C. E., *The Myths of Automation*, New York: Harper (1967).

Singer, H. W., 'Dualism Revisited', *I.D.S. Communications Series* No. 41 (mimeo) (1969).

Sklair, L., 'The Sociology of the Opposition to Science and Technology: With Special Reference to the Work of Jacques Ellul', *Comparative Studies in Society and History*, 13 (1971), pp. 217–35.

Sklair, L., *The Sociology of Progress*, London: Routledge and Kegan Paul (1970).

Smith, M. L. (ed.), *The Role of Science in the Development of Natural Resources*, Oxford: Pergamon (1964).

Snow, C. P., *The Two Cultures: and a Second Look*, New York: Mentor (1964).

Stehr, N., 'Societal Consequences of Science – Technology and the Public' (mimeo, 1971).

Storer, N., *The Social System of Science*, New York: Holt, Rinehart & Winston (1966).

Strauss, A. L. and Rainwater, L., *The Professional Scientist: A Study of American Chemists*, Chicago: Aldine (1962).

Sultan, P. and Prasow, P., 'Automation: Some Classification and Measurement Problems', *Labour and Automation Bulletin*, 1 (1964), pp. 1–25.

Tannenbaum, P. H., 'Communication of Science Information', *Science* (1963), pp. 579–83.

Taylor, C. W. and Barron, F. (eds), *Scientific Creativity*, New York: Wiley (1963).

Terman, L. M., 'Scientists and Nonscientists in a Group of 800 Gifted Men', *Psychological Monographs, General and Applied*, 68 (1954), pp. 1–44.

UNESCO, *Statistics on Research and Experimental Development Activities, 1967*, Paris (1970).

Vaitsos, C. V., 'Bargaining and the Distribution of Returns in the Purchase of Technology by Developing Countries', *Bulletin of the Institute of Development Studies*, 3 (1970), pp. 16–23.

Vollmer, H. M., 'The Social Organization of Science and Technology' (mimeo), Stanford Research Institute, Menlo Park, California (1964); 'Organizational Socialization among Scientists', SRI (1967); 'Dimensions and Parameters of Technical Obsolescence', SRI (1967).

Watson, J. D., *The Double Helix*, London: Weidenfeld and Nicolson (1968).

Weber, M., *From Max Weber* (ed. by Gerth and Mills), New York: OUP (1958).

Weinberg, A. M., *Reflections on Big Science*, Oxford: Pergamon (1967).

Weisner, J. B., *Where Science and Politics Meet*, New York: McGraw-Hill (1965).

West, S. S., 'The Ideology of Academic Scientists', *I.R.E. Transactions on Engineering Management*, EM-7 (1960), pp. 54–62.

Woodruff, W., *The Impact of Western Man*, London: Macmillan (1966).

Zilsel, E., 'The Genesis of the Concept of Scientific Progress', *Journal of the History of Ideas*, 6 (1945), pp. 325–49.

Zuckerman, H., 'The Sociology of the Nobel Prizes', *Scientific American*, 217 (1967), pp. 25–33.

Index

CLASSES, CRISES & COUPS
Themes in the Sociology of Developing Countries

Peter C. Lloyd

Classes, Crises and Coups examines the social tensions of developing nations, focusing specifically on India, the countries of Central and West Africa, and the states of north-eastern Latin America.

Analysing these culturally diverse areas by means of a single conceptual framework, the author relates existing social tensions to changes in patterns of social stratification. Through case studies of tribal, caste, and peasant societies, he demonstrates the impact of Western economic domination in widely varying spheres. Comparing the effects of technological developments on rural and urban societies, he analyses mass rural uprisings from millenarian movements to peasant rebellions, poverty, unemployment, and the experience of migrants from the countryside in the rapidly expanding cities.

In a detailed consideration of ruling élites and their varying interests and capacities to accede to the demands of the masses, the author attempts to explain why change is achieved through peaceful means in some societies but is preceded by revolution and violence in others. His fascinating discussion of violence and rapid change includes case histories of Nigeria, Columbia, Peru, Cuba, and Tanzania.

THE DRUGTAKERS

The Social Meaning of Drug Use

Jock Young

Illicit drug use is often falsely explained as a result of
personality defects. In denoting drug users as inadequate, and
describing their subcultures as inauthentic or even non-
existent, psychologists and psychiatrists are engaging in an
invidious form of social control. For reactions, both popular
and professional, against drug use are really reactions not
against drugs per se but against drug users. It is not drugs
but cultures that are condemned.

Jock Young explores in detail the nature, extent and origins
of international drug use today, the various drug subcultures,
and the all-important question of social policy. He
demonstrates how out of touch British legislation is with the
essential problems. Viable control of drug taking can only
come through the drug subcultures themselves, allowed and
encouraged to regulate their own activities.

SOCIETY, SCHOOLS AND HUMANITY
The Changing World of Secondary Education

Douglas Holly

In an examination of the political, social and economic implications of the changing educational picture, Douglas Holly looks first at the traditional apparatus of British secondary schooling and charges it with having lost its meaning. He argues that present reforms merely reshape the basic pattern, and that the comprehensive school is no guarantee of a comprehensive education, though a vital step towards it. What is needed is a more fundamental change in perspective, a greater concentration on the social relationship between teacher and taught and, above all, the abandonment of a system which alienates and dehumanizes through its emphasis on 'success' and 'failure'.

'This book may well be seminal; certainly, it is an outstanding contribution to the present debate and should be required reading for all one-dimensional thinkers in education.'   TIMES EDUCATIONAL SUPPLEMENT

'Its subject-matter gives it a right to the widest possible audience.'   MORNING STAR

'As a contribution to the sociology of education, Douglas Holly's book has the advantage of being prescriptive rather than descriptive. It adopts a dynamic perspective of the developing educational system.'   THE TEACHER

'The book is marked by intelligence and a grasp of the questions at issue which should commend it not only to those who would share his point of view but to the many who would find it unacceptable.'

TIMES LITERARY SUPPLEMENT

'This book could hardly have been published at a more opportune time.'   SOCIALIST COMMENTARY